60

AN INTRODUCTION TO
ANIMAL PHYSIOLOGY

PLATE I. TOADS WITH THEIR CHROMATOPHORES IN DIFFERENT STATES

The two had been under similar conditions for an hour before they were photographed, except that the dark one was on a black background and the light one on a white background. They were placed together on a white background for photography.

AN INTRODUCTION TO
ANIMAL
PHYSIOLOGY

BY

W. B. YAPP, M.A.

SECOND EDITION

OXFORD
AT THE CLARENDON PRESS
1960

Oxford University Press, Amen House, London E.C.4

GLASGOW   NEW YORK   TORONTO   MELBOURNE   WELLINGTON
BOMBAY   CALCUTTA   MADRAS   KARACHI   KUALA LUMPUR
CAPE TOWN   IBADAN   NAIROBI   ACCRA

'Come, tell me how you live,' I cried,
'And what it is you do.'

THE WHITE KNIGHT

FIRST EDITION	1939
REPRINTED	1941
,,	1944
,,	1946
,,	1948
,,	1955
SECOND EDITION	1960

PRINTED IN GREAT BRITAIN

PREFACE TO SECOND EDITION

IT is twenty-one years since this book was written, but in spite of the great advances that have been made in our knowledge of some aspects of physiology, it has worn well and has sold steadily throughout its life. I began work on a revision two years ago, and I apologize to my readers for the delay in the preparation of a new edition. Many parts have been completely rewritten, and the whole has been brought as nearly up-to-date as I have found possible. No doubt the book contains errors, but I hope that there is little in it that the conscientious student will later have to unlearn. In spite of some arguments to the contrary, I have left the arrangement of the matter much as it was before, with only a little renumbering of the sections and some subdivision. I hope the second edition will bring me as many friends as did the first.

My colleague Mr. H. Asher gave me much help with the section on sense-organs, and Dr. R. W. Murray and Dr. B. Schofield patiently answered my inquiries on particular points. Dr. W. V. Thorpe read the biochemical portions in manuscript. To all of these I am grateful.

W. B. Y.

Glenridding,
April 1958.

FROM THE PREFACE TO THE
FIRST EDITION

I AM well aware that in attempting to cover in one elementary volume almost the whole range of animal physiology, I am treading on ground where no English angel has been before me. I wish that it were otherwise, for the scope of physiology is so vast that few men can claim personal acquaintance with more than one or two small parts of it, and the risk of error is great. But in the country of the blind the one-eyed man is king, and I have written this book with the object of giving students a fuller and more accurate account of animal physiology than is at present available.

The book was written not for examination requirements but because I believe that young zoologists should know more physiology than they usually do. Nevertheless, it will, I hope, be useful for the First M.B., Higher School Certificate,[1] and College Scholarship examinations, for all of which an increasing knowledge of physiology is demanded. In addition it should serve for junior University students.

No author could have been more fortunate in his helpers than I have been. To all of them I offer my thanks, but especially to Dr. G. R. de Beer and Mr. P. F. Haggart, both of whom read the whole manuscript and left it better than they found it; to Mr. C. W. Carter for reading the book in proof; to Mr. J. Z. Young for reading section 5, and to Professor C. M. Yonge for reading most of section 1; to Professor J. H. Orton, Professor A. D. Ritchie, Mr. H. Lob, Mr. D. M. Hall, and Mr. E. G. MacGregor

---

[1] Now (1958) replaced by the General Certificate of Education Advanced and Scholarship levels.

for advice on particular points; and to Mr. William Holmes for advice and for assistance with the Index.

Lastly, I must record my thanks for the great help I have received from the officials of the Clarendon Press.

W. B. Y.

Manchester
December 1938

CONTENTS

CONTENTS

LIST OF PLATES

ACKNOWLEDGEMENTS

THANKS are due to the authors, editors, and publishers of the following works and journals for permission to reproduce the figures specified.

Academische Verlagsgesellschaft m.b.H. for Fig. 29; L. C. Beadle in *The Biological Reviews of the Cambridge Philosophical Society* (Cambridge University Press), vol. 18, for Fig. 46; L. A. Borradaile and F. A. Potts, *The Invertebrata* (Cambridge University Press), for Figs. 8 and 19; J. R. G. Bradfield in *Symposia of the Society for Experimental Biology*, 1955, for Fig. 18; J. Gray, *Experimental Cytology* (Cambridge University Press), for Figs. 20 and 22; J. Gray in *The Proceedings of the Royal Society*, B, 93, for Figs. 1 B and 21; R. W. G. Hingston, *Problems of Instinct and Intelligence* (Edward Arnold & Co.), for Fig. 40; A. L. Hodgkin in *The Biological Reviews of the Cambridge Philosophical Society* (Cambridge University Press), vol. 26, for Fig. 33; S. J. Holmes in *The Journal of Comparative Neurology*, vol. 15, for Fig. 39; O. Löwenstein in *The Biological Reviews of the Cambridge Philosophical Society*, vol. 11 (Cambridge University Press), for Fig. 35; G. H. Parker, *Humoral Agents in Nervous Activity* (Cambridge University Press), for Fig. 30; C. F. A. Pantin (1956) in *The Journal of Experimental Biology*, vol. 13, for Fig. 28; O. P. Pearson in *Condor*, vol. 52, for Fig. 49; C. W. Rees, *The Neuromotor Apparatus of Paramaecium* in University of California Publications in Zoology, vol. 20, for Fig. 32; Starling's *Principles of Human Physiology*, edited by C. Lovatt Evans (J. & A. Churchill, Ltd.), for Fig. 12 and Schema 8; J. Stephenson, *The Oligochaeta* (Clarendon Press), for Fig. 39; V. B. Wigglesworth, *Insect Physiology* (Methuen & Co., Ltd.), for Fig. 7; V. B. Wigglesworth in *The Proceedings of the Royal Society*, B, 106, for Figs. 13 and 14; Samson Wright, *Applied Physiology* (Oxford University Press), for Figs. 27 and 31; the Council of the Marine Biological Association for Figs. 1 A and 23; and the Council of the Royal Society for Figs. 18, 45, and 46.

The quotation on the back of the title-page is from *Through the Looking-Glass*, by Lewis Carroll.

INTRODUCTION

EVERY elementary student of biology learns that his subject is divisible, as it might be vertically, into botany and zoology, and horizontally into morphology and physiology. Of the latter division as applied to plants he sees much, but his knowledge of animals tends to consist for a long time of only the structure of their parts, with which the names of certain rather ill-defined functions are connected. In the present book an attempt is made to explain these functions more fully, and in so doing to give an account of the way in which an animal, considered as a machine, works. This is very much the same thing as describing what it does and how it does it, provided that the peculiar acts of individuals are neglected. In experimental work particular individuals and particular species must be used, and the latter are often named in the text, but in practice there are usually only minor differences in the physiology of all the members of one class; we are most interested in the generalizations made inductively from particular observations, and such generalizations have been made wherever it seems reasonable to do so.

In addition to a certain amount of intelligence and common sense, two things are assumed in the reader; some knowledge of biology as usually taught for the Advanced Level of the General Certificate of Education or First M.B. examinations, and a similar knowledge of chemistry. The first is not likely to be lacking, and, indeed, if it is this book is useless, for physiology must be based on a sound knowledge of morphology. A few anatomical structures which are frequently neglected in the books are described or illustrated, but no attempt is made even to remind the reader of things with which he should be familiar. Unfamiliar names or points of classification should be looked up in one of the ordinary zoology text-books as they occur. Similarly with the biochemistry it has been assumed that so much of this subject as is usually taught for the botanical side of First M.B. biology will be available to the reader in books even if he does not remember it. In a few places a knowledge of physical chemistry possibly above that of the examinations mentioned will be useful. Such parts must be skipped by those who cannot understand them; they have been inserted because for those who can follow them they make the physiology clearer and easier.

The book proper begins with a chapter called Nutrition. This deals with the food which an animal needs, how it gets it, and what it does with it in order to be able to absorb it; the absorption itself, and the intermediate metabolism, that is, the way in which the food is built up to become part of the body. The next chapter, Excretion, deals with the elimination of waste products, and so finishes the story of what happens to the food, although a big gap has been left in the middle. The third chapter is called, rather inadequately, Respiration and the Provision of Energy. Since most energy is obtained by oxidation, this chapter contains a discussion of the oxygen supply.

That finishes the more narrowly chemical side of physiology. The fourth chapter, Effectors, describes the working of those tissues which do things in the sense of having an effect on the outside world—muscles, glands, cilia, and so on. Next comes Co-ordination, dealing with the methods by which the processes described in the other sections are kept running in such a way that the animal reacts as an individual, and not as a vast number of independent units. This section includes divisions on nerves, hormones, and sense organs. The sixth chapter is called Behaviour, and tries to show, without being dogmatic as to metaphysics, that much of what the animal does as an individual can be usefully studied from the same mechanistic standpoint as are its isolated parts in the traditional physiological laboratory.

After that comes a chapter on Reproduction, which needs no explanation, and lastly a short section dealing with some of the ways in which the higher animals have become independent of their environment.

1

NUTRITION

THE food of animals is used in two ways, as a fuel to supply energy, and as raw material to be incorporated in the tissues of the body. In the second case it may be used to make completely new material (growth in the strict sense) or it may merely be used for repair of structures broken down in the life processes of the organism. The animal must first obtain raw material (feeding); this must be prepared for absorption (digestion), and after it has been absorbed it must suffer chemical changes according to the purpose to which it is to be put. In the present section these processes will be treated in order. The final provision of energy, and the disposal of the waste products, will be dealt with in the chapters on Respiration and Excretion respectively.

1.1. The Foodstuffs, their Nature and Source

Since the ultimate chemical analysis of any animal is always approximately the same, it follows that certain elements must be present in the food. A full list of those necessary for any species is probably at present impossible, but careful analyses and feeding with rigidly purified food have shown that many more than the common half-dozen or so biological elements are required. Some animals are very efficient in obtaining particular elements from their food. Most tunicates have in their blood a protein which is rich in vanadium, yet this substance is barely detectable in the sea-water in which the animal lives, its concentration being of the order of 1 mg/cu. m. or 1 part in 10^9. In other tunicates it is replaced by niobium. Nearly all marine arthropods and molluscs possess haemocyanin, which contains copper, the concentration of which in sea-water is about the same as that of vanadium. Some Protozoa (Radiolaria Acantharia) form shells of sulphate of strontium, an element which again is scarcely present in the sea. These facts have led a few people to suggest that the animals concerned can transmute the elements, but this is hardly likely.

It is in many cases necessary not merely that a certain element be present in the food, but that it be present in a particular form of combination, and this is strikingly so for the elements which are required in the greatest proportion, that is for carbon, hydrogen, and nitrogen. Taking account of this, it is convenient to divide the food of animals into the following classes:

> Proteins
> Fats
> Carbohydrates
> Other organic compounds
> Inorganic substances.

1.11. Proteins

Proteins make up an essential part of protoplasmic structure, and in the normal way the food from which they are derived consists also of proteins. In structure they are compounds of very high molecular weight built up from aminoacids joined together by peptide linkages,

$$-\overset{\displaystyle O}{\underset{}{C}}-\overset{\displaystyle H}{N}-$$

each of which is formed by the condensation of the carboxyl group of one acid and the amino-group of its neighbour. The proteins of food are mainly broken down to aminoacids before absorption, and it would therefore be expected that the latter could be used instead. This is the case, but since not all the aminoacids can be converted one into another and some of them cannot be made by animals it is necessary that certain quantities of particular acids be present. Tryptophan, for instance, which has the formula

$$\begin{array}{ccc} & CH & CH_2{-}CH \cdot COOH \\ HC & C{-}C & NH_2 \\ HC & C & CH \\ & CH & NH \end{array}$$

cannot be synthesized by animals, and it must therefore be present in the food, either free or combined in a protein. For the same reason proteins are not all of equal value, since varying amounts of them are necessary to supply the required aminoacids. Maize, for instance, contains no tryptophan, and is in consequence an inadequate food if it is the sole source of protein. The number of essential aminoacids varies from species to species, and it may also vary with age during the life of one animal. In man ten seem to be required, and the others are synthesized by a reaction called transamination, in which the amino-group is shifted from one organic molecule to another. Speaking generally, less protein is needed if it is of animal origin than if it comes from plants. Proteins which contain most of the necessary aminoacids in proportions suitable for animals are called first-class, and while most animal proteins are in this group (gelatin is a notable exception) it includes but a few vegetable proteins. Casein, the protein of milk, provides all the aminoacids that are necessary for *Drosophila* larvae, and perhaps for some other animals. Breakdown of intracellular protein occurs continuously, and since mammals do not store protein to more than a very slight extent, a continual supply is necessary in the diet. The minimal quantity seems to vary with the other food and with the past history of the subject. For many animals, particularly carnivores, protein is important also as a source of energy, and it is the chief source of sulphur.

There is no evidence that any animals other than the photosynthetic green flagellates, whose metabolism is that of plants, can live on food which is lacking in animoacids, though some nitrogen may be obtained from other sources. From time to time revolutionary claims have been made that certain species can live on such a diet, but in all cases it has later been shown that symbiosis with plants was taking place. *Drosophila* larvae can live on mineral salts, sugar, and ammonium tartrate, $(CHOH \cdot COONH_4)_2$, but if they are carefully cleared of the yeasts which are normally present in the gut, they die on this food. Some experimenters thought that the ciliate *Colpidium* could live on ammonium glycerophosphate,

$$CH_2OH \cdot CHOH \cdot CH_2O \cdot PO \cdot (ONH_4)_2,$$

but Bacteria were found to be present. Termites live symbiotically on *Trichonympha* and other flagellates which live in the gut; they can grow successfully when fed only on the purest filter-paper, which contains but 0·0006 per cent. of ash. The source of the nitrogen in this case remains a mystery. As shown later (p. 53), mammals can manufacture aminoacids from ammonia, and rats can utilize ammonium ions present in the food.

Artiodactyls, the animals which chew the cud, get some 40 per cent. of their nitrogen requirements from symbiotic Bacteria. Cocci in the rumen synthesize protein from carbohydrate and from ammonia produced by other

Bacteria, and are digested by the host. Urea can be used as a source of the ammonia.

1.12. Fats

Fats are an important constituent of most foods, and it seems that in the mammal some of the energy must be supplied from this source or from the fatty acids from which they are derived. Moreover, fatty acids in the form of phospholipides such as lecithin enter intimately into protoplasmic structure. Nevertheless, fats can be formed from carbohydrate, and in animals such as those Protozoa which digest fat scarcely at all this is the source from which the protoplasmic fat presumably comes. In fly larvae, fat is formed from protein, but it appears unlikely that this occurs in the mammal, unless the amount of protein in the diet is very high. In rats, not only are fats necessary, but amongst them must be at least one which is unsaturated, such as that derived from linoleic acid, $CH_3(CH_2)_4CH:CHCH_2CH:CH(CH_2)_7COOH$, which is present in linseed oil and lard.

1.13. Carbohydrates

Carbohydrates are in most animals the chief source of energy, and although they can be formed both from fat (p. 54) and from protein (p. 52) a certain amount, which differs for different species, must generally be present in the food. The ciliate *Glaucoma* (= *Tetrahymena*) *piriformis* can live on a diet of proteins (containing ten essential aminoacids) and vitamins only, but if carbohydrate is present it is used, and less deamination (p. 50) takes place. Carnivores need less carbohydrate than herbivores. In mammals absence of carbohydrate upsets the metabolism of fat and protein.

The chief carbohydrates of food are the hexoses glucose, fructose, and galactose, or their derivatives such as starch which are hydrolysed to them in digestion. Since up to 25 per cent. of the dry weight of grass may be pentose-carbohydrates, these may be important in the diet of herbivores. One must not assume, however, that because a substance is present in the food it is an important source of nourishment, or even that it is used at all. *Lyctus*, the powder post beetle, does not need wood, but it does need starch and sugar, and many lepidopteran larvae cannot digest the cellulose of the leaves which they eat.

1.14. Other Organic Compounds

It is probable that no further organic substances, other than those which may be classed as vitamins (pp. 63–82), are necessary for animals, but there are some which can be used fairly widely, and others which are used by a few species. Alcohol can be oxidized and has some possible calorific value, and a number of mammals have been shown to utilize acetic acid. This, and some other acids, appear to be important sources of energy for the colourless Phytomastigina, but their ecological value for Metazoa is doubtful.

Waxes, which resemble fats in being esters of higher acids, but differ from them in that the alcohol from which they are formed is not glycerol, are not attacked by the enzymes which split fat, and cannot be digested by most animals. The larva of the moth *Galleria* feeds on beeswax, and so do the tropical birds called honey-guides (Indicatoridae). Both are able to digest about half the wax that they take in, and probably in the birds and possibly in the insect, symbiotic organisms are necessary for this utilization.

1.15. Inorganic Substances

Besides the oxygen required for respiration certain other compounds and elements are necessary. Water, although it is formed in small quantities in the body by oxidation of organic materials, is lost in far larger quantities by evaporation and in urine and faeces. The deficit must be supplied in food and drink, and in man four-fifths of the daily loss must be obtained in this way. In small terrestrial animals, particularly insects, the control of water loss is very important, as it is one of the most difficult foods to supply. The ions of sodium, potassium, and chloride are present in protoplasm and body fluids, and are necessary for the efficient functioning of membranes, and must be supplied in the food.

The majority of the elements which in small quantity are necessary for life and growth are probably supplied in the form of inorganic ions. They include, for various animals, calcium, chromium, copper, iron, magnesium, manganese, molybdenum, and zinc. Calcium helps to form many skeletons, and is essential for the cell membrane. Chromium is possibly part of the permanent structure of the red blood cell. Copper is a constituent of the haemocyanin present in the blood of most arthropods and molluscs (section 3.22) and also of a number of vertebrate enzymes; in the fowl and several mammals it is necessary for the formation of the blood. In cattle and sheep it has an important action as an antagonist for molybdenum; on certain pastures there is an excess of this in the herbage, and the result is a disease which can be cured by the addition of small quantities of copper sulphate to the grass. Besides its well-known occurrence in haemoglobin, iron is present in several oxidative enzymes, including the cytochromes (section 3.12). Magnesium is an activator of enzymes such as adenosine triphosphatase (section 3.14). Manganese activates various oxidations, and the actions of intestinal aminopeptidase and of bone phosphatase, so that deficiency leads to malformation of the skeleton; birds need relatively large quantities of it. Molybdenum occurs in the prosthetic groups (p. 21) of some enzymes, including xanthine oxidase, which is important in the formation of uric acid (section 1.41). Zinc is a constituent of carbonic anhydrase (section 3.3) and other enzymes. Cobalt is a constituent of vitamin B_{12} (section 1.529), but cattle and sheep, which need far more of it than do other animals, get it from their symbiotic organisms (section 1.313), which have themselves probably synthesized it from inorganic cobalt.

By contrast, the non-metallic elements iodine, phosphorus, and sulphur are often obtained in organic form. Iodine occurs in the thyroid hormone; some of it is absorbed as iodide. Phosphate ions are important in many reactions and are universally present in cells; they are obtained from organic compounds such as nucleoproteins (p. 24), or directly from inorganic salts. Sulphate ions also are present in cells, and are derived from the sulphur of proteins by oxidation.

1.16. The Food Requirements of Man

The normal food requirements of man depend in part on the amount of external work which he does, but even when this is reduced as near to zero as possible some energy, and so some food, is still required. The heart and some other organs are working continuously, and energy is lost in the form of heat. The energy output of a fasting resting animal which is doing no external work is called its basal metabolism. When this is calculated per unit of body-weight it is found to be greater the smaller the animal. This is to be expected, for the smaller an animal the higher is the ratio of its surface to its volume, and so the more rapidly does each gramme of it lose heat. If basal metabolism is calculated per unit of area of body-surface of a given species it is generally found to be fairly constant.

In young men it is about 40 kcal/sq.m./hour, but it falls with age and is about 10 per cent. less in women and much higher in children. The heavier a man is the higher will be his basal metabolism, but small men have a greater energy output per pound. If minor differences in shape are neglected it is possible to construct a nomogram connecting surface with height and body-weight, and from this the basal metabolism of any man for whom the usual physical dimensions are known can be calculated. The average height of Englishmen is 171 cm (5 ft 7 in.) and weight 70·3 kg (11 stone). This corresponds to a surface area of 1·8 sq. m., which gives a basal metabolism of 71 kcal/hour. When allowance is made for the increased metabolism when the man is up and about, and for an average amount of external work, the energy requirement comes to about 3,000 kcal/day. There can, of course, be no exactness to this figure, since it is at best an approximate mean. Men in sedentary occupations will need less, those doing heavy manual labour more. A tailor has been calculated to need but 2,500 kcal, and a woodcutter as much as twice this. Women need about four-fifths of what a man does, and small children still less.

There is quite a large loss in cooking so that a food supply of about 3,400 kcal a day is generally recommended, although there is a tendency to reduce this figure. Further, as has been said above, it is necessary for a healthy life that some of the energy should be supplied from fat and some from protein, although men have succeeded in living on diets very low in both of these. In England about 11 per cent. of the energy is supplied by protein, of which half is first-class, and a quarter is supplied by fat. This means that at least 70 g (2·5 oz) of protein should be taken per day. The need for increased protein for growing children, who are forming new protoplasm, is obvious, and women need more during pregnancy and lactation.

1.2. Feeding and Feeding Mechanisms

The method by which an animal obtains its food depends on the class to which it belongs, and also, and even more, on the nature of its food. On the latter basis it is possible to divide animals by their feeding mechanisms into three or four main types:

> Microphagous feeders
> Macrophagous feeders
> Detritus feeders
> Fluid feeders.

1.21. Microphagous Feeders

Microphagous feeders are animals which live on small particles, usually plankton. It is a characteristic of these that they scarcely ever stop feeding, and they are often, though by no means exclusively, sedentary or sluggish. Perhaps the commonest method which they use is to draw a current of water to the mouth by means of cilia, food particles being abstracted and the water expelled. This is found in nearly all phyla from the Protozoa to the chordates (with the obvious exception of the nematodes and arthropods, which possess no cilia). The long cilia in the oral groove of *Paramecium* draw a cone of water towards the cytoplasmic mouth, and food particles thus brought into contact with this are ingested. Some sea-anemones, such as *Metridium*, are covered with cilia which may beat towards the mouth, to which they convey plankton. For most of the time they beat in the opposite direction, so that waste products are removed, this being one of the few cases where reversal of cilia undoubtedly takes place. In the lamellibranchs there is a complicated arrangement of cilia on the gills, palps, and mantle, by which a current of water is brought into the shell, particles of a certain size selected and carried to the mouth, and water and waste material ejected. In the sea-mussel *Mytilus* an outline of

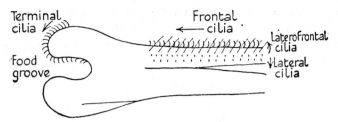

FIG. 1 A. Diagrammatic lateral view of gill filament of *Mytilus edulis*.
Modified from Orton.

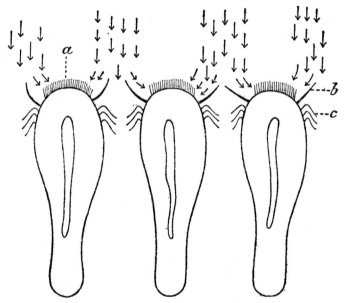

FIG. 1 B. Transverse section of three gill filaments of *Mytilus edulis*, showing
the deflection of the vertical current on to the frontal cilia.

a. Frontal cilia; *b.* laterofrontal cilia; *c.* lateral cilia. After Gray.

what happens is as follows. The inhalant current is caused
by cilia on the gills where they occupy the three positions
shown in Fig. 1. The lateral cilia cause an inward current directed on to the gills, and the particles carried in

this are diverted by the laterofrontal cilia on to the edge of
the gill filaments. Here the frontal cilia carry them down
to the groove in the free edge of the gill, where they are
carried forward to the palps. On these there is mechanical

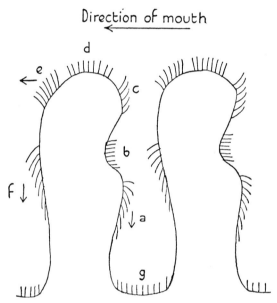

FIG. 2. Diagrammatic section through two ridges on the
palp of an oyster. The whole palp is covered with cilia, but
for clarity these are shown in seven separate blocks according
to their direction of beat. Blocks *a*, *e*, and *f* beat in the direction shown by the arrows; block *b* through the plane of the
paper towards the base of the palp; block *c* diagonally
towards the mouth; and blocks *d* and *g* through the plane of
the paper towards the upper margin of the palp. Recon-
structed from Yonge.

selection of particles by size. A simplified section of a palp
of an oyster is shown in Fig. 2; light particles are thrown
over the tops of the ridges and go to the mouth, while
heavy particles fall into the grooves and are taken to the
edge of the palp. Cilia on the mantle cause a current which

takes these rejected particles, together with other waste products, to the *inhalant* siphon. In some species muscular contraction of the gills and palps helps in the transport of the particles. The most advanced forms with ciliary feeding are the tadpoles of frogs and toads, which scrape off small particles with the buccal rasp. These and other particles are gulped into the mouth, and then taken to the oesophagus by cilia. In *Bufo bufo* and *Rana temporaria* there is probably no peristaltic swallowing. Well developed ciliary feeding is also found in the ammocoete larva of *Petromyzon*.

There are other types of microphagous feeding. In some species of Crustacea setae on various appendages are used to create a current of water, and the larva of *Culex* feeds so efficiently in this manner that it is said even to be able to feed on colloidal particles, though it cannot get enough of them to grow if other food is not available.

The secretion of mucus often helps in the transport of particles, and in some animals it has become all-important. *Urechis campo* (Annelida, Gyphyrea), *Vermetus* (Gastropoda), and the larvae of *Chironomus plumosus* (Diptera) secrete threads or nets of mucus which float into the water, and are then withdrawn and ingested, together with the particles which they have trapped. A similar method is occasionally used by *Nereis*. *Ciona* and other tunicates use continuous mucous sheets secreted by the endostyle.

The particles ingested by filter-feeders are usually a few microns in diameter. The mucus-feeders extract even smaller particles, but though a few can retain haemocyanin molecules none can retain average proteins. Tadpoles and water-snails feed on the surface-film of water, which consists of a thin solid layer of protein probably derived from decaying plant material. A tadpole may take in 0·5 sq. cm./sec, which in stagnant water, where the film is thickest, means that it could in this way consume its own mass of protein in a day.

1.22. Macrophagous Feeders

Macrophagous feeders are those which feed on comparatively large masses of food, and which in consequence only feed occasionally. Examples, from the Protozoa to man, are fairly obvious. The Rhizopoda ingest particles of food in a number of ways. In some (e.g. *Amoeba proteus*), water is taken in with the food, so that a vacuole is formed at once, while in others (e.g. *Actinosphaerium*) the food is taken practically dry, and water is then secreted round it. The food particle may simply be drawn into the cytoplasm, the whole animal may flow round it, or two definite pseudopodia may be used to surround it. The last is the method normally used by *Amoeba proteus*. *Amoeba* can cut a paramecium into two pieces. All the Hydrozoa, although they move very little, are nevertheless macrophagous, animals which touch the tentacles being paralysed by the nematocysts (p. 205). The tentacles carry the prey to the mouth, and in *Hydra* as soon as this is touched they withdraw so that the animal stretches itself over its food 'like a serpent or an automatic stocking'. Swallowing, at least in some species of *Hydra*, is stimulated by glutathione released from the prey by the nematocysts.

In macrophagous forms the food has often to be broken up before the digestive enzymes can act on it, or even before it is taken into the mouth. Occasionally there is very vigorous external digestion. The rhizopod *Vampyrella* pours out a cellulase to dissolve the wall of the Alga *Spirogyra* on which it feeds and the ciliate *Glaucoma* and others liquefy gelatin in the medium, so that they must produce an external proteinase. The starfish *Asterias* extrudes its stomach over its prey, such as a mollusc, and a considerable amount of digestion takes place before the food is swallowed. A number of species inject a protease into living animals. Most of the cephalopods do this, and so do the larvae of the beetles *Dytiscus* and *Lampyris* (the glow-worm). The first of these insects lives on almost any living thing that it can catch—tadpoles, for instance—and the second on snails and slugs. Spiders likewise inject prot-eases into the flies which they have caught. The external digestion of the food is so complete that the material actually taken into the body is liquid, and any parts not dissolved are rejected. Blowfly larvae likewise liquefy their food before they swallow it, and since many of them are always present together they change the solid flesh, on the surface of which they begin life, into a semi-fluid pulp. Some of the enzymes concerned in this are present in the excreta.

More often the food is broken up by mechanical means. In decapod Crustacea such as *Astacus* food is first torn by the chelae, and then pulled to pieces by the endopodites of the second and third maxillipeds while being held in the mandibles. After it has been taken into the mouth it is further broken up in the gizzard, a special part of the fore-gut bearing internal teeth or pyloric ossicles. Insect jaws and palps are used to the same purpose as the mouth-parts of Crustacea, and species which feed on hard food (Coleoptera, Orthoptera, some Hymenoptera) have well-developed mandibles. The radula of such gastropods as the snail is used for cutting pieces of leaf of suitable size; for this purpose it works against a hard pad on the roof of the mouth. For the most part the lower vertebrates swallow their food whole: this is so in the dogfish, where whole crabs may often be found in the stomach, and in the frog and snake. The egg-eating snake *Dasypeltis scabra* has an interesting special adaptation. The haemal spines of the cervical vertebrae project into the oesophagus, and as the egg is pressed against them while it is being swallowed, its shell is broken. Most birds also swallow their food whole, though parrots break it up very finely with the beak and tongue, and thrushes and some shore birds break the shells of molluscs before eating the soft parts. The gizzard is very muscular, but has no hard parts; instead, it contains small stones which have been accidentally or deliberately swallowed or fed to the chicks by their parents. Food is crushed by being worked against these. In mammals, the teeth, in addition to being used to seize the food, may also serve to crush it in the mouth. In accordance with this the type of food has a close connexion with the form of the teeth, particularly of the cheek teeth. The molars of carnivores have cutting edges, but are not used for grinding: those of herbivores have ridges, and of omnivores rounded cusps, both being suited to chewing. Animals which live on small invertebrates, badly called insectivorous, have cheek teeth with sharp points. Piscivorous species do not chew their food, and have simple conical molars adapted for holding their prey.

1.23. Detritus Feeders

Detritus feeders, those which feed on the organic matter in soil and mud, are perhaps best placed with or near macrophagous forms. They include burrowing species like *Lumbricus* and other worms which suck in soil by the protruded pharynx, those which shovel sand into the mouth like the holothurians, and a few such as the sturgeons which suck mud with the lips. In all cases in order for the animal to get enough food a great deal of useless mineral matter has to be passed through the body.

1.24. Fluid Feeders

There remain several species which feed on food which is already liquid. Most of these suck fluid through some sort of mouth apparatus. The majority of them are insects. The chief free-living forms are Lepidoptera, bees, and blowflies, which have three different types of sucking apparatus developed from the mouth-parts. The ecto-parasitic insects such as bugs, mammal-lice, and mos-quitoes also mostly get their food in this way, but here the

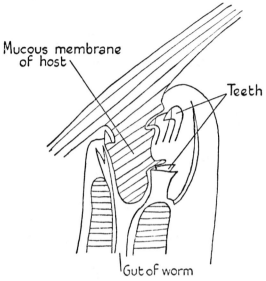

Fig. 3. Diagrammatic L.S. of anterior end of *Ankylostoma* attached to the wall of the gut. In part after Brumpt, *Précis de Parasitologie*, Masson et Cie, in part after Keilin.

mouth-parts are capable not only of sucking but of first piercing through the epidermis of the host. Ectoparasites of other classes, such as ticks and leeches, use a similar method. Both of these last groups have been shown to pro-duce an anticoagulin to prevent clotting of the blood while it is being sucked. A few endoparasites also use this method: the liver-fluke lives mainly on blood which it draws in through the mouth, which is surrounded by the anterior sucker, and some nematodes such as *Ankylostoma* browse on the mucous membrane of the gut wall and obtain much blood (Fig. 3).

The more extreme endoparasites, such as the Sporozoa, Cestoda, and *Sacculina*, absorb food over practically the whole body-surface, and the liver-fluke can absorb monosaccharides in this way. It has been suggested that free-living animals might be able to absorb organic matter directly, either through the gut wall or through the outer surface. There is some circumstantial evidence for this, such as the fact that although Leptocephali larvae of the eel live and grow in the Atlantic for three years little food has ever been found in them, but it is unlikely that the small amounts of organic matter in either fresh or sea-water (10 mg/litre) can ever be very important.

1.25. Symbiosis

Many animals are assisted in their feeding by others, with which they are said to be commensal; the hermit-crab feeds on particles dropped by the anemone which it carries, and the hawfinch on the stones of haws dropped from the trees by thrushes. In symbiosis there is a more intimate physiological connexion between two species, and it is common for Metazoa to carry in their gut micro-organisms on which they are more or less dependent. Many of these are important in breaking down cellulose, which is otherwise difficult to attack, and this aspect of symbiosis is dealt with in sections 1.313 and 1.33. Others manufacture vitamins; the bacteria in the rumen of cattle make several B-vitamins, and it is probable that accessory factors are made by symbionts in insects. Bacteria in the gut of some Aphidae, beetles, and moths can fix atmospheric nitrogen and so make it available for their hosts.

1.3. Digestion

It is characteristic of animals that much of their food consists of complex organic substances, which are chemically relatively inert and often insoluble. They cannot be

directly used for the metabolism of the body, but must
first be broken down into simple diffusible products. Such
preparation of the food is called digestion. The products
must not only be soluble, but they must also be such as the
body-cells can absorb and deal with. A further need for
digestion lies in the fact that, even if the food is soluble, it
is of a different nature from the tissues of the body. All
proteins are made up of combinations of relatively few
aminoacids, but one protein cannot be converted to
another unless it is first broken down to its constituent
aminoacids. A protein molecule is like a model made of
a constructional toy in which the strips of steel of different
sizes represent different aminoacids. An aeroplane and
a saw-mill may consist of nearly the same aggregate of
parts, but they are arranged in different ways, and the
one can be converted into the other only by being first
completely dismantled. Polysaccharides are similar, and
even disaccharides, though crystalline and diffusible, must
be broken down to monosaccharides before the cells can
use them.

In the majority of animals digestion goes on in the gut,
so that it is internal but extracellular. External digestion
has already been dealt with under feeding mechanisms
(p. 14). Intracellular digestion, in which substances are
taken into the cells for breakdown, is normal in Protozoa,
sea-anemones, Platyhelminthes, and lamellibranchs. It is
possible that it takes place in the vertebrate small intestine,
preliminary soluble breakdown products formed in the
gut lumen being absorbed for further action.

Digestion is generally carried out by enzymes, which
are commonly defined as 'thermolabile organic catalysts',
or in some similar way. If the term catalyst is given its
classical definition of 'a substance which alters the rate of
a chemical reaction', this is inaccurate, and gives an
entirely false picture of what enzymes do. There is no

evidence that the reactions in which they assist go on slowly or at all in their absence; the cane sugar in one's tea is not slowly turning into glucose and fructose, nor does glucose in the air gradually become carbon dioxide and water, yet both of these changes are rapidly carried out by enzymes in the body. In so far as the same end-products can be produced without enzymes (for example glucose and fructose by acid, carbon dioxide and water by heat) the reactions that go on are quite different. It is possible to redefine 'catalyst' to meet the difficulty, but this is clumsy, and introduces difficulties for inorganic chemistry. It is better to define an enzyme, in terms of what it is and does, as 'a protein which initiates and takes part in a reaction or a chain of reactions in such a way that it is itself largely restored at the end'. Generally the name of every enzyme ends in -ase, this suffix being added to the root of the name of the substrate with which it reacts, where that is possible, or to some other root that indicates the nature of the reaction that it mediates.

An enzyme is always affected by the acidity of the medium in which it is acting, and optima have been measured in many cases. The exact values, however, seem to vary according to the degree of purity of the enzyme, and according to the salts and other substances present, as well as with the substrate and the species. It is therefore only possible to indicate in a general way the optimum for an enzyme for the natural conditions under which it works. Temperature optima result from two processes: chemical reactions, whether enzymic or not, are hastened by rise of temperature, but at the same time enzymes are progressively destroyed. The apparent optimum is simply the point at which the destruction of the enzyme just outweighs the increase in the rate of the reaction for purely physical reasons, and will be higher the shorter the time for which the high temperature is allowed to continue.

Many enzymes will not work unless their active group is attached to a prosthetic group, which is not a protein. Others need a coenzyme, a substance with a much smaller molecule, which also differs from a prosthetic group in that it is not combined with the active group, or is so weakly attached that it is easily separated from it. Co-enzymes are not thermolabile. Activators are substances which react with an enzyme before it carries out its action. They may be organic or inorganic, and sometimes convert an inactive pro-enzyme into the active form. They may do this by removing a part of the molecule so that the active group is, as it were, exposed, a process which may be called unmasking, or by counteracting the effect of an interfering substance, which is called deinhibition, but the mode of action of many activators, especially the inorganic ions, is unknown.

1.31. Digestion in the Mammal, especially Man

The process of digestion consists mainly of a series of hydrolyses, and follows a generally similar course in all vertebrates: our knowledge of the details is largely obtained from experiments on dogs, confirmed by clinical observations on man. The whole of the process goes on in the alimentary canal, the parts concerned being as follows.

The saliva in the mouth is produced partly by small buccal glands, but chiefly by three or four pairs of salivary glands—the submaxillary, the sublingual, the parotid or retrolingual, and the infraorbital. The last is absent from man but present in the dog and rabbit. In man about a litre of saliva is produced a day. It contains a protein called mucin, and its chief value is to act as a lubricant. It is secreted at pH 6·4–7·0, but it is said to go alkaline on standing through loss of carbon dioxide.

The gastric glands of the stomach are tubular and form

gastric juice: this contains, besides mucus and enzymes,
0·2–0·6 per cent. of free hydrochloric acid, sufficient to
give a pH of 1 even in the presence of proteins, which act
as buffers. (Tenth Normal acid is about 0·4 per cent.)
This acid is a disinfectant, though not all Bacteria are
killed by it. Enzymes, mucus, and acid are secreted by
different types of cell.

The secreted contents of the intestine come from four
sources. Brunner's glands, in the submucosa at the upper
end only of the duodenum, produce mucus, the function of
which is to protect the epithelium from the acid of the
stomach. Succus entericus, the intestinal juice proper, is
produced mainly by tubular glands in the Lieberkuhn's
follicles (the crypts between the villi) of the duodenum.
The pancreas produces pancreatic juice. The liver produces bile, which contains no enzymes, but which is nevertheless of great importance in digestion. After secretion it
is in most mammals, including man, stored in the gall-
bladder, where water is absorbed until the solids are ten
times as concentrated as they were on arrival. The bile
contains sodium chloride and bicarbonate, the pigments
bilirubin and biliverdin (which are breakdown products
of haemoglobin), lecithin and cholesterol, and the characteristic bile salts. These vary in different animals, but are
always salts of acids closely related to cholesterol. In man
the chief are sodium taurocholate and sodium glyco-
cholate.

The secretions of Brunner's glands and the pancreas are
alkaline, the bile is nearly neutral, and the succus entericus
has a pH of 6·0. Although the pH of the pancreatic juice
is not above 8·9 it represents about N/10 base, since the
alkalinity is caused by bicarbonate, which acts as a powerful buffer. The acidity of the food passing into the intestine
from the stomach is partially neutralized, but actual
alkalinity is probably never reached. The pH of the duo-

denal contents is 4·5–5·1, that of the ileal contents
6·0–6·5.

1.311. Digestion of Proteins. There is no digestion of
protein in the mouth. In the stomach the acid breaks up
the collagen which forms the white fibres of connective
tissue, and so liberates the individual cells, which are then
more readily acted on by the enzymes. The elastin of
elastic fibres is not attacked. The chief enzyme is a proteinase called pepsin, which hydrolyses most edible proteins to proteoses and peptones and a few aminoacids, all
of which are soluble. Pepsin attacks only those peptide
bonds that are formed from the carboxyl of an *l*-dicar-
boxylic acid and the amino-group of an *l*-aromatic acid.
The chief acids that it liberates are consequently *l*-tyro-
sine and *l*-alanine. By this attack protoplasmic cell walls
are broken down, and their contents liberated. The droplets of fat from the food give a milky appearance to the
stomach content, which is then called chyme. Pepsin is
active below pH 4·5, and has an optimum which varies
from 1·5 to 2·5 according to the substrate. It is secreted as
a pro-enzyme, pepsinogen, which is unmasked by the
removal of a polypeptide by hydrochloric acid, or by
pepsin that is already present.

In the stomach of some young mammals there is another
enzyme, rennin, which has somewhat similar properties
to pepsin. It is secreted as prorennin, which is activated by
acid and then hydrolyses the same peptide bonds as does
pepsin, but with a pH optimum of about 4. It is best
known for its action on milk, which is also shared by
pepsin. The soluble protein casein is converted to para-
casein, which is precipitated as the calcium salt, so that
the milk flocculates, although the acid of the stomach may
bring the casein back into solution as the hydrochloride.
The physiological function of all these changes is obscure.

Rennin is probably absent from man, but is the chief enzyme in the abomasum (p. 28) of foetal calves (and perhaps lambs), where it is gradually replaced by pepsin after birth.

In the duodenum proteins are attacked by a battery of enzymes which hydrolyse them progressively to polypeptides, dipeptides, and aminoacids. The whole active principle from the pancreas was formerly called trypsin, but that name is now used in a more restricted sense for the pancreatic proteinase. The collection of proteases (or proteolytic enzymes—those which assist at any stage in the breakdown of proteins) in the succus entericus was formerly called erepsin, but that term has now gone out of use. The constituents into which 'trypsin' and 'erepsin' have so far been analysed are shown in Table 1. It is possible that some of the final stages of proteolytic digestion may be intracellular.

There are substances in nuclei, and in such cytoplasmic structures as mitochondria, called nucleoproteins, in which a protein of low molecular weight is combined with a nucleic acid. This consists of about fifteen to one thousand nucleotides, each made up of phosphoric acid, a pentose carbohydrate, and four purine and pyrimidine bases. In nuclei the carbohydrate is mostly d-2-desoxyribose, giving desoxyribose nucleic acid, and elsewhere it is almost exclusively d-ribose, giving ribonucleic acid. Nucleoproteins are hydrolysed by the acid in the stomach, and the protein is digested in the ordinary way. The nucleic acids are split to simple nucleotides by nucleases from the pancreas, and then nucleotidases from the intestinal mucosa split off phosphate, and nucleosidases from the same place separate the pentose from the bases.

1.312. Digestion of Fats. Both mastication and the action of pepsin on the nitrogenous cell walls cause the

TABLE I. *Proteolytic Enzymes of the Small Intestine of Mammals*

Place of secretion	Enzyme	Activation	pH optimum	Substrate	Point of application	Products
Pancreas	Trypsin	Trypsinogen unmasked by enterokinase, or by trypsin already present	8–11	Proteins Proteoses Peptones	Peptide links at ends of chain and in middle, formed from carboxyl group of lysine or arginine	Polypeptides, and aminoacids, especially lysine and arginine
,,	Chymo-trypsin	Chymo-trypsinogen unmasked by trypsin	7·5–8·5	Proteins Proteoses Peptones	Peptide links at ends of chain and in middle, formed from carboxyl group of an aromatic acid	Polypeptides, and aminoacids, especially tyrosine and phenylalanine
,,	Carboxy-peptidase (probably many)	Procarboxy-peptidase unmasked by trypsin	c. 7·3	Polypeptides	Terminal peptide link adjacent to free carboxyl group	Dipeptides and aminoacids
,,	Elastase	Proelastase unmasked by trypsin	8–9	Most proteins except keratin and collagen, but especially elastin		Soluble proteins
Small intestine	Amino-peptidase (probably many)	By metallic ions	8·0	Polypeptides	Terminal peptide link adjacent to free amino-group	Dipeptides and aminoacids
,,	Dipeptidases (probably many and specific)	By metallic ions	7·5–8·0	Dipeptides, e.g. glycyl-glycine	Amino—and carboxyl groups, and peptide link	Aminoacids

presence of droplets of fat in the chyme. There is a fat-splitting enzyme or lipase in the stomach, but it is possibly only regurgitated from the intestine and in any case it is unimportant as it has only slight activity at the acidity of the gastric contents, and that chiefly on finely divided fats such as those of egg-yolk. In the small intestine there are two lipases, one from the pancreas and one from the mucosa. Both are strongly unspecific, attacking a wide range of glycerol esters to form diglycerides, monoglycerides, and free glycerol, with one, two or three molecules of fatty acid respectively. The ease with which the action is carried out, and the pH optimum, depend on the length of the fatty acid molecule. The pancreatic lipase, which is the more important of the two, attacks most readily triglycerides of long chain-length, and has a pH optimum ranging from 7 to 9 as the length increases. The digestion of fat is greatly helped by the presence of bile, the salts of which lower surface tension, so breaking up the droplets of fat to a finer emulsion. Since the intestinal contents are never alkaline, soaps cannot be formed.

1.313. Digestion of Carbohydrates. Starch grains, the commonest form of polysaccharide in food, consist of a central core of amylose, making about a quarter of the mass, and a husk of amylopectin. Both these substances consist of chains of glucose units, but in amylopectin lengths of chain containing twenty or twenty-four glucose units are joined to form a branching chain. These branches are not separated by any digestive enzymes. Glycogen has a similar structure to amylopectin, but the branches have only twelve to eighteen glucose units. The saliva of most mammals is free, or nearly free, from enzymes, but that of Primates, pigs, elephants, and some rodents contains an endo-amylase called ptyalin (optimum pH 6·2–6·8), which attacks the simple links of both amylose and amylopectin and splits off a series of maltose molecules leaving dextrins, as may be represented in a simplified form thus:

amylose → erythrodextrin → achroodextrin
+maltose   +maltose.

Maltotriose molecules (containing three glucose units) are apparently also formed in the proportion of one for every 2·3 molecules of maltose. Glycogen is hydrolysed similarly also to maltose.

The activity of digestive amylases is greatly reduced, and their pH optima altered, in the absence of chloride ions. The extent to which salivary digestion goes on depends on the time during which the food remains in the mouth. When the swallowed food is made strongly acid in the stomach the action of amylase is stopped, but the acid takes some time to diffuse into solid food, and it may be as long as forty minutes before hydrolysis ceases. By this time very little starch is left. Ptyalin is quite incapable of attacking raw starch grains. These must first be broken down, either in the preparation of the food as by boiling, by chewing, by Bacteria, or by enzymes contained in the food itself.

The gastric juice contains no enzymes which act on carbohydrate, but the duodenal contents regurgitate into the stomach. The acid hydrolyses cane sugar, and also inulin, which, since it is the normal storage compound of the Compositae, will occasionally occur in the food of man in such things as the Jerusalem artichoke and salsify. Since vertebrates have no inulase, the action of the acid is the only way in which inulin can be digested, unless it is attacked by symbionts.

The small intestine contains an amylase and a maltase from the pancreas, and a sucrase, a maltase, and a lactase from the succus entericus. Pancreatic amylase has the same properties as ptyalin, except that it can attack raw starch grains and can split maltotriose to maltose and glucose; it is probably a mixture. The other enzymes, which are called collectively glucosidases or disaccharases, hydrolyse the appropriate disaccharides to monosaccharides; maltase splits maltose to two molecules of glucose and can also split sucrose, sucrase splits sucrose to glucose and fructose, and lactase splits lactose (milk sugar) to glucose and galactose. Lactase is especially prominent in young mammals and is the only amylolytic enzyme produced by the calf for the first month of its life.

Cellulose is very resistant; lignocelluloses are seldom digested, and the simpler types can only be attacked by special enzymes called cellulase and hemicellulase, which are not formed by vertebrates. In connexion with the long time taken to digest cellulose, it is significant that herbivores have a much longer gut than carnivores of similar size, and food may remain in the gut for a long time. The cellulose cell walls in the food of herbivorous mammals are dissolved partly by autolysis of the dead cells by their own enzymes, and partly by the action of symbiotic Bacteria. These are very prominent in the rumen of artiodactyls. Food is swallowed without being chewed, and passed into a complicated 'stomach' (Fig. 4), the last chamber of which, or abomasum, is the only one which contains gastric glands and so corresponds functionally to the stomach of other mammals. All four parts, however, develop from the normal stomach rudiment. After being swallowed the food is circulated through the rumen and reticulum, where the cellulose is attacked by Bacteria. The food is regurgitated into the mouth and chewed, and then swallowed a second time. It undergoes further mechanical trituration by the folds of the psalterium, and then goes to the abomasum for normal digestion. In cattle the food takes seven to ten days to pass through the gut, of which about four days are spent in the rumen. The Bacteria in the rumen produce large quantities of volatile fatty acids, especially acetic, propionic, and butyric, not only from cellulose but from other carbohydrates and proteins as well. These acids are absorbed in the rumen, and from them the animal gets at least one-sixth of its total supply

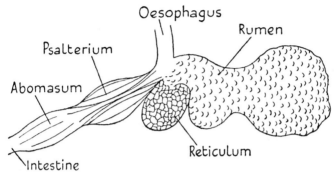

FIG. 4. Stomach of sheep, cut open, semi-diagrammatic.

of energy. The rumen is well buffered, largely by the saliva, and the pH range is from 7·5 (in starvation) to 5·8. The Bacteria produce also large quantities of carbon dioxide and methane, the carbon in which is wasted; the whole process is, from the thermal point of view, very inefficient. There is some evidence that dead Bacteria are digested in the abomasum and small intestine, so that the animal makes further use of them as food.

Also present in the rumen are a number of peculiar ciliates of the Spirotrichida and Holotrichida. According to some authors they ingest the Bacteria, and are themselves digested by the host to provide up to one fifth of its protein requirement, but they are also able to digest cellulose and other carbohydrates, producing lactic, acetic, and butyric acids. They also build up reserve carbohydrates (glucosans) within their cells, and break these down to the same acids when starved, and produce proteins of higher biological value than do the bacteria. They may therefore be of use to the host in providing a reserve food supply when grass is not available. It has been shown that sheep can live without them. Similar ciliates occur in the large intestine of the African elephant, the rhinoceros, the tapir, the guinea pig, the chimpanzee, and the gorilla.

A comparable symbiotic digestion of cellulose with production of fatty acids occurs in many other mammals. In a kangaroo, *Setonix brachyurus*, Bacteria act in an enlarged stomach. In the horse they are present chiefly in the caecum and ventral colon, and in the rabbit in the caecum. The fatty acids are presumably absorbed from the large intestine in the horse, and they may be in the rabbit, but in this animal a peculiar habit known as pseudorumination or refection or reingestion has developed. When food is first eaten, it passes rapidly through the alimentary canal to the caecum, and after one or two days is passed, early in the morning, as soft faeces. These are eaten by the rabbit, and pass to the cardiac stomach, and remain there while fresh food passes straight through as before. The twice-swallowed food is digested in the stomach and intestine in the ordinary way; it does not re-enter the caecum, but water is absorbed in the large intestine, so that dry faecal pellets are produced. Refection is also known in other lagomorphs, in many rodents, and in the common shrew.

1.314. Absorption. The first condition for absorption is that the substance must be able to pass through the walls of the epithelial cells. The ease with which these can be penetrated does not depend only on the size of the particle concerned, for although the walls are impermeable, as would be expected, to proteins, peptones, and the larger peptides, they appear also to be impermeable to the ions of magnesium, nitrate, and sulphate, and to disaccharides, while they allow much larger fatty acids to pass through. In the simple case, any molecules that can pass through the gut-wall will tend to distribute themselves uniformly, so that they diffuse along the gradient from regions of high concentration to regions where it is low, but the simple distribution may be upset in two ways. Where a membrane has differential permeability to various ions, the electric forces between the anions and cations produce a different grouping, and what is known as a Donnan equilibrium, from the name of the chemist who first investigated it, is set up. Secondly, there may be active or assisted transport, in which by various chemical processes a molecule is taken against the concentration gradient, or along the gradient more rapidly than it could diffuse. Active transport needs energy, and depends on a living and respiring membrane, while diffusion and the Donnan equilibrium occur with non-living membranes of the appropriate properties. A molecule that takes part in any reaction which leads to its active transport may be said to be primarily assisted, while molecules that are redistributed only as a result of the movement of primarily assisted substances may be said to be secondarily assisted.

The stomach absorbs some water, and small amounts of simple substances, but the main absorptive organ is the small intestine. Its surface is greatly increased by the villi, which have a characteristic structure (Fig. 5), and it is into these that the digested food goes. They undergo a constant pumping action, which helps to empty the lacteals into the plexus of lymphatics with which they connect, and also make swaying movements which constantly renew the fluid in contact with the absorptive surface. The milky liquid in the lacteals is called chyle. The lymphatics finally open into the left jugular vein by the thoracic duct. The free surface of the cells of the intestine is produced into closely packed projections, a few ten-thousandths of a millimetre long, forming what is called a brush-border. Similar structures are common where absorption is taking place, but they also occur in connexion with secretion. Some are present in the stomach.

Aminoacids are readily absorbed into the blood vessels of the villi, and are taken away by the portal system.

Fatty acids, and probably monoglycerides, are absorbed by the epithelial cells of the villi, the process being possibly assisted by phosphorylation to a lecithin-like substance. Glycerol is also absorbed, and in the cells neutral fat is resynthesized and passes into the lacteals and so to the blood. Some short-chain fatty acids, not more than 40 per cent. of the whole, are absorbed directly into the blood capillaries. The bile salts are hydrotropic, that is they form molecular complexes with substances such as fats, fatty acids, and calcium soaps, and so bring them into true solution. Bile certainly assists the absorption of fat, and it has been claimed that in the presence of fatty acid and monoglycerate it can bring neutral triglycerides into a state in which they are directly absorbed without hydrolysis. Other workers, however, deny this, as well as the absorption of diglycerides. The extent to which a fatty meal can be utilized without bile depends on its nature, but in general in men without bile something of the order of one half of the ingested fat is absorbed.

The hexoses glucose, fructose, and galactose are completely absorbed into the blood-stream. Galactose is absorbed slightly more rapidly than glucose, and both about twice as rapidly as fructose, and all are absorbed more readily from the duodenum than from the ileum. Absorption normally occurs along a concentration gradient, but is also assisted, possibly, in the case of glucose, by its conversion to glucose-6-phosphate and lactate in the cells.

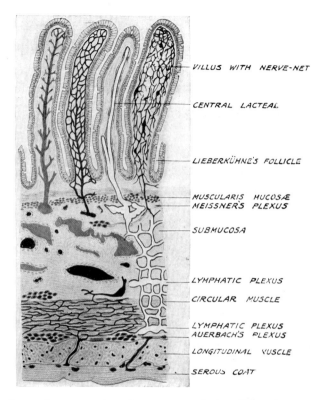

VILLUS WITH NERVE-NET

CENTRAL LACTEAL

LIEBERKÜHNE'S FOLLICLE

MUSCULARIS MUCOSÆ
MEISSNER'S PLEXUS

SUBMUCOSA

LYMPHATIC PLEXUS

CIRCULAR MUSCLE

LYMPHATIC PLEXUS
AUERBACH'S PLEXUS

LONGITUDINAL MUSCLE

SEROUS COAT

FIG. 5. Diagrammatic section through wall of small intestine to show vascular and lymphatic arrangements. After Schaffer.

This keeps the concentration of glucose in the cells low, and so maintains a false gradient of free glucose which facilitates its entry. Before it passes into the blood, the glucose-6-phosphate is hydrolysed back to free glucose. Pentoses are absorbed without assistance, but since if they are injected directly into the blood-stream they are rapidly excreted, they are unlikely to have any great value as food except under special circumstances.

The ions of sodium, potassium, and chloride are absorbed whether the concentration gradient is in their favour or not, so that there must be assistance, but the mechanism is unknown. The absorption of calcium is assisted by vitamin D, and is decreased by phytic ($=$ inositol-hexaphosphoric) acid, which is present in cereals.

In the small intestine practically all the food and much of the water has been absorbed. The material passed into the colon consists mainly of water, mucus, ions from the digestive juices, dead Bacteria, and excretions such as bile and salts of heavy metals. Only when the food contains a large amount of indigestible cellulose is any appreciable part of it present. Some more water and ions are absorbed, and the remains are ejected through the anus as faeces.

Food has generally passed through mouth, stomach, and small intestine in $4\frac{1}{2}$ hours. The stay of any residue in the colon is much longer, up to 3 or 4 days or more.

1.315. The Movement of the Food. In man and many other mammals the food in the mouth is masticated, that is to say it is broken up by the cheek teeth and rolled into a bolus by the tongue. The degree of chewing which is possible depends on the jaw articulation and this on the food. In Carnivora the dentary has a hinge-like joint with the squamosal, and lateral movement of the jaw is impossible: there is no chewing. In Artiodactyla the glenofd surface is flat, and the dentary can be moved widely from side to side so that the cellulose walls of the food can be broken up. The rabbit's jaw is somewhat similar, but the lower cheek teeth are nearer together than the upper, so that the teeth of the two sides cannot grind the food at the same time. Man, omnivorous, is intermediate, with some sideways movement. Mastication is voluntary, but it may be reflex, each closure of the jaws acting as a stimulus for their reopening.

After chewing, the bolus is swallowed: deglutition or swallowing starts as a voluntary movement, but its accomplishment is a chain of reflexes involving the movement of the food by peristalsis, the closure of the nasal and tracheal openings, and the cessation of breathing. The trigeminal, glossopharyngeal, vagus, and hypoglossal nerves are involved. Peristalsis is the chief form of muscular contraction characteristic of the gut, and consists of a wave of contraction of the circular muscle which moves from the oral to the anal end, so that its effect is to move the contents in the same direction. Antiperistalsis, which sometimes occurs by a local reversal of the reflex, moves the food in the opposite direction. The peristaltic wave in the oesophagus is started reflexly at the upper end by the contact of food entering from the pharynx, and travels downwards at about 2 cm/sec. If the food is fluid it enters the stomach 6 sec after the beginning of the act (so moving faster than the peristaltic wave), but if it is solid it takes much longer, up to 15 min to pass down the oesophagus.

As food enters the stomach its muscular wall relaxes, and the organ expands to hold, if necessary, large volumes of matter. Soon afterwards waves of contraction, three or four a minute, pass from the middle of the stomach to the pylorus. They tend to drive the food in the same direction, but since the pylorus is closed there is axial reflux, giving very good mixing. This peristaltic contraction, which starts on the entry of food, is myogenic, that is to say its co-ordination is independent of any nerve supply. After a time—about a minute when water has been swallowed—the pylorus relaxes at each wave, allowing some of the stomach contents to enter the duodenum. The mechanism by which the pylorus is controlled is not clear, but the central nervous system seems to be involved. Fat stays in the stomach longer than carbohydrate, but all food has generally left after 3 hours, while fluids usually pass through in 1 to 4 min. Vomiting is caused by compression of the stomach by a violent contraction of the diaphragm. Anti-peristalsis is normal in the stomach and oesophagus of artiodactyls, so that food is returned to the mouth.

In the small intestine the food continues to be moved by peristalsis, controlled by the deep nerve plexus (Auerbach's). In the duodenum there is some antiperistalsis, which gives good mixing, and food can be regurgitated into the stomach, particularly when that viscus is empty. Two types of peristalsis occur in the jejunum and ileum, slow waves travelling at about 2 cm/min and proceeding only short distances, and occasional rushes which travel further at about 10 cm/sec. The small intestine also undergoes segmentation movements, by which the food contents are thoroughly mixed. The wall becomes constricted into a number of segments, and then about 5 sec later the constrictions disappear and are replaced by another set exactly out of phase with the first (Fig. 6).

The ileal contents begin to pass into the colon about 4 hours after the meal, and there move more slowly, propelled by infrequent powerful contractions which occur especially when food is taken, to arrive at the rectum 14 hours to 3 days later. The normal stimulus for defecation is the filling of the rectum, and it is carried out by contraction of this viscus, aided by that of the voluntary abdominal muscles.

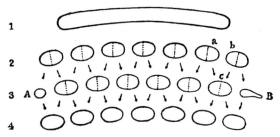

FIG. 6. Diagram of the 'segmentation' movements of the intestines as observed by Röntgen rays, after administration of bismuth.

1. A continuous column, intestinal movements being absent.
2. The column broken up into segments.
3. Five seconds later, each segment divided into two, the halves joining the corresponding halves of adjacent segments.
4. Condition (2) repeated five seconds later.
   After Cannon.

1.316. The Co-ordination of Secretion. There is a complicated and varied mechanism for ensuring that the digestive juices are available when they are wanted. Saliva is secreted as the result of taste stimuli picked up in the mouth by the fifth and ninth cranial nerves. The glands are stimulated by parasympathetic fibres in the trigeminal, facial, and glossopharyngeal nerves, and by the cervical sympathetic. As a result of the formation of conditioned reflexes (see section 6·4) saliva may be formed on the receipt of any stimulus, such as a dinner gong, connected with meals, or even by an advertisement or the mere thought of food. Gastric secretion is started by meat in the mouth through a similar appetite reflex, which may also become conditioned to new stimuli, and is continued in two other ways. Peptones in the stomach cause the pyloric mucosa to produce a hormone, gastrin, which circulates in the blood and stimulates the gastric glands, and the presence of digested food in the duodenum causes the production of another hormone, which stimulates a further small production of gastric juice. Nervous stimulation gives a juice rich in pepsin, acid, and mucus, while the hormones produce a more dilute juice.

Both the intestinal juice and the mucus from Brunner's glands are produced by mechanical stimulation, Meissner's plexus being apparently involved in the former, but there are possibly also two further duodenal hormones, enterocrinin causing the production of juice and duocrinin that of mucus. The pancreas is stimulated to produce enzymes by the vagus, and also by a hormone called pancreozymin which is formed in the duodenal mucosa when proteoses or peptones make contact with it. Another hormone, called secretin, is formed similarly when acid comes in contact with the mucosa, and causes the pancreas to secrete bicarbonate. The neutralization of the stomach contents is therefore under automatic control, for the acid acts as a stimulus for the production of base, and when the intestinal contents are nearly neutral no more secretin, and so no more bicarbonate, is produced.

Bile is at least in part an excretion and its production by the liver is continuous. It is, however, increased by the presence in the intestine of protein, fat, bile salts, or dilute acid, or by the presence of secretin in the veins. Bile is stored in the gall-bladder where it is concentrated by absorption of water and salts and receives mucin and possibly cholesterol. The gall-bladder is innervated by the vagus, in which motor impulses that cause contraction are induced by the sight of food or the act of eating; the gall-bladder is also stimulated by a hormone called cholecystokinin, formed by the duodenal mucosa on contact with digested food, particularly when this is rich in fats, which need bile salts for their digestion. In those mammals, such as perissodactyls and elephants, that have no gall-bladder, the passage of bile into the duodenum is presumably continuous.

1.32. Digestion in Other Vertebrates

The general course of digestion seems to follow the same lines in other vertebrates as in mammals. Salivary digestion is rare, but an amylase is present in the saliva of frogs and toads, and of the fowl. The stomach secretes a pepsin-like enzyme acting in acid medium, the intestinal proteases are distributed as they are in mammals, and the intestine contains amylase, disaccharases, and lipase. In bony fishes, however, both amylase and maltase are secreted predominantly by the pancreas. Small amounts of gastric lipase occur in some birds and fishes. Little work has yet been done on the identity of the enzymes in the different classes, but the individual proteases are very similar, if not identical, in fish, Amphibia, reptiles, and mammals. Salmon pepsin has been shown to be different in specificity from that of mammals and of the fowl.

The stomach contents are seldom so acid as they are in man and the dog, pH values from 2·5 to 4·5 being common in fish, Amphibia, and birds. In some rays and bony fish the stomach is alkaline, even though pepsin is present, but by contrast sharks have been reported as having an acidity twice that of man. The stomach is absent from Holocephali, Dipnoi, and many teleosts. Since the protochordates do not possess a stomach and do not produce pepsin, it is possible that the organ developed within the vertebrates, parallel with the change from microphagy to macrophagy. It may originally have been a storage organ, which is very necessary in carnivores, and high acidity and pepsin may have come later to kill the prey and give the possibility of preliminary digestion of protein. In Amphibia, including the frog, more pepsin is produced by the oesophagus than by the stomach.

In the fowl there is preliminary digestion in the crop by autolysis and by Bacteria, with production of lactic acid.

1.33. Digestion in Invertebrates

For a long time the only method available for investigating the presence of enzymes in invertebrates was to make an extract of the gut or of a gland, and observe its effect on various substrates *in vitro*. This has been done for most of the phyla, and it has been found that nearly all animals possess, in greater or less degree, proteases, carbohydrases, and lipases, only a few groups being lacking in one or other of the last two. Since the food of animals consists of proteins, carbohydrates, and fats, and of little else, these results merely give us proof of what might with little risk have been assumed *a priori*. The methods of extraction which have been used have often been rather crude, and it is often by no means certain that the enzymes identified are really secreted into the gut in the sense of being passed outside the cells. The more recent and valuable work on enzymes has involved careful preparation of the extract, exact quantitative following by analytical methods of the change of the substrate to its scission products, and meticulous attention to the hydrogen-ion concentration and other physical properties of the medium. In the 1930's Willstätter and Waldschmidt-Leitz introduced adsorption methods which enabled enzymes to be separated from one another. This for the first time made it possible to compare the enzymes of different animals. In the light of this last method of attack the earlier work, on the mere occurrence of the three great groups of enzymes, is of little interest. Beyond showing that enzymes were present, the only result of importance which it gave was the observation that the relative concentration of the enzymes in the gut bore a general relation to the type of food. For example, the closely related flies *Glossina* and *Calliphora* both contain protease, carbohydrase, and lipase, but while the blood-sucking *Glossina* has much protease and little of the other two, conditions in the vegetable-feeding *Calliphora* are exactly the reverse.

Careful adsorption methods, similar to those used to separate the proteases of vertebrates, have been applied to only a few other animals. In the crab *Maia squinado* and in the marine snail *Murex anguliferus* it has been found that the gut contains four proteases resembling those present in vertebrates, namely proteinase, carboxypeptidase, aminopeptidase, and dipeptidase. Morevoer, the pH optima are of the same order as those for the vertebrate enzymes. Since the exact values of these optima depend on the degree of purification, exact equality is hardly likely to be obtained, but the proteases of these two animals are certainly very similar to those of vertebrates. The *Maia* proteinase does not need activation, but after it has been purified it becomes inactive, and can be re-activated by enterokinase. This suggests that the proteinase of *Maia* is similar to or identical with that of vertebrates, but that in the crab it is secreted along with its activator, which is separated in the purification by adsorption. Experiments on insects, on *Helix pomatia*, on the cuttlefish *Sepia officinalis*, and on a coral, have shown that in all these the protease consists of several components. In Orthoptera, beetles, lepidopteran caterpillars, and other insects the protease consists of a tryptic proteinase, a carboxypeptidase, an aminopeptidase, and a dipeptidase. For *Sepia* the pH optima are about the level of those for trypsin, and the proteinase requires activation by an extract of the caecum of the animal. This extract can be replaced by enterokinase, and can itself activate vertebrate trypsin: there is therefore little doubt of its close similarity to enterokinase. The general conclusion which may be drawn from all these results is that certainly in the Mollusca, Crustacea, and insects, and probably in the coelenterates, protein digestion is carried out by the same series of enzymes as are present in the intestine of vertebrates, and that it is at least possible that some of them are identical in all these classes.

Invertebrates probably possess nothing which corresponds to pepsin, but a few, such as the annelid *Pheretima*, have been said to have proteases which work in a slightly acid medium.

An interesting case is that of the larva of the clothes-moth *Tineola biselliella*, which lives largely on keratin and related compounds, which are not in the ordinary way attacked by enzymes. The pH of the gut is 10, and under these conditions the keratin is reduced by a system present in a special part of the gut to products on which the animal's proteinase can act. This proteinase cannot act on proteins *in vitro* (that is, in glass vessels), but it does act on keratin which has been attacked by a weak reducing agent. Dermestid larvae have a similar method, except that the pH is not above 8·2.

The carbohydrases of invertebrates have not been so fully investigated as the proteases, but something has been made out as to their nature and distribution. Amylase from a number of groups has been shown to be very similar to vertebrate amylase: it hydrolyses starch to maltose, but cannot attack pure starch grains, and usually has a pH optimum slightly on the acid side of neutrality. In the oyster activation by salts is necessary, just as with ptyalin. In most cases it has not been separated from its associated maltase, but in the oyster they occur separately.

Inulase is present in the snail and some other animals. Cellulase and hemicellulase have been found in a number of invertebrates, notably the earthworm, the snail, the boring bivalve *Teredo*, some insects, and possibly the cray-fish. There is some evidence that in the snail cellulase and hemicellulase are identical, but that the enzyme consists of more than one component, a true cellulase breaking the cellulose to an intermediate sugar, and another hydro-lysing this to glucose. While some wood-boring insects have cellulase, phytophagous species do not, although a few, such as the earwig, have hemicellulase. A few animals, such as the snail and some insects, can digest chitin. In *Helix pomatia*, where the action is rather weak, chitin is broken down to N-acetylglucosamine. This may be a side-effect of the cellulase, since enzymes of this class sometimes have weak chitinase activity.

The three common disaccharases—sucrase, maltase, and lactase—have been found very widely in invertebrates, but next to nothing seems to be known about their rela-tions with each other or with the vertebrate enzymes. In some animals many more sugars than sucrose, lactose, and maltose can be hydrolysed, so that either several di-saccharases are present or else one enzyme can act on more than one substrate. The snail in particular can digest a very full list of sugars and related substances—at least seventeen. As there is only a limited number of hexoses from which the other sugars are built up, the second explanation is quite probable.

Lipases as a group are much less specific than proteases and carbohydrases, and all glycerol esters seem to be hydrolysed to some degree by any enzyme of this class. Invertebrate lipases differ in a number of points from those of vertebrates; they are differently affected by ions, they are inhibited in different ways, and they differ in the ease with which they attack different substrates. Many of them attack esters of lower fatty acids more readily than oils or fats, so that they are more properly called esterases than lipases. The distinction, however, is a very fine one, and it seems that even in the same species the action is sometimes stronger on fats, sometimes on esters.

In the vertebrates, the different constituents of the enzymes acting on proteins and carbohydrates are very largely produced by different glands, and to some extent act in different parts of the alimentary canal. It was therefore easy to recognize that more than one enzyme of each sort was present, even before the modern work on separating them by adsorption was begun. On the other hand, all the enzymes of an invertebrate are often produced by a single gland, and they nearly always act together in one part of the alimentary canal. This, while it means that the recognition of separate entities is difficult, also means that anatomically the gut of invertebrates is relatively simple. About such specialization as there is it is very difficult to generalize, so that each of the major groups must be taken separately. It can, however, be said that intracellular digestion is primitive, and as such is the normal method in the coelenterates and Turbellaria. It has also been retained in some higher animals which feed in such a manner as to make it possible. Of these the chief are the lamellibranchs and lower gastropods, which feed on minute vegetable particles, and the arachnids, which break down the food externally to fluid and small particles which can easily be absorbed by the cells. In many echinoderms and lamellibranchs there is a special form of intracellular digestion; large food particles may be taken up and ingested by wandering amoebocytes, which in lamellibranchs may even go outside the animal and ingest food in the mantle cavity. They can attack all three classes of food and are probably of some importance.

The advantages of extracellular digestion are many. It reduces the internal area of the gut necessary for absorption, it hastens digestion and the voiding of indigestible matter, and it enables the enzyme-secreting glands to become specialized. The last process has only just begun in invertebrates, but as described above it is well developed in the vertebrates.

1.331. Digestion in Protozoa. In the Protozoa digestion goes on in vacuoles. In all the genera which have been investigated by modern methods it has been found that the vacuoles rapidly become acid (they reach a pH of 4·0 in *Paramecium*) and that digestion goes on under these conditions. The acidity may be due at least in part to the cytolysis of the food, as the prey is always killed before there is any great departure from neutrality. When digestion is finished the hydrogen-ion concentration gradually returns to normal, and defecation occurs somewhere between pH 5·0 and pH 7·0. Protozoa seem to find proteins the easiest food to digest, many having difficulty with carbohydrate and fat. *Amoeba proteus* digests fat to glycerol and fatty acids, which pass into the cytoplasm and are there resynthesized, but *A. dubia* takes some days to digest olive-oil and *Typanosoma evansi* seems to contain neither lipase nor carbohydrase. A number of soil-living rhizopods have both cellulase and chitinase, which are presumably useful if miscellaneous organic particles are used as food. The predaceous ciliate *Didinium* is unable to synthesize peptidase, but obtains it from the Paramecia on which it lives. The enzyme is, therefore, a vitamin for this animal.

An account of protozoan digestion would be incomplete without a reference to the fact that the green flagellates are photosynthetic and sometimes (e.g. *Euglena*) saprophytic as well. Photosynthesis is, however, typically a phytological phenomenon, and it would be out of place to discuss it here.

1.332. Digestion in Coelenterata. In the coelenterates there are no special digestive glands, but in the Scyphomedusae the glandular cells are concentrated on the gastric filaments and in the Anthozoa on the mesenterial filaments. The enteron contains a proteinase which starts the hydrolysis of proteins. The further breakdown of these, and the entire digestion of fats and carbohydrates, are intracellular. Before the food particles are absorbed they may be moved about by peristalsis or ciliary currents or both. Indigestible parts of the food are extruded by the mouth, and may be removed by the ciliary currents. The green Algae which live symbiotically with many corals are of no help in supplying food.

1.333. Digestion in Platyhelminthes. Most of the Turbellaria which have been examined resemble the coelenterates in that only the preliminary breakdown of proteins is extracellular, but in some digestion goes on in the meshes of a temporary syncytium formed by processes from amoeboid cells. In some of the Rhabdocoelida digestion is mainly or perhaps entirely extracellular. The pharyngeal glands of the Turbellaria secrete mucus, and in some species of Rhabdocoelida their secretion contains enzymes which are used for external digestion.

1.334. Digestion in Annelida. The pharynx of the earthworms contains a proteolytic enzyme and a fair concentration of cellulase and chitinase; they probably come from the pharyngeal (salivary) glands, which also produce mucus. In the intestine, digestion of all types of food takes place, and in general, secretion seems to be carried out by the gut wall. Little seems to be known of digestion in polychaetes; in serpulids and sabellids the transport of the food is by cilia throughout.

1.335. Digestion in Arthropoda. There is no intracellular digestion in the Crustacea, and all the movement of the food is by muscles, since cilia are entirely absent from the group. In the decapods the food is well broken up in the gastric mill, and is at the same time attacked by a protease which is sent forward from the digestive diverticula.

At the entrance to the latter there is a complicated filter which allows only fine particles to pass. All the further digestion and most of the absorption take place here, the main midgut region being extremely short. Substances similar to or identical with the bile salts of vertebrates are present, and presumably help in the digestion of fat. Material is taken into the diverticula by the contraction of longitudinal muscles, and expelled by the contraction of circular muscles. Some decapods and copepods have a peritrophic membrane similar to that of insects.

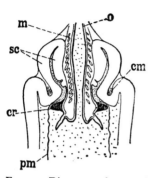

FIG. 7. Diagram of gut of earwig, *Forficula*. After Wigglesworth. The peritrophic membrane is squeezed out as a tube surrounding the food by a press formed from the posterior part of the foregut.

cr., circular ring forming inner wall of press; *cm.*, circular muscle compressing the outer wall against this ring; *m.*, sphincter muscle; *o.*, oesophagus; *pm.*, peritrophic membrane; *sc.*, cells secreting the substance of the membrane.

In some insects the labial glands contain an enzyme, for instance amylase in the cockroach and a protease in the larva of *Corethra* (Diptera), and they nearly always form a liquid which softens the food. Glands seldom open into the crop, but digestion may take place here by enzymes sent forward from the midgut, as for example in the cockroach, where fat is digested and absorbed in this region. In this animal and many others the crop is the chief site of digestion, but this is carried out mainly by yeasts and Bacteria, which are subsequently themselves digested by their host. Midgut digestion is by enzymes in the normal way, and it is also from this region that the proteases used in external digestion are generally obtained. When an insect is feeding on solid food, the bolus on leaving the foregut is enclosed in a thin sac of chitin called the peritrophic membrane (Fig. 7). This is permeable to both enzymes and digested food, and absorption takes place through it. It is absent from many fluid-feeders, such as bugs, adult Lepidoptera, fleas, lice, and tabanid flies, and from many carnivorous beetles, in which the midgut cells break down completely. The chief function of the hindgut is to absorb water, loss of which is very dangerous to insects, but in some beetle larvae digestion of symbionts and absorption of the products takes place.

Where there is a marked metamorphosis there is often a complete change-over in the enzymes produced, corresponding to the change in food. Many adult butterflies and moths have no digestive enzymes except invertase, and some, such as *Lymantria*, which has vestigial mouthparts and does not feed, have none at all. Even when invertase is present and sugar is taken, it seems not to be essential, for many moths can lay just as many eggs if they are fed on water as if they are given syrup. Many male adult Diptera and some females do not need protein, but in other species the females must have a meal of protein before they can lay eggs.

1.336. Digestion in Mollusca. The Lamellibranchia are peculiar amongst relatively advanced animals in that most of their digestion is intracellular, although some authors have maintained that the cells of the digestive diverticula fragment, and so liberate proteolytic and lipolytic enzymes into the gut. The only enzyme certainly set free in the gut is the amylase formed in the crystalline style. The latter is a rod of material consisting largely of globulin (a protein), but containing food particles and the enzyme as well (Fig. 8). It is secreted in a style sac in the intestine, and is rotated by means of cilia, its speed in the young oyster being about 70 r.p.m. It is gradually worn down in front so that the amylase is liberated and at the same time brought into very close contact with the food. The function of the protein is to maintain the pH of the gut at about 5·5, which is optimal for the amylase. In many genera the stomach has a special filtering mechanism which allows only small particles to pass into the digestive diverticula, in the cells of which further digestion takes place. Muscle is almost entirely absent from the gut, so that all the movement of the food is by cilia, which maintain a circulation through the diverticula. The more primitive Gastropoda closely resemble the lamellibranchs in their methods of digestion.

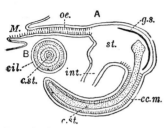

Fig. 8. Sections of part of the alimentary canal of *Donax*.

A. Longitudinal section, showing *cc.m.*, caecum of the intestine containing *c.st.*, crystalline style; *g.s.*, gastric shield; *int.*, intestine; *M.*, mouth; *oe.*, oesophagus; *st.*, stomach. B. Transverse section across the caecum showing *cil.*, ciliated epithelium, and *c.st.*, crystalline style composed of concentric layers of material. After Barrois.

Some, such as *Crepidula*, possess a style, and this produces the only extracellular enzyme, which is an amylase. In *Patella* and other genera which are without a style the amylase, again the only extracellular enzyme, is produced by lateral diverticula of the foregut. In carnivorous forms, such as *Murex*, there are extracellular proteases, which may be formed by the digestive diverticula or by buccal glands or both. In the Pulmonata, such as *Helix*, most of the digestion is extracellular, but it seems that the digestion of protein goes on only in the cells, though the evidence is conflicting. In all gastropods most of the digestion, as well as absorption, takes place in the digestive diverticula. The radula is an important feeding organ, and is lubricated by the secretion of the buccal glands. In *Dolium* and *Murex* these produce also the sulphuric acid for the solution of the calcareous shells of the bivalves on which these animals feed.

1.4. Intermediate Metabolism

All the soluble materials which the blood obtains from the small intestine suffer one of two fates: they may be built up into the tissues of the body, or they may be broken down to supply energy. In either case they undergo complex chemical changes, and in recent years, largely through the technique of introducing radioactive isotopes into the molecule, much has been learnt both of the details of the reactions and of their speed. There is an extremely rapid turnover, many atoms changing their position in the body and their state of chemical combination several times a day. Thus in 24 hours the mass of iron removed from human blood plasma is 32 mg, which is eight times that present at any one time, and half of this is used for the manufacture of haemoglobin in the bone marrow. The haemoglobin in the blood contains about 3–4 g of iron, so that all of it must be renewed once in a hundred days or so. The proteins of the rat liver have a half-life of only 6–7 days, and those of the skin of even less. The great lability of the atoms means that, from a chemical point of view, it is impossible to draw sharp dividing lines at particular points in a series of reactions which begin with those of assisted transport as the molecules enter the cells, and end only when the waste products are finally expelled from the body. Functionally, however, we may distinguish three stages. There is first the build-up of protoplasm, enzymes, reserve food substances, and any compounds that are used in the body. This is called in this book intermediate metabolism; it is in general anabolic in character. Secondly, there are the processes that lead to the formation and elimination of waste products, or excretion, and thirdly there are the katabolic processes the main or only function of which is to provide energy. In a resting egg, or in an animal in diapause, the atoms are caught at the end of the first stage; anabolism is complete, and the katabolic processes are greatly slowed down or have effectively ceased. In the active animal no such separation can be made.

In a discussion of intermediate metabolism it is convenient to deal with the three chief classes of foodstuff separately.

1.41. Protein Metabolism

Proteins are formed from aminoacids, and experiments with labelled nitrogen have shown that the complete formation of a protein molecule may take 25 min, but the mechanism of the process is unknown. It is presumably enzymatic, and in some cells the nucleus seems not to be necessary.

The nitrogen of the food, which is almost entirely in the form of protein, is generally far more than is needed for the making of new substances in repair and growth, and this is especially true of carnivores. Accordingly many of the aminoacid molecules absorbed from the gut go through a series of processes in which the nitrogen is removed and ultimately excreted, and the remainder of the molecule is made available for other uses. Since the same thing may happen to molecules of aminoacids derived from tissue proteins, the old distinction between endogenous nitrogen, which was thought of as having a semi-permanent status in the body, and exogenous nitrogen, which was that which was directly eliminated, is no longer useful.

Two processes, transamination and deamination, are important in the removal of the amino-group from aminoacids in mammals; both can go on in most tissues, but the latter is only known to occur rapidly in liver and kidney. In transamination the amino-group is exchanged for the keto-group of an α-ketoacid, and in deamination there is

$$\underset{\text{-glutamic transaminase}}{}$$

$$\underset{\substack{\text{aminoacid}}}{R \cdot CH \cdot NH_2 \cdot COOH} + \underset{\substack{\text{α-ketoglutaric acid}}}{COOH \cdot CO \cdot CH_2 \cdot CH_2 \cdot COOH} \rightleftharpoons \underset{\substack{\text{α-ketoacid} \\ \text{(e.g. pyruvic)}}}{R \cdot CO \cdot COOH} + \underset{\substack{\text{glutamic acid}}}{COOH \cdot CH \cdot NH_2 \cdot CH_2 \cdot CH_2 \cdot COOH}$$

$$\underset{\text{l-glutamic dehydrogenase}}{}$$

$$\underset{\substack{\text{glutamic acid}}}{COOH \cdot CH \cdot NH_2 \cdot CH_2 \cdot CH_2 \cdot COOH} \rightleftharpoons \underset{\substack{\text{iminoacid}}}{COOH \cdot C : NH \cdot CH_2 \cdot CH_2 \cdot COOH} + 2H$$

$$\underset{\text{(probably spontaneous)}}{}$$

$$\underset{\substack{\text{iminoacid}}}{COOH \cdot C : NH \cdot CH_2 \cdot CH_2 \cdot COOH} + H_2O \rightleftharpoons \underset{\substack{\text{α-ketoglutaric acid}}}{COOH \cdot CO \cdot CH_2 \cdot CH_2 \cdot COOH} + NH_3$$

SCHEMA I. Transamination and deamination, sometimes called transdeamination. Italics indicate enzymes.

an oxidation which removes the nitrogen as ammonia. Most commonly the two are combined, as in Schema 1.

Codecarboxylase (pyridoxal phosphate, p. 73) is required as a coenzyme in the transamination, and either coenzyme I or coenzyme II (p. 71) is needed as an acceptor of hydrogen in the first stage of the deamination. This scheme seems to account for most of the ammonia that is produced, but some aminoacids go through other pathways, such as direct deamination by l-aminoacid oxidase or by specific deaminases, or transamination in which acids other than α-ketoglutaric take part. It seems that lysine is not deaminated at all.

The ammonia produced by aquatic animals may be execreted directly (pp. 90–91) but in terrestrial animals it undergoes further changes. In mammals these take place chiefly in the liver, and are described in section 2.13. The ammonia formed in other tissues combines with glutamic acid to form glutamine, and in this form it is carried in the blood to the liver, and is also held in many tissues so that it forms a store of ammonia.

The non-nitrogenous parts of the molecules—the 'aminoacid residues'—are ketoacids which ultimately help in providing energy for the animal by taking part in one of the schemes of oxidation described below, but before doing so they may have undergone synthesis to other compounds. The residues from all the non-essential aminoacids and from a few essential ones can give rise to glucose, and are called glucogenic; the reactions that take place will be understood from section 1.43, and they are presumably of great importance in carnivores. The residues from most of the essential aminoacids either are not synthesized, or they give rise to fatty substances, when they are called ketogenic.

Since transamination is reversible, and the ketoacids that take part in it can be formed from carbohydrate, there can be synthesis of some aminoacids from non-protein sources. Experimentally the nitrogen can be supplied, as would be expected, by ammonia, but this is unlikely to be important except in special cases such as the ruminants with their symbionts, where it is known that urea can be a useful food.

Protein metabolism in the Amphibia appears to be in general similar to that in the mammals. Little is known of nitrogen metabolism in invertebrates, but it seems that in annelids, decapod crustacea, and molluscs it begins by the separation of ammonia from aminoacids, just as it does in vertebrates, and since most invertebrates produce ammonia, deamination, with or without transamination, is likely. Some silkworms are unable to digest starch, and are probably able to synthesize carbohydrate from protein. Maggots can use protein for making fat.

1.42. Fat Metabolism

Fatty substances enter into cell structure in two ways; they may be an essential constituent of protoplasm, where they are particularly important in the structure of membranes and mitochondria, or they may be present as formed materials which are easily removed and which are by no means essential for life. The structural fats are mostly combined with phosphoric acid as phosphatides, and may form structural complexes with proteins, while the reserve fats are usually in the form of neutral triglycerides, the ordinary fat of common speech. Both forms are in part built up by the animal from the fatty acids absorbed by the small intestine. There is some general connexion between the fats in the depot and those taken in the food, but each tissue of each species maintains its fats fairly constant in composition, so that there must be some power to change one fatty acid to another.

Whatever its subsequent fate, most dietary fatty acid

undergoes a process called β-oxidation, because the carbon atom next to that to which the carboxyl group is attached is first attacked. By a series of reactions involving several enzymes and coenzymes the fatty acid with two fewer carbon atoms than the original one is produced, and the process is repeated with gradual shortening of the chain. At each step the two carbon atoms that are removed appear in combination with coenzyme A (p. 73) as acetylcoenzyme A. The reactions take place mainly in mitochondria, and chiefly in the liver.

Acetylcoenzyme A is a highly reactive substance which takes part in many series of reactions. By a reversal of β-oxidation it can be synthesized to higher fatty acids, which unite with glycerol to form fats, and this mode of synthesis explains why most natural fatty acids have an even number of carbon atoms (that is, an odd number in the chain plus a carboxyl group). Since the acetyl portion of acetylcoenzyme A is also formed from glucose (p. 58), fats can be formed from carbohydrate. Most of the acetyl-coenzyme A formed from glucose is, however, oxidized to water and carbon dioxide by the tricarboxylic acid cycle (p. 59) and this is also the fate of much of that which comes from fats. When it is being produced in large amounts two molecules condense to form acetoacetic acid, which is carried to other tissues for oxidation, or exceptionally may be excreted. Acetate is probably not converted to pyruvate, so that fatty acids do not give rise to carbohydrates. In ruminants much acetic acid is produced by the Bacteria in the rumen and absorbed into the blood, and the milk fat is largely produced from this in the mammary gland.

The glycerol derived from fats is oxidized, with adenosine triphosphate as a coenzyme, to triose phosphate, and this may be either oxidized through the tricarboxylic acid cycle or synthesized to glucose and glycogen, as shown in the next section. By this means a little carbohydrate may be formed from fat.

Fat is carried in the blood largely in the form of soluble complex lipids, which are made especially in the liver. Lecithins, for example, are formed from glycerol, two aliphatic acids (not necessarily the same), and an amine-substituted phosphoric acid. The depot-fat in mammals has a high rate of turnover, the half-life being 6 to 8 days.

Fat is commonly stored in the connective tissue of all vertebrates, though Amphibia have little of it. Cold-blooded animals tend to have a higher proportion of unsaturated fats than do mammals and birds, and marine fish have much fat which is based on acids with twenty, twenty-two, or twenty-four carbon atoms. In mammals nearly all the fat is derived from acids with sixteen or eighteen carbon atoms. Fishes must therefore have a different, although presumably related, enzyme system. The salmon increases the proportion of long-chain acids in its fat when it goes to sea. Fat is also found as a storage compound in many invertebrates, as in the Platyhelminthes, in the yellow cells of earthworms, in molluscs, and in the digestive diverticula and gonad of crustaceans.

1.43. Carbohydrate Metabolism

The chief carbohydrates absorbed from the gut are hexoses, substances with six carbon atoms in the molecule. Most of the carbon atoms—five in glucose, mannose, and galactose, four in fructose—together with an oxygen atom form a ring, and the remaining one or two form a side-chain. All hexoses can form phosphates by reaction with phosphoric acid, and through these they are mutually inter-convertible. For convenience the carbon atoms are numbered. In glucose those in the ring on each side of the oxygen atom are 1 and 5, and that in the side-chain is 6, and the numbers in other hexoses correspond.

In the liver the four common hexoses are phosphorylated, and then in general built up into glycogen by a series of reactions which are shown in Schema 2, which shows also, briefly, two alternative fates. The reaction with glycogen is carried out by inorganic phosphate, but in every other reaction in which phosphate is introduced into a molecule it is obtained from adenosine triphosphate (p. 124) which is converted to adenosine diphosphate at the same time. The initial phosphorylation of the hexoses is not reversible. Most of these reactions are almost universal in living tissues, including those of plants, but they go on at different rates in different parts of the body, and the liver is the chief site of them in mammals.

The direction in which these reversible reactions move is determined by the needs and activities of the animal, and is largely under endocrine control, as described below. If energy is needed fructose-1-6-diphosphate is broken down by a series of reactions known as glycolysis. It involves many enzymes and coenzymes and can go on in all tissues. It begins by the splitting of the hexose molecule into two three-carbon units, or triose phosphates, and eventually each of these gives rise to a molecule of pyruvic acid. Each molecule of hexose has thus given two molecules of pyruvic acid, and at the same time it has lost four hydrogen atoms, which are taken up by substances called hydrogen acceptors, which are themselves reduced.

$$C_6H_{12}O_6 \rightleftharpoons 2CH_3.CO.COOH + 4H.$$

The most important of these acceptors is coenzyme I. In skeletal muscle, when oxygen is absent, the hydrogen taken up by this reduces the pyruvic acid to lactic acid. The lactic acid is carried away by the blood, and in the liver the oxidization of one-fifth of it supplies enough energy for the resynthesis of the rest to glycogen.

Pyruvic acid is oxidized in two stages. In the first, it

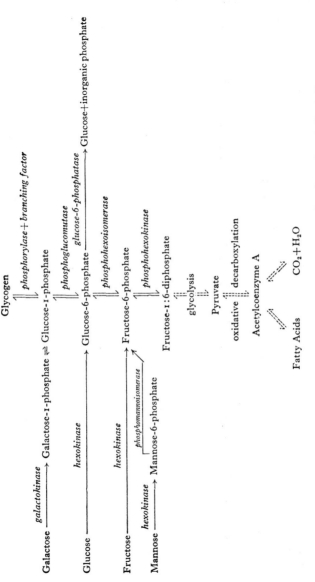

SCHEMA 2. Intermediate carbohydrate metabolism. Dotted lines indicate series of reactions, italics indicate enzymes.

reacts with coenzyme A to form acetylcoenzyme A, and at the same time loses a molecule of carbon dioxide and two hydrogen atoms. This is known as oxidative decarboxylation, and is not reversible. It needs other coenzymes, cocarboxylase (thiamine pyrophosphate, p. 69) and lipoic acid (which may be combined) and coenzyme I. Acetylcoenzyme A is then oxidized by a series of reactions called the tricarboxylic or citric acid cycle, in which it reacts with oxaloacetic acid, which is ultimately regenerated (Schema 3). Oxaloacetate is itself derived from pyruvate, and various links in the chain may be formed from noncarbohydrate sources, as shown in the schema. Molecular oxygen is not used, the oxidation taking place by the addition of water followed by dehydrogenation. In the end two molecules of carbon dioxide are formed from each acetyl radical. In total, therefore, three have been formed from each pyruvic molecule, the carbon of which is thus completely oxidized. All the enzymes of the citric acid cycle are present in mitochondria, but some are also present in the cytoplasm.

Glycolysis and the tricarboxylic acid cycle probably account for more than 90 per cent. of the oxidation of glucose in mammals, but a small part goes through an alternative pathway sometimes called the shunt, in which glucose is converted to pentose with the formation of one molecule of carbon dioxide. The reactions may be summarized:

$$6 \text{ hexose phosphate} + 3 \text{ O}_2 \rightarrow 6 \text{ pentose phosphate} + 12\text{H} + 6\text{CO}_2$$
$$6 \text{ pentose phosphate} \rightarrow 5 \text{ hexose phosphate} + \text{PO}_4^{---}$$

$$\text{hexose phosphate} + 3\text{O}_2 \rightarrow 12\text{H} + 6\text{CO}_2 + \text{PO}_4^{---}$$

The hydrogen atoms are removed by coenzyme II.

Little work seems to have been done to find out whether the tricarboxylic acid cycle occurs in animals other than mammals. Many of the necessary enzymes are present in

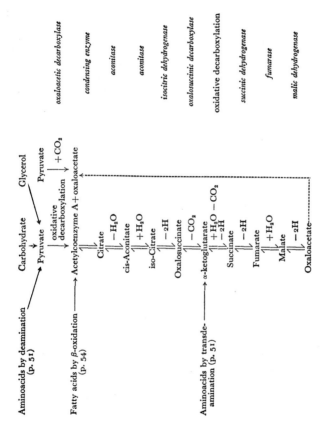

SCHEMA 3. The tricarboxylic, or citric, acid cycle. Italics indicate enzymes.

locusts, but as succinic dehydrogenase, which is a key-enzyme in the cycle, could not be detected, it is unlikely that the cycle is important in these animals.

Intermediate carbohydrate metabolism is regulated by several hormones, chief of which are those from the islets of Langerhans in the pancreas. Insulin causes glucose to disappear, and it does so by acting on all four of the chief lines of change that glucose can undergo—conversion to lactate, and to fatty acids, oxidation to carbon dioxide, and synthesis to glycogen. It therefore probably affects the reaction that precedes all of these, that is the conversion of glucose to glucose-6-phosphate by adenosine triphosphate, and there is evidence that it does so both by increasing the rate of entry of glucose from the tissue-fluids to the cell, so having a mass-action effect, and by altering the end-point of the phosphorylation directly. Insulin is liberated into the blood whenever the concentration of glucose in the blood is raised. In the disease diabetes mellitus its production is deficient, the blood sugar rises, and is then excreted in the urine. The disease can be treated by the administration of insulin, which must be carefully regulated in amount to prevent too much glucose being removed. A deficiency of insulin also causes impaired synthesis of proteins and fatty acids, but these effects may be secondary to that on carbohydrate.

Glucagon, another hormone from the islets, increases the blood sugar by accelerating the phosphorylation and breakdown of liver glycogen to give glucose-1-phosphate, and shifting the equilibrium to the right. It therefore assists insulin in aiding the utilization of glucose in muscle.

Adrenaline also assists the phosphorylation of liver glycogen, and as it increases also the production of lactic acid from muscle glycogen it provides more material from which liver glycogen is made. Cortin, from the adrenal cortex, has complex effects, the chief of which seem to be an increase in the formation of carbohydrates from fats and proteins, and a slowing of oxidation. Adrenocortico-tropic hormone from the anterior pituitary acts by stimulating the activity of the adrenal cortex, and it increases also the production of adrenaline. Growth hormone, also from the anterior pituitary, has complex effects, most of which may be secondary to its effect in increasing protein synthesis.

The link between all the processes of metabolism is the transport carbohydrate, which is normally and chiefly glucose though in the foetus of artiodactyls and the horse there is much fructose. Glucose enters the blood not only from the gut during digestion, but from the liver, where it is formed by the reversal of the path of glycogen synthesis, and is formed indirectly from muscle glycogen (via lactic acid and liver glycogen) and from protein and fat. Its concentration in the blood is kept sensibly constant in man at about 100 mg/100 ml by the action of all these hormones and by the sympathetic nervous system. Stimulation of the hepatic branch of the vagus causes the conversion of glycogen to glucose, and stimulation of the pancreatic branch causes the secretion of more insulin. The effects of the hormones are summarized in Schema 4.

Other vertebrates, while probably similar in general, differ in detail. The concentration of blood sugar of birds is about twice that of mammals, and this may be connected with the poverty of the pancreas in β-cells and its richness in α-cells. Removal of the pancreas from grain-eating birds causes only a mild hyperglycaemia, which disappears within a week, but a similar experiment on an owl caused extreme hyperglycaemia and death, just as it would in a mammal. Hyperglycaemia can be induced in a pancreatectomized duck by feeding it with meat. Lizards are sensitive to glucogen but not to insulin, and so removal of the pancreas causes hypoglycaemia. Pancreatectomy

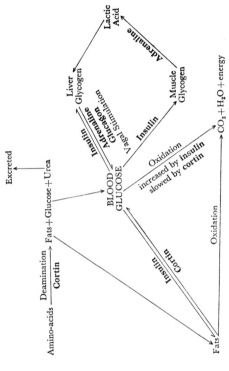

SCHEMA 4. The control of blood sugar in mammals. Modified from Moore. Hormones are in heavy type.

in urodeles causes a hyperglycaemia that is not relieved by removal of the pituitary.

Glycogen is apparently one of the main storage substances in all vertebrates, and that of the cod appears to be similar to that of mammals. The question of storage in the invertebrates seems to have been little investigated, but glycogen is common, as it is found in *Pelomyxa* (a rhizopod), the peritoneum of earthworms, the connective tissue and gonads of molluscs, and the digestive diverticula of crustaceans. The snail *Helix pomatia* contains also a substance galactogen, which is similar to glycogen but is not attacked by amylase, and on acid hydrolysis yields galactose instead of glucose.

1.5. Vitamins

During the last half-century there has gradually developed the knowledge that the classical constituents of a diet—water, carbohydrates, fats, proteins, and mineral salts—are not by themselves adequate to ensure growth or maintain a healthy life. To the accessory food substances which are required in addition Funk in 1912 gave the name vitamine, the terminal 'e' being afterwards dropped when it became certain that the vitamins had no particular connexion with amines. The number of known vitamins increases as research progresses, and many of them are now available in crystalline form and have had their chemical composition determined.

For a substance to qualify as a vitamin three properties only are necessary: it must be organic; a small quantity of it must be enough for life; and the animal must be unable to manufacture it, or at least unable to manufacture enough of it. In spite of the apparent simplicity of these criteria a formal definition of a vitamin is difficult. Some substances are 'partial vitamins', that is, the animal can make some, but not enough; an example is choline, which mammals can make from the amino-acid methionine, or from proteins such as casein which contain this, although man at least always needs some choline in the diet. There may be a series of increasing ability to synthesize a given vitamin, so that in the limit one species can make all it needs and the substance ceases to be a vitamin at all. The rat, for instance, needs ascorbic acid (vitamin C) just as does man, but can synthesize all it wants from glucose. Sometimes the form in which the substance is supplied in the food is slightly different chemically from that in which it is used in the body, so that one can distinguish the 'provitamin' in the diet from the vitamin in the tissues—and here, strictly speaking, the vitamin is made by the animal. Examples are β-carotene which is the precursor of vitamin A, and thiamine, which is phosphorylated in the tissues to co-carboxylase.

One possible way of defining vitamins would be to say that they are all those organic substances, other than carbohydrates, fats, and proteins, which are required in the food either in the active form, or as simple precursors th at are not themselves carbohydrates, fats, or proteins. This would have the advantage that it would settle the position of those substances which, although they belong to one or other of the three main groups, have sometimes been regarded as vitamins because of their essential nature and requirement in small quantities. Examples are the aminoacid phenylalanine, a constituent of many proteins and probably a precursor of adrenaline, and the un-saturated acids linoleic, linolenic, and arachidonic, which are important constituents of the phospholipids of yolk and nervous tissue.

The functions of many vitamins are now known, and most of them are coenzymes in various chemical processes. The clinical signs and symptoms by which the early vitamins were recognized are expressions of an underlying upset of chemical processes caused by their deficiency or absence.

A diet poor, but not completely lacking, in a particular vitamin, may cause general ill development without the presence of any recognizable disease. Adding milk, which is rich in many vitamins, to an institutional diet previously regarded as adequate, caused a gain in growth-rate of 3 lb in weight and nearly an inch in height per boy per year. Since, of people living together on similar diets, some may show signs of disease and others not, either there must be different individual requirements for vitamins or there must be different abilities to synthesize them. Both of these may depend in part on the differing activities, either in destruction or synthesis, of the micro-organisms in the gut and other parasites.

In an assessment of the value of a food as a source of vitamins care must be given to the effects of cooking and other forms of treatment. Meat, fish, and eggs in general suffer little loss in the ordinary processes to which they are subjected, but there is some loss of the B-vitamins in cooking and canning. Milk suffers little loss in pasteurizing or spray or roller drying, but there is a big loss of vitamin C and of thiamine in evaporated milk and smaller losses in sweetened condensed milk. The heaviest loss in vegetables is by shredding, especially by a blunt knife, which causes subsequent oxidation of vitamin C and of carotene as a result of the damage to the cells.

The basic requirements for vitamins appear to be broadly similar throughout the vertebrates. Some species or groups can synthesize what others cannot, but the chief differences arise in those animals such as the ruminants which have important symbionts in the gut. These may be able to synthesize all or nearly all of the hosts' needs for many of the accessory factors.

The vitamins were formerly known only by the letters of

the alphabet, but those of which the chemistry is known are now generally called by definite names. The classification into water-soluble and fat-soluble is probably not important, and so for convenience the list which follows is arranged in alphabetical order.

1.51. Vitamin A

Vitamin A_1 is fat-soluble and is present in all body tissues but particularly in the waxy part of the fat of both mammalian and fish liver, and to a lesser extent in milk-fat and eggs. It is not destroyed by ordinary cooking and keeps well. It is also formed in the intestinal mucosa from β-carotene, one of the constituents of the green pigment of plants, which is therefore an important dietary source, particularly in herbivores. The formula of β-carotene is

This can be split *in vitro* into two molecules of vitamin A_1, which is but it is said that in the animal only one molecule is produced. Vitamin A_2, which occurs in the livers of fish and Amphibia, usually in addition to vitamin A_1 but occasionally by itself, differs from vitamin A_1 in possessing a second double bond in the $3:4$ position of the ring and has about 40 per cent. of its biological activity. While the free alcohol of vitamin A circulates in the blood, the form stored in the liver is the ester.

The most striking effects of an inadequate supply of vitamin A are certain defects of the eyes—in children xerophthalmia, an inflammation of the cornea and conjunctiva, and in adults night-blindness, an inability to see in twilight. With these are associated other symptoms, particularly in children a diminution of rate of growth, maldevelopment of bone and teeth, and an increased susceptibility to the common skin infections like rashes and boils. The feature common to many of these is an increased keratinization of epithelia, which leads to the disease either directly, or indirectly by making it easier for Bacteria to invade the affected part. The effects of deficiency on bone and teeth depend on a reduced activity of the epiphyseal cartilage and osteoclasts and on a degeneration of the odontogenic epithelium. In tissue cultures, chick ectoderm deprived of vitamin A becomes keratinized, but if it is given excess of the vitamin it becomes a mucus-secreting ciliated epithelium instead of developing normally. Corneal epithelium similarly comes to resemble conjunctiva. Vitamin A_1 aldehyde (retinene) is the non-protein part of the visual purple of the retina (p. 302), and night blindness is caused by non-formation of this pigment. The protective value of vitamin A applies only to epithelia. As, however, this type of tissue is widespread, and as many of the parasites which infect man must pass through epithelia by their own efforts in order to do so, the importance of an adequate supply of the vitamin is obvious. Excess is toxic, and occurs in animals and men who eat too much polar-bear liver.

1.52. Vitamins of the B-group

In the early days of the investigation of vitamins a deficiency of one water-soluble substance was thought to be the cause of a wide variety of symptoms, but it was soon shown that several substances, called vitamin B_1, B_2, and so on, were concerned. They have little in common except that they often occur together in food, and it is best to use their individual names. Eleven are now well established, and there are probably others. Nearly every one of them forms part of a coenzyme necessary for the metabolism of protein, fat, or carbohydrate. Many of them can be synthesized by Bacteria present in the normal mammalian gut and all of them by those in the rumen of artiodactyls. These mammals consequently have requirements of the vitamins which are different from, and in general lower than, those of others. Rodents also get an adequate supply of some B-vitamins through their habit of coprophagy. Rats provided with sorbitol, an alcohol related to glucose, can also survive without either coprophagy or B-vitamins, apparently because this substance enables the intestinal Bacteria to make enough of them.

1.521. Thiamine

Thiamine, or aneurin, or Vitamin B_1, is nowhere present in large quantities but is widely spread, and occurs in wholemeal, peas, beans, yeast, milk, and eggs. It is not appreciably destroyed by 3 hours' heating at 100° C, so that dried eggs and wholemeal bread and biscuit are satisfactory sources. At 120° C it is rapidly destroyed, so that it is absent from canned food. Many biological materials, including raw fish-flesh and bracken

and other plants, contain thiaminases, and so are poisonous
unless accompanied by excess of the vitamin. The formula
of the transport form of thiamine is

$$
\begin{array}{c}
\text{N}=\text{C}-\text{NH}_2 \\
\text{H}_3\text{C}-\text{C}\quad\text{C}-\text{CH}_2-\text{N}\underset{\underset{\text{CH}_3}{|}}{\overset{\diagup\text{CH}-\text{S}}{\diagdown}}\text{C}=\text{C}-\text{CH}_2-\text{CH}_2\text{OH} \\
\text{N}-\text{CH}\qquad\text{Cl}
\end{array}
$$

The chief disease produced by a deficiency is beri-beri,
in which there is muscular wasting, anaesthesia of the
skin, and finally paralysis of the muscles. Beri-beri is
associated with a diet of polished rice, that is rice with the
embryo and pericarp removed, these being the parts which
contain the vitamin. Experimentally its deficiency causes
similar diseases, particularly polyneuritis in birds. The
fundamental effect is an upset of respiration, for the active
form of thiamine is the pyrophosphate, which is co-carboxylase, one of the coenzymes responsible for the oxidative decarboxylation of pyruvic acid and α-ketoglutaric
acids (p. 58). This is also the path by which carbohydrate
is converted to fat, and rats need less thiamine on a high-
fat diet than on a low one. Indeed, if their diet is completely free from carbohydrate they can survive for months
without thiamine, so that it is not necessary for the provision
of energy from fat alone.

1.522. Vitamin B$_2$

The original vitamin B$_2$ was first split into riboflavin
and nicotinamide, and then other constituents were discovered, so that although the name is sometimes applied
to the former it is best abandoned.

1.5221. Riboflavin

Riboflavin or lactoflavin is found in most tissues, but

the best sources are milk, liver, kidney, and egg-white. Its
formula is

$$\text{H}\quad\text{CH}_2\text{—CHOH—CHOH—CHOH—CH}_2\text{OH}$$

(structure of riboflavin)

Its deficiency results in man in inflammation of the mouth,
nostrils, and scrotum, and in crying and fatigue of the
eyes. Mild degrees of deficiency are common, and are
presumably signs of an upset of oxidation in the cells, for
riboflavin is a constituent of two coenzymes, riboflavin-
5-phosphate or flavin mononucleotide (FMN), and riboflavin adenine dinucleotide (FAD), which are bound to
proteins as flavoproteins and are hydrogen acceptors.
Reduction occurs across the two —N= double bonds.

1.5222. Nicotinamide

Nicotinamide, and nicotinic acid from which it is
easily derived, are widespread, but the chief sources
are meat, liver, yeast, and wheat germ. The formulae are:

(structures of nicotinamide and nicotinic acid)

Nicotinamide   Nicotinic acid

Nicotinic acid may be synthesized to some extent in
most mammals, including man, and in fowls, from the

aminoacid tryptophan, so that deficiency occurs only when the diet is low in both the vitamin and protein; it causes the disease pellagra, the symptoms of which are diarrhoea, dermatitis, and dementia. It is almost entirely a maize-eaters' disease, and was formerly very common in the southern states of the United States of America, and followed the introduction of maize into Europe and Africa. The disease arises because the vitamin, though present in the cereal, is in a bound form in which it is not available, though it can be liberated by alkaline hydrolysis. Deficiency in other mammals does not produce such marked symptoms, except for the disease black tongue in dogs.

Nicotinamide is the active constituent of diphospho-pyridine nucleotide (DPN, coenzyme I), which is the hydrogen acceptor in most dehydrogenase reactions, and of triphosphopyridine nucleotide (TPN, coenzyme II), which is the acceptor in a few dehydrogenations, such as that of glucose-6-phosphate in the shunt (p. 58). Two hydrogen atoms are added to the benzene ring, with loss of a double bond.

1.523. Biotin

Biotin, formerly known as vitamin H, is found in liver, kidney, yeast, egg-yolk, and milk, and has the chemical structure

$$NH—CH—CH—(CH_2)_4—COOH$$
$$CO \qquad | \qquad S$$
$$NH—CH—CH_2$$

Raw egg-white contains a protein called avidin which combines with biotin in the gut and prevents its absorption, so that the easiest method of producing biotin-deficiency in an animal is to give it a diet with much egg-white. Natural deficiency probably never occurs. Biotin probably assists in a number of reactions, such as the decarboxylation of oxaloacetic acid, the deamination of aspartic acid, and the synthesis of oleic acid, but its exact function is unknown.

1.524. Inositol

Inositol is widely distributed; the chief foods containing it are liver, beef, fruits, and cereals. It is one of the stereoisomers of hexahydroxycyclohexane, and has the formula

$$
\begin{array}{c}
H \\
O \\
| \\
C \\
H \\
\end{array}
$$

HO—CH   HC—OH

HO—CH   HC—OH

$$
\begin{array}{c}
H \\
C \\
| \\
O \\
H \\
\end{array}
$$

It has been known since 1850, when it was isolated from muscle, and called 'muscle sugar'. Experimental deficiency causes reduced growth and loss of hair in rodents, but its status in man is unknown. Its hexaphosphoric ester, or phytic acid, reduces the absorption of calcium.

1.525. Choline

Choline is present in all cells, chiefly as a constituent of lecithins, and so is commonest in such foods as egg-yolk, liver, kidney, and the germ of cereals. Its formula is

$$(CH_3)_3N(OH)—CH_2—CH_2OH$$

and most mammals can synthesize it from methionine and aminoethanol. Experimental deficiency leads to fatty livers in mammals and to a shortening and thickening of the bones (perosis) in birds. Its chief function is to supply methyl groups, which can also be obtained from methionine, and its vitamin status in man is doubtful. As a constituent of phospholipids it is important in the transport of fats and in the formation of cell-membranes, and it is the normal substance from which acetylcholine (p. 252) is formed.

1.526. Pantothenic Acid

Pantothenic acid is found in most cells, but the best sources are liver, kidney, green stuff, and yeast. Its formula is

$$HOCH_2-\underset{\underset{CH_3}{|}}{\overset{\overset{CH_3}{|}}{C}}-CHOH-CO-NH-CH_2-CH_2-COOH$$

Chicks deprived of it fail to grow, and develop dermatitis, while rats are similarly affected but also show anaemia and greying of the hair. Deficiency in man is unknown. Pantothenic acid is a constituent of coenzyme A, which is of great importance in intermediate metabolism (p. 54).

1.527. Pyridoxal

Pyridoxal or vitamin B_6 is widely distributed in foods, the principal sources being meat, liver, green vegetables, and wheat germ. Pyridoxin and pyridoxamine also occur in foods and are converted into pyridoxal in the body. The formulae are:

Pyridoxal   Pyridoxin

$$CH_2NH_2$$

Pyridoxamine

Experimental deficiency of pyridoxal in man and other mammals causes anaemia, loss of weight, and other symptoms. Both pyridoxal phosphate and pyridoxamine phosphate are coenzymes in various decarboxylations, particularly in transamination (p. 50), and are known as codecarboxylases.

1.528. Folic Acid.

Folic or pteroylglutamic acid, or vitamin M, occurs chiefly in green vegetables, fruit, cereals, and liver. It consists of para-aminobenzoic acid linked at one point to glutamic acid and at another to a pterin (a compound with a double ring of six carbon and four nitrogen atoms), and is converted in the liver, with ascorbic acid as a catalyst, into folinic acid, which differs by the presence of three extra hydrogen atoms and a formyl group. This is the most active form of the vitamin; a number of other related substances have similar biological properties. Deficiency in man causes the tropical disease called sprue, and an anaemia in which the red cells are enlarged. Folinic acid takes part in the synthesis of many nitrogen-containing compounds, such as methionine, purines, choline, and desoxyribosenucleic acid, and is necessary for the proper formation of erythrocytes.

1.529. Cyanocobalamin.

Cyanocobalamin or vitamin B_{12} is found in liver, kidney, meat, and milk. Its formula is $C_{63} \ H_{90} \ O_{14} \ N_{14} \ P \ Co$, many of the carbon atoms being arranged in a series of rings, and the cobalt being attached to nitrogen atoms by co-ordinate bonds. Other closely related compounds occur and are easily converted to this. It is the only vitamin which, so far as is known, contains a metal atom.

As cyanocobalamin is absent from plants, deficiency occurs in strict vegetarians, but more important is the disease pernicious anaemia. In this the vitamin is present in the food but it is not absorbed because of the absence of a substance called intrinsic factor, which is normally secreted by the gastric mucosa. Cyanocobalamin is involved in the metabolism of proteins, fats, carbohydrates, and nucleic acids, presumably because it enters into a reaction basic to all these, but there is no evidence as to what this may be. Desoxyribosenucleic acid, and probably ribonucleic acid, are not made without it. Both cyanocobalamin and folinic acid are necessary for the formation of red blood cells, and the latter can largely, but not entirely, replace the former.

1.53. Ascorbic Acid

Ascorbic acid or vitamin C is water-soluble; there are small quantities in milk and liver, but it is found chiefly in fresh fruits and vegetables, though its distribution is not very uniform. The Mediterranean lemon (*Citrus medica* var. *limonum*) is a good source, but the West Indian lime (*C. medica* var. *acida*) is a poor one. It is very easily oxidized, particularly in alkaline solution; lemon-juice brought to a pH of 12·5 and left exposed to the air loses all its vitamin C in 3 hours, but at pH 7·0 it is hardly affected by a week's exposure to the atmosphere. Vegetables and potatoes cooked in the ordinary way lose less than half their ascorbic acid, and it is sometimes present in canned foods, if these are acid and have been preserved in absence of air.

Ascorbic acid has been synthesized from *d*-galactose,

and exists in an oxidized and a reduced form, the formulae of which are

reduced   oxidized

So far as is known, all mammals except primates, guinea-pigs, and marmots can synthesize it, probably from both glucose and galactose.

Deficiency in man causes scurvy, a painful and often fatal disease characterized by haemorrhage of the limbs and gums. The fundamental cause of these symptoms is a defective formation of the cement substance that binds cells together, so that the endothelial cells of capillaries are more easily separated and bleeding through the walls readily occurs. The ease of transformation from the reduced to the oxidized form suggests that it may be a coenzyme in some dehydrogenase reactions, but the means by which it prevents scurvy are unknown. It is needed also for the production of collagen in bone and other tissues, and it is possible that in deficiency the constituent that goes wrong is a mucopolysaccharide; there is a failure of the matrix of bone, not of calcification. There is a low concentration of ascorbic acid in the body in tuberculosis, and scorbutic guinea-pigs have an excessive liability to infection, so that it may confer some general protection against disease.

1.54. Vitamin D, Calciferol

Vitamin D is fat-soluble, but it is not found in high concentration in any common foods. The best source is fish-liver oil, particularly from the cod, halibut, and tunny. Some is present in egg-yolk, oysters, and mushrooms. Although all these are unusual or expensive foods a deficiency of D is not common except in northern countries, because it is readily formed by ultra-violet irradiation of ergosterol, which is widely distributed, and of 7-dehydrocholesterol; both these substances are therefore provitamins. Sunlight is an adequate source of the radiation, and the reaction can take place in the skin of animals, including man.

Vitamin D occurs in two forms, calciferol (vitamin D_2) and cholecalciferol (D_3), the former having an extra methyl group. Both have molecules based on the structure of the steroids (p. 236), but the B-ring is broken between atoms 9 and 10. Mammals can use either, but poultry need D_3. The name vitamin D_1 was given in error to an impure product containing calciferol, and is not now used.

Deficiency of vitamin D causes true rickets in children from 9 months to 2 years old, adolescent rickets in older children, and osteomalacia in adults. In all of these there is malformation of bone and dentine, caused in growing children by a failure to lay down calcium and phosphate in the new tissue, and in adults by the removal of these minerals, so that the bones bend and become distorted in rickets and fracture in osteomalacia.

Rickets can be produced experimentally not only by restriction of vitamin D, but also by a deficiency of calcium or phosphorus in the food, and by an unusual calcium/phosphorus ratio. Rickets is associated with a deficiency of phosphorus in the blood, and the associated tetany with a similar deficiency of calcium, so that it is unlikely that vitamin D acts by increasing the rate of deposition of these in the bone. More probably it increases the net absorption of them from the gut. In rickets nearly all the calcium taken in the food is passed out with the faeces, and so is two-thirds of the phosphorus. In normal animals much smaller quantities are lost. Excess of vitamin D given to dogs reduces still further the amount of these two elements in the faeces, increases the amount in the blood, and leads to increased calcification, and calcification in improper places such as the arteries and kidneys. Many vegetable foods contain substances that reduce the absorption of calcium, and therefore produce rickets when taken in large quantities. The best known of these is phytin, present in cereals, especially oats. Fortunately on slow boiling it is largely destroyed by phytase, so that little remains in porridge.

The method by which vitamin D increases absorption is unknown.

1.55. Vitamin E or Tocopherols

The tocopherols are fat-soluble, but, like A, are present in the waxy, not the fatty, parts of such fats as those of the embryos of seeds, green leaves, and to a lesser extent milk, flesh, and egg-yolk. They are quite stable, but are destroyed in rancid fats. Four naturally occurring tocopherols are known. The formula of the most active, α-tocopherol, is

$$H_3C \underset{\underset{\displaystyle CH_3}{|}}{\overset{\overset{\displaystyle CH_3}{|}}{\underset{5}{\overset{7}{\bigcirc}}}} \overset{CH_3}{\underset{H_2}{\overset{O}{\bigcirc}}} \overset{|}{\underset{H_2}{C}} -(CH_2)_3 \cdot \overset{CH_3}{\overset{\cdot}{CH}} \cdot (CH_2)_3 \cdot \overset{CH_3}{\overset{\cdot}{CH}} \cdot (CH_2)_3 \cdot \overset{CH_3}{\overset{\cdot}{CH}} \cdot CH_3$$

β-tocopherol, which lacks a methyl group at position 7 in the benzene ring, has only 40 per cent. of the activity of the α-form, γ-tocopherol, which is without the methyl group at position 5, has 8 per cent. and δ-tocopherol, with neither of these methyl groups, has only 1 per cent.

Absence of tocopherol causes sterility in rats in both male and female. In the former the seminiferous tubules degenerate, the sperms lose their motility, and the animals lose their normal interest in the opposite sex. When all the tubules have degenerated the effect is irreversible. In the female a lack of tocopherol produces defects of the allantois and yolk-sac which lead to asphyxia and starvation of the foetus, and its resorption in a late stage of pregnancy. This is a temporary effect, and if tocopherol is administered in time the next pregnancy is normal.

The effects on males are similar in dogs, rabbits, and monkeys, and on females in mice and guinea-pigs, but deficiency has not been shown to occur in man. In all the above species, and in ruminants and domestic birds, deficiency also causes skeletal muscular dystrophy and weakness, and in some species cardiac and smooth muscles are affected.

The fundamental action of vitamin E probably lies somewhere in the field of oxidation, possibly in the cytochrome c reductase system (p. 119). Deficiency leads to excessive utilization of the reserves of vitamin A in the liver, and the tocopherols probably protect other substances from oxidation in a similar way.

1.56. Vitamin K

Vitamin K_1 is fat-soluble and occurs most abundantly in green vegetables, tomatoes, and pig liver. It is 2-methyl-3-phytyl-1:4-naphthaquinone, and has the formula

$$\text{C—CH}_2\text{—CH=C·(CH}_2)_3\text{—CH·(CH}_2)_3\text{—CH·(CH}_2)_3\text{—CH—CH}_3$$

A related substance, vitamin K_2, with a longer side-chain, is formed by Bacteria, including those of the gut, from which it may be absorbed.

In deficiency the liver does not form adequate amounts of the substance prothrombin, which is necessary for normal blood coagulation, and small cuts therefore cause prolonged bleeding. Deficiency is common in new-born babies. A number of other naphthaquinones, including 2-methyl-1:4-naphthaquinone, called vitamin K_3, also promote the clotting of blood. A substance called dicoumarin, which is present in the plants called melilots, *Melilotus officinalis* and *M. alba*, of which the former was formerly cultivated for fodder but has been long replaced in Great Britain by clover, antagonizes the action of vitamin K, so that improperly cured hay in which this substance is present in highly poisonous to cattle.

1.57. Other Vitamins

A few other vitamins, the importance or even the existence of which is doubtful, have been described. Flavonal glucosides found in lemon juice are said to be necessary to prevent capillary haemorrhage in guinea-pigs and have been called vitamin P, while methylnornarcotine, which has been alleged to be antiscorbutic, has been called vitamin R. Some unsaturated fatty acids—linoleic, linolenic, and arachidonic—are essential nutrients and have been called vitamin F but they cannot be made to fit into any reasonable definition of vitamin. They occur in the animal body chiefly as phospholipides, but arachidonic is present in small quantities in storage fat of cattle and pigs. The other two are present in seeds, and their esters make up a large part of the drying oils of commerce, but their presence in animal storage fats seems to be doubtful.

1.58. Vitamins in Invertebrates

It will be clear from what has already been said that while most of the B-vitamins are coenzymes in fundamental chemical processes that go on in almost all living cells, the fat-soluble vitamins and ascorbic acid are of more specialized function. It is therefore not surprising that B-vitamins are needed by many invertebrates, but that the others are required much less widely. Only in the insects and a few Protozoa has much systematic work been done.

Most of the insects which have been studied (chiefly Orthoptera, Coleoptera, Lepidoptera, and Diptera) need six members of the B-complex—thiamine, riboflavin, nicotinic acid, choline, pantothenic acid, and pyridoxal—and some need biotin and folic acid. The differences between the requirements of the various species are probably due not so much to any different needs of the animals as to the presence or absence of symbiotic micro-organisms. Many insects bear yeasts or bacteria intracellularly in special structures called mycetocytes, and have arrangements for infecting the eggs with them. Those of two species of beetle have been shown to manufacture several of the B-vitamins. These symbionts are chiefly found in insects with restricted diets, such as the louse, *Rhodnius*, and the tsetse fly, where the larva as well as the imago feeds on blood, and are absent from species such as the gnats and fleas where the larva has a more generalized diet. Insects seem not to need vitamin A or ascorbic acid but some need α-tocopherol. Most of those which have been tested need cholesterol or a related sterol, but they are unable to utilize calciferol.

Many Protozoa need one or more members of the B-group, and some trypanosomes and the flagellate *Trichomonas* need ascorbic acid or some other substance as a substitute for it. The snail *Helix pomatia* seems to need some unidentified B-vitamins and sterols for growth, and the growth and reproduction of *Hymenolepis diminuta*, a tapeworm of rats, are greatly reduced if the host is fed on a diet containing thiamine but lacking the other B-vitamins. The anaemia caused by *Diphyllobothrium latum* is due to its accumulating cobalamin from the food of its host.

Carotene is widespread in the invertebrates, but vitamin A, which has recently been sought in all the main phyla, is much less common. Vitamin A_2 has not been found, and A_1 occurs in a few nematodes and perhaps echinoderms and annelids, and in many molluscs and Crustacea. In the cephalopods and Crustacea it is present in the well-developed eyes, and it seems to function here in a similar way to what it does in vertebrates (p. 302). The position in insects is obscure. Vitamin A has not been found, but its aldehyde retinene is present in the eyes of honey-bees, and it seems unlikely that the biochemistry of vision in insects would be fundamentally different from that in Crustacea—unless, indeed, as has been suggested, the two groups arose independently from a pre-annelid ancestor. Cephalopods, which have much esterified vitamin A in the liver, may use it more generally, as do the vertebrates, and *Helix pomatia* also needs it for growth.

It is at least possible that some invertebrates might need as vitamins substances quite different from those required by mammals, but the only definite examples seem to be carnitine, a betaine with the formula

$$(CH_3)_3N^+\!\!-\!\!CH_2\!\!-\!\!CHOH\!\!-\!\!CH_2COO^-,$$

which is essential for the growth of the mealworm, and the peptidase required by *Didinium* (p. 44).

2

EXCRETION

Iɴ many of the chemical reactions which go on in the animal body, whether their object is to provide energy or to make some definite substance which the animal needs, by-products are formed for which there is no immediate use. Any process by which these by-products are so treated that they take no further part in metabolism is called excretion. The term is not generally applied to the voiding of material which enters the body and passes out unchanged: thus the nitrogen which leaves the lungs of tetrapods, and the undigested cellulose in the faeces of herbivorous animals, are not regarded as excretory products. It is, however, difficult to delimit the latter exactly, and it is obviously impossible in the ordinary way to distinguish between those molecules of a substance such as water which were formed by chemical action in the body, and those which were merely taken in with the food. The analogy with the waste products of a chemical factory is a fairly close one: the method of dealing with the unwanted material depends on its quantity and nature, and the harm which it would do in its place of origin.

2.1. Substances Excreted

For convenience the materials which are excreted may be put into four groups:

2.11. Water

Most animals, whether they live on land or in ponds or in the sea, take in large quantities of water with their food, and mammals and birds drink it as well. Expulsion of this water is not strictly excretion, but some is also formed in the complete oxidation of fats and carbohydrates, and in all the class of reactions called condensations. Further, the surface of the animal cell is normally a semipermeable membrane and the osmotic pressure of the protoplasm greater than that of fresh water; this means that fresh-water animals will take up water osmotically. Unlike plants, animals seldom have rigid cell walls, and so this last process would, in the absence of special arrangements, go on indefinitely. In such animals the regulation of this osmotic water is more important than the excretion of that from the first two sources; it is considered in section 8.3. Feeding animals with deuterium oxide (heavy water) has shown that there is rapid interchange of water between the gut and the cells. It is, therefore, impossible to distinguish between molecules of water from the three sources.

2.12. Carbon Dioxide

Carbon dioxide is the normal end-product of the carbon of any material which is oxidized to give energy. The organ systems which get rid of it are generally those which bring oxygen into the animal, and so its excretion is considered under the heading of respiration; an account of the chief process in mammals is given in section 3.3. It need only be said here that small quantities are dealt with in other ways, for example, by being converted into urea (p. 85) or calcium carbonate.

2.13. Nitrogen Compounds

Nitrogen compounds are so much more important than the other groups that excretion in many cases means in effect nitrogenous excretion.

The processes of deamination and transamination, by which in mammals the nitrogen of most of the ingested

protein is sooner or later separated as ammonia, have been
described in section 1.41, and similar reactions probably
occur in other animals. Sometimes the ammonium ion is
eliminated in combination with other radicals, and in the
mammalian kidney it is also formed by the hydrolysis of
glutamine and oxidation of other aminoacids, and
excreted directly. More often ammonia undergoes further
changes before it is voided from the body. In the mammalian liver it joins with carbon dioxide and phosphate
derived from adenosine triphosphate (ATP p. 124) to
form carbamyl phosphate,

$$NH_3 + CO_2 + ATP \rightarrow NH_2CO \cdot H_2PO_3 + ADP$$

Glutamate and enzymes from mitochondria are required.
Carbamyl phosphate is then converted to urea by a series
of reactions, shown in schema 5, which are known as the
ornithine cycle because of the reaction with and regeneration of that aminoacid. The same cycle has been demonstrated in the livers of elasmobranchs and of the frog and
tortoise, but it does not occur in teleosts and birds. There
must therefore be other pathways for the formation of urea
in vertebrates, and some of these are probably subsidiary
to the ornithine cycle in mammals.

Aminoacids, or their derivatives, such as hippuric acid
(benzoyl glycine, $C_6H_5CO \cdot NH \cdot CH_3COOH$), may be excreted, and some animals get rid of insoluble protein. In
mammals creatine breaks down to creatinine

$$HN = C \underset{\displaystyle \underset{CH_3}{|}}{\overset{\displaystyle \nearrow NH - CO}{\underset{\displaystyle \searrow N - CH_2}{}}}$$

which is lost in the urine. In some animals, such as marine
teleosts, trimethylamine oxide $(CH_3)_3N:O$, is lost, and
in elasmobranches this substance is formed, but retained

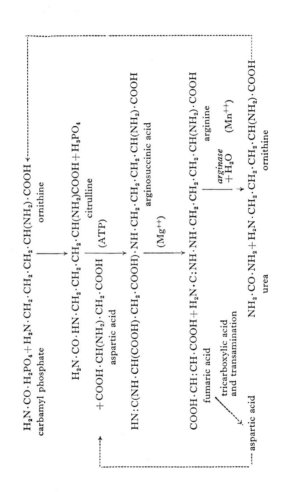

SCHEMA 5. The ornithine cycle.

in the blood to help to maintain the high osmotic pressure (p. 376).

The purines derived from nucleoproteins in the food may, like aminoacids, either be built up into constituents of the body or be broken down immediately. On digestion of nucleic acid, adenine (6-amino-purine)

and guanine (2-amino-6-hydroxypurine)

are formed. The first of these then loses ammonia by two routes. Some of it is deaminated by the enzyme adenase to hypoxanthine (6-hydroxypurine), but most of it first combines with ribose-1-phosphate to form inosinic acid (a nucleotide) which gives inosine (the corresponding nucleoside), which then splits to form hypoxanthine and ribose-1-phosphate. Hypoxanthine is oxidized to xanthine (2-6-dihydroxypurine)

by xanthine oxidase. Guanine, which is very insoluble and probably much less important than adenine, is hydrolysed directly to xanthine by guanase. Xanthine is further oxidized by xanthine oxidase to uric acid (2-6-8-tri-hydroxypurine) with flavine adenine dinucleotide (p. 119) as the hydrogen acceptor. All the purines can exist in two isomeric forms, and in uric acid the keto-form (which is not shown for the substances above) probably predominates. The change for uric acid is

enol form   keto-form

In most mammals a further enzyme, uricase or urico-oxidase, is present, which acts on the uric acid giving allantoin,

in which the purine ring has been broken. Uricase is absent from man and the higher primates, so that these animals excrete uric acid. It is not a true acid, but in its enol form it dissolves in alkalis giving monobasic acid urates of the type RHU, dibasic neutral urates, R_2U, and quadriurates, $RHU \cdot H_2O$. When it is in solution in animals it is usually in the form of acid or quadriurates, in mammals generally the latter.

The distribution of the enzymes that carry out these processes is erratic, man, for example, apparently possessing no adenase; but some such system of degradation of nucleoproteins seems to occur in all vertebrates and probably in many invertebrates. The Amphibia and fish possess uricase, and also allantoinase, which breaks the purine ring again and hydrolyses allantoin to allantoic acid,

and allantoicase, which hydrolyses this substance to two molecules of urea and one of glyoxylic acid,

CHO—COOH. In these forms, then, the nitrogen from nucleoproteins is excreted as urea. Invertebrates take the degradation even further, splitting urea to ammonia and carbon dioxide by means of urease, but most insects stop at uric acid, Diptera and gastropods at allantoin, and freshwater lamellibranchs at urea.

Birds and the Squamata (lizards and snakes) excrete most of their nitrogen as uric acid, whether it starts by being part of a protein or of a nucleoprotein. In birds uric acid is formed basically from ammonia, carbon dioxide, glycine, and formate, which, with the help of glutamate and ribose-1-phosphate, give hypoxanthine, which is oxidized to uric acid by the usual route. Birds do produce some urea, probably by the action of the little arginase that they possess on arginine directly derived from proteins in the food.

The vertebrates can therefore be divided into three groups. The teleosts, the tadpoles of Amphibia, and the Crocodilia excrete their nitrogen chiefly as ammonia, and may be called ammoniotelic; elasmobranchs, adult Amphibia, and mammals form chiefly urea, and are ureotelic; while the birds and Squamata form uric acid and are uricotelic. Chelonians are intermediate: aquatic species produce chiefly ammonia, or approximately equal quantities of ammonia and urea, amphibious species mostly urea, and xeric species mostly uric acid with fair quantities of urea. Dipnoi produce ammonia when they are active, urea when they are in their cocoons. The adult of the aquatic amphibian *Xenopus laevis* produces chiefly ammonia, like the tadpole. The relationship with the mode of life is obvious, and more is said of this in section 8.2. The changeover from ammonia to urea at metamorphosis in Amphibia appears to be connected, like other changes at that time, with the activity of the thyroid, for when metamorphosis is induced in the axolotl by thyoxine, or similarly made to occur precociously in the frog, the ratio of urea to ammonia increases.

A similar division of the invertebrates can be made, but most excrete largely ammonia. The insects, and to some extent the gastropods, are uricotelic.

2.14. Other Substances

There is scarcely an element which has not at some time been found amongst the excretory products of animals. The inclusion of all substances other than water, carbon dioxide, and nitrogen in one group has no justification except that the remaining substances are quantitatively much less important. Qualitatively they may be just as important to the animal as nitrogen. The chief are phosphorus, usually as phosphate, sulphur as sulphate derived by oxidation of aminoacid residues (p. 52), and calcium. They are generally eliminated by the mechanism which deals with nitrogen.

The Felidae are peculiar in excreting fat in the urine. In tigers it appears to be secreted by the proximal convoluted tubules of the kidney.

2.2. Methods of Excretion

The object of excretion is to remove from the sphere of chemical action of the body end-products which may be harmful, and which in any case will, if they are allowed to accumulate, upset equilibrium by their mass-action effect. The simplest way to do this is by a method sometimes used in the treatment of poisoning, that is by converting the obnoxious substance into some insoluble derivative. In this state it can do no harm. Any part of the body which seems to be specially used for storing such materials is sometimes called a 'kidney of accumulation', though there is no suggestion that there is any similarity to the mammalian kidney other than very generally in function.

It is possible that in some animals such insoluble waste products, originally quite useless, have become of some benefit to their possessors. It is noteworthy that many skeletal materials contain elements which are often excreted. Chitin contains 4 per cent. of nitrogen, the acid portion of calcium carbonate is a form of carbon dioxide, and bone is largely made of calcium phosphate, itself a common excretory product. It is impossible to be dogmatic as to whether a particular substance is primarily excretory or useful, but sometimes the probability is great on one side or the other. For example, it may safely be said that the uric acid which forms the chief pigment of butterflies of the family Pieridae (the Whites) was primarily excretory in origin, and the same is probably true of the uric acid which appears to be regularly present, though in varying quantities, in vertebrate exoskeletons such as feathers, hair, and hooves.

Even where excretory products are made insoluble and stored they usually sooner or later escape to the exterior and are lost. Exoskeletons are shed, and insoluble material in the coelom goes out by pores. But more often there is some definite mechanism by which the unwanted material is voided. The word 'kidney' has often been applied to any organ which appears to be concerned in this, but it seems better to restrict the word to the particular type of organ which carries out nitrogenous excretion in the vertebrates. Alternative names are available in all groups, and 'excretory organ' is good enough for general purposes.

The morphological nature of the excretory organ varies from group to group. Details of structure may be found in the ordinary textbooks of zoology, but some general classification is necessary to render intelligible what follows.

First, the surface of the body may be used, either, as in Protozoa and coelenterates, the unspecialized cell surface, or, as in the skin of man, an epithelium specially developed into such glands as the sweat glands.

In many invertebrates the nephridium is important. This is an ectodermal derivative, centripetal in growth, with an intracellular lumen, and primarily ending in a flame cell (solenocyte). It is found in Platyhelminthes, Rotifera, Annelida, Mollusca, and *Branchiostoma*, and it is customary to consider it homologous in all these. The classification of nephridia is difficult, but they are called protonephridia if they do not open into the coelom, and metanephridia if they do. The external opening of a nephridium is a nephridiopore, and the internal opening of a metanephridium a nephridiostome.

Some authors consider that the original function of the coelom was to store excretory matter. However that may be, excretion is often carried out by coelomoducts, which are paired structures almost exactly opposite to nephridia in their properties. They are mesodermal, centrifugal in growth, have an intercellular lumen, and do not have flame cells at their ends. They are found in Annelida, Mollusca, Arthropoda, Echinodermata, and Chordata, and are considered homologous in all these groups. Although they were probably evolved as genital ducts, in all these phyla they assist also in excretion.

In some animals, particularly the polychaetes, nephridium and coelomoduct are closely associated to form a compound organ, the nephromixium. This may retain both genital and excretory functions, or may be excretory only.

In many animals the gut is excretory, and in a few (Crustacea, insects, spiders) a diverticulum of it is the chief organ. It is doubtful whether the specialized structures in the different groups can be regarded as homologous.

There remain a few special types which can be put in

none of the above groups. They are mainly small organs in which waste products accumulate. The fat body of insects is an example.

2.3. The Vertebrate Kidney

By far the best known of all excretory mechanisms is the vertebrate kidney. It eliminates water, nitrogen, and many other substances, and has shown itself capable of adaptation to very varied circumstances. In addition to dealing with waste matter it is also an important osmotic regulator; this aspect of its function is dealt with in section 8.3. Although its structure varies to some extent with the evolutionary level of its possessor (it is a mesonephros in fishes and Amphibia, and a metanephros of somewhat different origin in the amniotes) and also with the environment, it is always built on the same general plan. It consists of a mass of coelomoducts opening into a single longitudinal collecting duct. The detailed arrangement in the mammals is as follows (Fig. 9). The coelomoducts have lost their original openings to the general coelom, and each starts as a blind Bowman's capsule. In the concavity of this is a bundle of blood capillaries, known as the glomerulus, derived from the renal artery. Bowman's capsule and the glomerulus are together known as the Malpighian body. From Bowman's capsule the coelomoduct continues as a coiled proximal convoluted tubule, then as the loop of Henle, and finally as the distal convoluted tubule. The cells of the proximal tubule are square in section and have a brush border. Several distal convoluted tubules open into one collecting tubule, and this joins with others to form large ducts which finally open into the ureter. The whole part distal to Bowman's capsule is spoken of collectively as the tubule. Blood is brought away from the glomerulus by a single vessel which breaks up into another set of capillaries surrounding the tubule. From them blood

goes into the renal vein. There are some differences from
this structure in other classes of vertebrates; the marine
teleosts either have a much reduced glomerulus or are

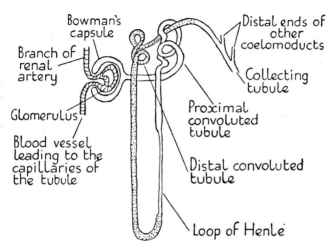

FIG. 9. Diagram of a single coelomoduct of a mammalian kidney.

without it altogether, and in those animals which have a
renal portal system the tubules (but not the capsules) are
supplied with a second system of capillaries containing
venous blood.

The difference in histological structure between the
capsule and the tubule, and the absence of the glomerulus
from some groups, suggest that these two parts of the kidney
have different functions; there is now no doubt that this is
the case.

In the Amphibia, Reptilia, and Mammalia it has been
possible by means of a micromanipulator to withdraw
small samples of the fluid from a capsule for analysis. This
'glomerular filtrate' (the reason for the name will appear
shortly) has been found to resemble a fluid obtained from

the blood by dialysis; with respect to every constituent for which the former can be analysed they are almost identical, and their electrical conductivities are the same. There is thus little doubt that the fluid in the capsule is blood plasma without its colloids. The only assumption that need be made to explain how this comes about is that the wall of the glomerulus together with that of the capsule acts as a membrane which is impermeable to colloids but permeable to water and crystalloids; that is, as a dialyser. If this is the case the conditions in the Malpighian body are that a membrane impermeable to colloids has water, crystalloids, and colloids on its one side, and water and crystalloids on the other. The ordinary laws of osmosis apply, and in the absence of any outside forces, water and crystalloids would pass through the membrane into the blood under the influence of the osmotic pressure of the colloids. But in fact they travel in the other direction, and this can only happen if there is a hydrostatic pressure acting in the opposite direction to the osmotic pressure. This is normally always present, since the blood is maintained above atmospheric pressure by the pumping action of the heart. Filtration should stop when the hydrostatic pressure in the glomerulus falls below the osmotic pressure of the colloids. This is the case; in mammals the colloids have an osmotic pressure of about 30 mm of mercury, and secretion of urine ceases when the arterial pressure falls below about 40 mm. (It is to be expected that the pressure in the capillaries will be somewhat less than that in a large artery such as the brachial where blood-pressure is usually measured.) Secretion may be stopped experimentally by ligaturing the ureter; in one experiment it ceased when the pressure in the ureter was 92 mm of mercury and that in the arteries was 133 mm. The difference, 41 mm, is obviously the maximum pressure available for forcing water and crystalloids out of the blood under these conditions, and it was just not enough to do so. The converse experiment, to increase the effective filtration pressure, has also been carried out; a certain volume of blood is removed, and replaced by Ringer-Locke fluid, which is isotonic with the blood but which contains no colloids. Under these circumstances, although the blood-pressure actually falls owing to the shock, the rate of excretion greatly increases.

Since the energy for the filtration comes from the heart, one would not expect an alteration in excretory rate to affect the oxygen consumption of the kidney. This is found to be the case. Furthermore, it would be expected that low temperature or respiratory poisons, while reducing those activities of the kidney which alter the composition of the glomerular filtrate, would not greatly affect the glomerulus. The urine would therefore have a much closer resemblance to the original glomerular filtrate than it normally does. This also has been experimentally confirmed, and at $25°$ C or when cyanides are added to the blood the urine (in excised and perfused dogs' kidneys) is very similar to the dialysate from plasma.

There is thus direct evidence that the Malpighian bodies act merely as ultrafilters which separate water and crystalloids from the plasma. By adding various proteins to the blood and observing if they appear in the urine, it has been found that the distinction is not strictly between crystalloids and colloids, but that the membrane is permeable to molecules of smaller molecular weight than about 70,000. Gelatin, of molecular weight 35,000, and haemoglobin, of molecular weight 67,000, are passed out, while the normal serum proteins of molecular weight not less than 72,000 are almost completely retained.

There remains the question of the part which the tubules play in excretion, and here the story is not so simple. Not only is the urine more concentrated than the glomerular filtrate, but its composition is different. The urine is normally poorer in aminoacids, sodium, and chloride, it contains no glucose, bicarbonate, or protein, is richer in potassium, phosphate, urea, and other waste products, and is less acid. The alteration could be brought about by absorption of water and differential absorption of the solutes, or it could be achieved at least in part by specific excretion of the different substances. In either case the urine would be concentrated and work would be done on it, so that oxygen would be needed. There is evidence showing that both processes go on.

Of the blood-plasma flowing through the kidney in mammals about one-fifth is filtered by the glomeruli, but the final production of urine may be as little as one-hundredth of this. In frogs, where it was first directly measured, it is not more than one-tenth. In general, then, 90 to 99 per cent. of the filtered water must be absorbed. Since glucose, chloride, aminoacids, and some other substances are decreased in concentration at the same time, they must be absorbed too, and to a greater extent than water. Some other substances, such as phosphate and (in mammals) urea, although in greater concentration in urine than in glomerular filtrate, are excreted at a slower rate than that at which they are filtered, so that they also must be absorbed.

It has become possible to withdraw fluid from different parts of the mammalian and amphibian kidneys, and by analysis of the samples to show where absorption is taking place. The proximal tubule and the loop of Henle are much the most important sites, absorbing all the glucose and most of the water and other solutes. The absorption of sodium, glucose, and some others is primarily assisted (p. 31) and chloride is secondarily assisted because it has to maintain ionic equilibrium as sodium is removed, while the absorption of water is secondarily assisted because the removal of solutes upsets the osmotic equilibrium. As the filtrate is concentrated, urea is absorbed down the concentration gradient in both proximal and distal tubules, but as it is not assisted its concentration in urine can never fall below that in plasma. Elasmobranchs, which have a high concentration of urea in the blood and reabsorb 90 per cent. of that which is filtered, must have assisted transport. Most mammals re-absorb uric acid and destroy it (p. 88), but the Dalmatian dog possesses a simple recessive gene which prevents absorption, so that this animal excretes uric acid in spite of the possession of uricase. There is only a little protein in glomerular filtrate, but that is absorbed by a peculiar process called athrocytosis; the molecules are taken up by the brush border of the cell and there flocculate and remain for some time before being passed into the capillaries.

The control of filtration and absorption is by hormones, and by the autonomic nervous system. Anything that increases blood-pressure or the rate of flow of blood through the kidneys must increase filtration. The antidiuretic hormone of the posterior pituitary (p. 234) reduces urine production, and hormones from the adrenal cortex (p. 236) are necessary for the absorption of sodium and chloride. Parathyroid hormone controls the absorption of phosphate. The production of all these hormones is very sensitive to the composition of the blood, probably acting through receptors in the hypothalamus. The final result is that however much water is absorbed from the intestine or lost in sweat, the composition of the blood is kept constant within very fine limits.

There is now plenty of evidence that the tubules also add substances to the urine. In marine teleosts there is no glomerulus, yet the urine contains waste products which can only have come from the blood through the tubules. There seems now to be little doubt that the renal portal vein of the frog goes only to the tubules. If the renal artery is ligatured, and the animal kept in oxygen to raise the oxyhaemoglobin content of the venous blood, excretion stops. If, however, urea is injected into the blood, it is excreted, together with some water. Further evidence comes from the argument that if the filtration be increased by any means, there should, if the tubules do nothing but absorb, be an equal effect on all the excretory products. But this is not the case. For example, owing to alterations in the pressure in the kidney there is increased filtration, with consequent diuresis, in the recumbent position in man; the output of water in one experiment went up by 237 per cent., that of chloride 123 per cent., of phosphate 50 per cent., of sulphate 41 per cent., of urea 64 per cent., and that of ammonia not at all. It follows that the solids must be in part excreted by the tubules, and that they are the sole source of the ammonia. In birds and the Squamata there is tubular excretion of uric acid.

There is little secretion in the true sense, that is extrusion of a substance actually formed within the cell, by the kidney. There may be some production of ammonia from glutamine, and in the cells of the distal tubule hydrogen ions are formed from carbon dioxide and water by the enzyme carbonic anhydrase (p. 140).

The tubules are continually doing work, and so require oxygen, and the glomeruli also need it to maintain the dialysing properties of the membrane. The respiratory quotient (p. 115) is between 0·8 and 0·9, and carbohydrate, protein, and fatty derivates can all be oxidized.

The urine passes to the bladder through the ureters, which have walls containing plain muscle, and which in man have about three waves of contraction passing down them per minute. The bladder can hold a gradually increasing volume of urine without showing any increase of pressure or of muscle tone. The act of micturition, volun-

tary in origin unless the bladder is over-full, is assisted by
several involuntary muscles, and results in the complete
emptying of the bladder.

The urine is the chief channel by which nitrogen escapes
from the body, in whatever chemical form the metabolism
of the animal may leave it (see section 1.41). In man, of
the 60 g of solid passed in the urine in the 24 hours, about
35 g are made up of organic nitrogen in various forms.
The sulphur obtained from proteins appears as sulphate
ions to the extent of about 2·5 g, and there are about 3 g
of phosphate measured as phosphorus pentoxide. About
10 g of chloride ions are present, though as this is obtained
unchanged from the food it is not strictly an excretion.
The chief cations present are potassium and sodium, of
which there are about 3 and 5 g respectively. All these
values vary widely with the food. Other metallic ions,
notably calcium, magnesium, and iron, are present, but
only in small quantities.

2.4. Other Vertebrate Excretory Organs

Waste products may pass to the exterior through other
channels than the kidneys. Water leaves by the skin, from
the lungs, and to a small extent in the faeces. Carbon
dioxide, mainly lost from the lungs, is considered in
section 3.3. About half the magnesium and calcium and
most of the iron leave through the intestine, the two former
being mainly in the form of insoluble phosphate and the
last chiefly sulphide. A small amount of nitrogen, about
1 gm per day in man, also goes out in this way. It is
largely in the form of breakdown products of haemoglobin
which are present in bile. The sweat contains most of the
common excretory substances, but in negligible quantities.
There seems to be no excretion by storage in the vertebrate, but the calcium phosphate of bone and the keratin

of hair and scales may perhaps be regarded as waste products which have been put to some use. This is certainly
the case with the urea and trimethylamine oxide in the
blood of elasmobranchs, which, as shown in section 8.3,
serve to maintain the plasma isotonic with sea-water.

In the embryos of the amniotes the allantois is used as
a deposit for renal waste which has been eliminated by
the mesonephros. In those mammals where the placenta
is highly permeable (e.g. rodents and man) the excretory
products are apparently simply taken away by the maternal blood; the mesonephros has only a very short existence,
and the allantois is a functionless stalk or (as in the mouse
and rat) never develops at all.

In the teleosts most of the ammonia and urea which are
formed are lost through the gills, the chief forms of nitrogen in the urine being creatine, creatinine, and trimethylamine oxide. This is connected with the marine habitat
(see section 8). The elasmobranchs are somewhat similar,
but the gills are much less permeable to urea, which is
largely retained in the blood.

2.5. Excretion in Invertebrates

The triple mechanism of filtration, resorption, and the
addition of solutes by active excretion has been shown to
be present in decapod crustacea, gastropods, and cephalopods, so that it must have arisen by at least three independent evolutions. Filtration and resorption are known also
in the insects and lamellibranchs, and resorption, with a
strong presumption of filtration, in annelids.

2.51. Excretion in Protozoa

There is no uniformity in the nitrogenous waste products
formed; *Amoeba* forms uric acid, *Glaucoma* and *Didinium*
ammonia, and *Paramecium* and *Spirostomum* urea according
to some authors and ammonia according to others. Since

Colpidium produces ammonia throughout its life-cycle but urea only when the culture is rapidly growing, there may be similar variation in *Paramecium*, or there may be specific differences. These products have been shown to accumulate in cultures of the animals named, but there is no evidence to show how they came to be outside the animal. The old story that the contractile vacuole is a specific excretory organ rests on a very insecure foundation, since attempts to show the presence in it of nitrogenous waste have failed. One author, for example, knowing the rate at which urea accumulated in a culture of *Paramecium caudatum*, and the rate of elimination of water by the vacuoles, was able to calculate that if all the urea excreted came from the vacuoles its concentration in them should be one part in from 2,000 to 3,000. He injected into the vacuoles Nessler's solution (for ammonia) and xanthydrol, which is sensitive to one part of urea in 12,000, but his results were negative. It is therefore probably sufficient to assume that soluble waste products diffuse out through the whole cell wall, just as it is assumed that carbon dioxide can diffuse out and oxygen can diffuse in. The contractile vacuole undoubtedly eliminates water, which probably contains waste products in solution, so that to a certain extent it assists in excretion, but it cannot be responsible for the whole or even a major part of it. Analysis of the fluid removed from the contractile vacuole of *Spirostomum* shows that it eliminates only one per cent. of the total urea produced.

It is probable that some of the crystals found in many genera are waste products stored in an insoluble form; in *Paramecium caudatum*, for example, granules of acid calcium phosphate have been demonstrated. The shells of Protozoa, which may be of calcium carbonate, strontium sulphate, silica, or a nitrogenous material, may be regarded as excretory; this view seems particularly likely to be correct where, as in *Polystomella*, most of the protoplasm is outside the shell, which can therefore hardly be protective.

2.52. Excretion in Coelenterata

Most chemical investigations have been negative, but uric acid has been found in *Anemonia sulcata*, and urea in other sea-anemones. There are no specialized excretory organs, and it must be assumed that waste products escape as they do in the Protozoa. In actinians it has been shown that injected substances, such as carmine, accumulate in certain regions, and this may mean that these places are specially active in excretion. Skeletons are common, both of calcium carbonate, as in the corals, and of nitrogenous organic material, as in the perisarc of Hydrozoa and in the gorgonians (Actinozoa). One function of the symbiotic green Algae in corals seems to be to remove end-products, such as carbon dioxide.

2.53. Excretion in Platyhelminthes

The flame-cell system, termed a protonephridium, and regarded as the forerunner of the nephridium of annelids, is usually regarded as the excretory system. It certainly expels a fluid, but the chemical investigations of this are few and unsatisfactory. There is some evidence that the nephridia are also osmotic regulators (e.g. their absence from the Turbellaria Acoela, which are all marine; variation in the rate of pulsation of the terminal vesicle in Cercariae with the external osmotic pressure; see section 8.3). It has, however, been shown that this is not the case in *Gunda ulvae*. The chief nitrogenous product of planarians, *Fasciola hepatica*, and *Taenia pisiformis* is ammonia, while *Trichinella spiralis* loses one-third of its nitrogen as ammonia and most of the rest as aminoacids and peptides.

2.54. Excretion in Annelida

Ammonia is the chief form of nitrogenous excretory product in the polychaete *Aphrodite* and in the medicinal leech, but in the earthworm *Lumbricus agricola* this makes up only 20 per cent. of the total, 40 per cent. being urea and the rest aminoacids, purines, and unidentified compounds. In the Indian earthworm *Pheretima posthuma* urea and ammonia are formed in approximately equal quantities, and significant amounts of creatinine are also produced. The nephridium was probably from its inception excretory in function, but it has in most species come into close relation with a coelomic funnel to form a nephromixium. The nephridium or nephromixium is certainly not the only, and probably not the chief, organ of excretion. The methods of excretion in the lumbricids are as follows.

Certain cells of the peritoneum, not near blood-vessels, are known as uric or bacteroidal cells, because they contain rod-shaped bodies, probably of uric acid. They act as a kidney of accumulation, but eventually disintegrate, and the insoluble particles which they contain are ingested by amoebocytes of the body cavity. These phagocytes may wander to the tissues and deposit their contents as pigment, or they may find their way to the surface and be lost from the body. In some species they collect as masses in the coelom, the 'brown bodies'. These, which may be up to 5 mm long, are found chiefly in the hinder segments, but they may occur in the genital segments and in the seminal vesicles. In addition to excretory particles they contain cysts of nematodes and of *Monocystis* and other gregarines, and shed chaetae. They disappear sooner or later, having probably escaped through the dorsal pores.

Phagocytes in the blood take up excretory matter and carry it to the gut wall, where they stay and become known as yellow cells (Fig. 10). They finally fall into the gut lumen and escape with the faeces. The yellowish chlorag-ogen granules of specialized cells of the gut-wall were formerly said to consist of guanine (p. 87), but they have now been shown to contain only 4 per cent. of nitrogen,

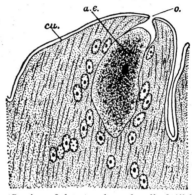

FIG. 10. Section of the oesophageal wall of *Allolobophora foetida*, showing a yellow cell or excretory amoebocyte in the act of traversing it.

× 500. *a.e.*, amoebocyte; *cu.*, cuticle of oesophageal epithelium; *o.*, opening in the oesophageal wall through which the amoebocyte will pass into the lumen of the alimentary canal. From Keilin in the *Quarterly Journal of Microscopical Science*, vol. 65 (1920).

so that they cannot be of any importance in excretion. The cells fall off into the coelom, and are dealt with in the same way as the uric cells.

The nephridium of the earthworm has been shown to be a true nephridium without any mesodermal elements (Fig. 11). Its physiology is unfortunately not so well known, since observers are not in complete agreement, but certain points are fairly clear. In the first place, coelo-mic fluid and the finest solid particles which it contains go down the nephridium to the exterior; in lumbricids chloragogen particles are much too large, but this does not apply to the whole phylum. Secondly, cells of the middle tube and the ampulla extract particles from the

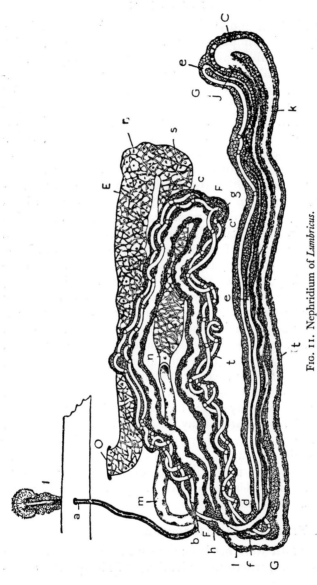

FIG. 11. Nephridium of *Lumbricus*.

a–h, the narrow part of the tube partly ciliated; *h–j*, ciliated wider tube expanding at *C* into ampulla; *k–n*, wide tube; *I*, funnel; *O*, external orifice; *t*, peritoneal layer; *s*, muscular fibres; *r*, nucleus of cell; *F*, *G*, second and third loops of nephridium. From Benham in the *Quarterly Journal of Microscopical Science*, vol. 32 (1891).

coelomic fluid and store them, although they gradually disappear. Their pigment is a haemochromogen, which must presumably have come from the blood pigment, but their chemical composition is otherwise unknown. Experimentally, these cells have been shown to take up particles of Chinese ink and coloured fluids which pass the nephridiostome. The osmotic pressure of the urine of earthworms is less than half that of the coelomic fluid, which is itself hypotonic to the blood. The nephridia thus appear to be osmotic regulators (see section 8.3). The urine is poorer than the other two liquids in almost every constituent, nitrogenous and otherwise, for which it has been analysed, so that there must be fairly general absorption of solutes. In particular, it contains much less protein than either the coelomic fluid or the blood, and agrees with the former in containing no glucose or fats, both of which are present in fair concentration in the blood. It is impossible, on the bases of these analyses, to determine whether all the urine comes from the coelomic fluid, or whether there is also filtration from the blood. The concentration of protein in the blood of *Pheretima* is about half that in human blood, so that, if the protein molecules are of about the same size, the blood-pressure necessary for filtration on the principle of the vertebrate kidney would be about 15 mm of mercury. This seems unlikely to be reached, and the function of the nephridial capillaries may be only to supply oxygen. According to some authors, there is intracellular excretion of granules, through the wall of the terminal reservoir to its cavity. The nephridium of earthworms empties at intervals of not less than three days, but that of *Arenicola* every 2 or 10 minutes.

2.55. Excretion in Arthropoda

Very little work has been done on the Crustacea except in decapods, where the chief forms of nitrogenous excretory products are ammonia and amino-compounds. The antennary gland of Malacostraca and the maxillary gland of Entomostraca, both of which are coelomoducts, are usually described as the excretory organs, but the liquid extracted from the green gland of decapods often contains less non-protein nitrogen than does the blood. It has, therefore, been suggested that in freshwater forms it acts as an osmotic regulator, but since it is also present in the marine species, that cannot be its only function. In *Cancer* the hydrostatic pressure of the body fluid is greater than the colloid osmotic pressure of the blood, and there is filtration of water and crystalloids followed by resorption of some ions and excretion of others, as in the vertebrate kidney. Other forms are probably similar, and the resorption is specially important in the freshwater crayfish and the estuarine shorecrab. The liver was shown long ago to be excretory, for its cells can extract foreign matter from the blood and eliminate it through the gut. In *Cancer* and some other genera it normally deals with purines in this way, but these could not be found in the crayfish. The exoskeleton, of chitin and calcium carbonate, may be in part excretory, and chromatophores of *Eriocheir* contain uric acid.

A number of amphipods and isopods have been shown to produce chiefly ammonia; in the marine *Ligia oceanica* this makes 70 to 80 per cent. of the total nitrogen, while in the terrestrial woodlice *Oniscus asellus*, *Porcellio scaber*, and *Armadillidium vulgare* it is 50 to 60 per cent., so that these animals appear to be only partially adapted to terrestrial life. Their total excretory nitrogen is however, only one-tenth of that of the aquatic species. In the woodlice, and also in the freshwater *Asellus aquaticus*, 5 to 10 per cent. of the non-protein nitrogen is uric acid. The chief excretory organs are the segmental glands of the second maxilla.

In insects uric acid is the normal nitrogenous excretory product, but traces of urea are excreted by many, and ammonia, urea, and amino-compounds are found in the clothes-moths. Ammonia is the chief product of dipteran maggots, which also break down uric acid to allantoin, which they excrete, as do the adults. Dytiscid and carabid beetles and some Orthoptera go further and hydrolyse this to allantoic acid, which they excrete. Guanine is unknown.

The Malpighian tubules, the standard excretory organs of the morphologists, actually are the most important part of the body in disposing of waste matter: they excrete both urates and carbon dioxide, which they receive from the blood in solution. The mechanism bears certain similarities to that in vertebrates, particularly birds; in *Rhodnius prolixa* (Rhynchota), for example, potassium or sodium urate is secreted in the upper part of the tubule, and water and base are resorbed in the lower part, leading to the precipitation of free uric acid as solid spheres. The same water and base are circulated and used repeatedly. This leads to conservation of water, which is very important in insects, where the method of respiration leads to much evaporation. An analogous process leads to the precipitation of calcium carbonate. There is normally no special mechanism for the expulsion of the contents of the tubes, but in Diptera they are muscular and peristalsis takes place.

There are subsidiary organs, of which the chief is the fat body, the parietal layer of which stores uric acid. The fate of this is different in different orders of insects. In the Collembola, which have no Malpighian tubules, it is stored throughout life, and the fat body is therefore the chief excretory organ, although the tubular glands opening by a common duct at the base of the labium in these insects and in the Thysanura are also said to be excretory. Uric acid is also stored throughout life in the Orthoptera, where the Malpighian tubules contain little or no uric acid. In the Hymenoptera it is transferred to the hind-gut during early imaginal life, and is voided when the insect emerges from the cocoon. A similar process occurs in muscid Diptera; here there is a period in metamorphosis when the tubules are completely broken down, and the fat body is therefore very important. Of less importance are the nephrocytes, chains of cells along the heart or oesophagus, which store nitrogenous matter which may later be taken away by phagocytes.

There are in many insects peculiar types of excretion, as, for example, in the celery-fly, *Acidia heraclei* (Diptera), where the calcium carbonate formed in the Malpighian tubules is deposited as large calcosphaerites, is dissolved during metamorphosis, and is laid down on the last larval skin and so eliminated—a process called ecdysial excretion. In some Dipteran larvae calcosphaerites formed in the fat body are eliminated in the same way. As in the Crustacea, chitin may be excretory, and in butterflies of the family Pieridae (the Whites), uric acid formed during larval life is stored in the fat body, and shortly before the emergence of the imago it is transferred to the wings and deposited as the familiar white pigment.

In spiders the Malpighian tubules excrete uric acid, probably as a sodium salt, and guanine. It is probable that the coxal glands eliminate urates. Uric acid is excreted by the Malpighian tubules of the Chilopoda.

2.56. Excretion in Mollusca

In lamellibranchs, ammonia and amino-compounds are the chief forms of excretory nitrogen, but urea and purines, including traces of uric acid, have been found. Sixty per cent. of the waste nitrogen of *Anodonta cygnea* is eliminated as ammonia. The concretions in the organ of Bojanus consist mostly of magnesium and phosphate, and uric acid is not present, but there is some nitrogenous material. Keber's organ acts as a kidney of accumulation, but in what form nitrogen is stored is not known. Of the gastropods, *Helix pomatia* eliminates ammonia, amino-compounds, urea, uric acid, and other purines, all in considerable quantity, some at least of them being got rid of by the kidney. During winter, uric acid and other purines are stored in the kidney. The slug *Limax agrestis* excretes chiefly urea, and the marine *Aplysia limacina* ammonia, amino-compounds, purines, and urea, in that order of quantity. The urine of cephalopods contains much ammonia, trimethylamine oxide, and amino-compounds, and smaller quantities of urea and purines. The molluscs illustrate very well the connexion between the habitat and the chief excretory products which was pointed out on pp. 90–91.

Both in lamellibranchs and in gastropods the cilia of the kidney withdraw water from the pericardium, but while in the former there are contractions of the organ which expel its contents, in the pulmonates general contractions of the body are required for its discharge. In terrestrial forms these occur every two or three weeks. In *Anodonta* and *Limnaea* the urine is hypotonic to the blood and pericardial fluid, but this does not mean that it is not excretory (cf. the glomerular filtrate of vertebrates, p. 95).

2.57. Excretion in Echinodermata

The fluid of the water-vascular system contains small quantities of ammonia, amino-compounds, urea, and uric acid. Since it is in communication with the surrounding sea-water, nitrogen is presumably lost from it.

3

RESPIRATION AND THE
PROVISION OF ENERGY

BY derivation, and in ordinary usage, the word 'respiration' means simply sucking air into the body and blowing it out again: it is in fact synonymous with breathing. Zoologists early recognized that the object of breathing was that the animal might absorb oxygen and give off carbon dioxide, and the meaning of respiration was extended to cover this gas exchange even where, as in the earthworm, it takes place without any special bodily movement. But further it became obvious that this taking up of oxygen from the atmosphere and giving up of carbon dioxide were simply the beginning and end of a process common to all animals (and indeed to all living matter) by which energy was made available for use when oxygen was taken to the tissues and entered into chemical reactions. In botany, since plants do not breathe, respiration has long meant merely the exothermic chemical changes by which energy is supplied, even when oxygen takes no part in them. It could logically be taken to include comparable processes in animals, and animal respiration would then be an exothermic chemical reaction (or series of reactions) by which energy is supplied for the use of the organism.[1] Where oxygen is required for these reactions

---

[1] In strict thermodynamic usage, since the increase in free energy is not necessarily equal to the liberation of heat, 'exergonic' should be used instead of 'exothermic', but for elementary and practical purposes the distinction is unimportant.

the whole mechanism whereby the gas is supplied would be included in the term, and where carbon dioxide is a by-product of the reaction its removal would be included. The word has never been used in connexion with the supply of reactants other than oxygen, nor with the removal of products other than carbon dioxide. A distinction would be made between external respiration, which covers the supply of oxygen and removal of carbon dioxide, and tissue respiration, which is the chemical processes in the cells.

Animal physiologists have never been entirely happy about this extension of the meaning of the word, and many of them have compromised by not using respiration unless oxygen comes in at some stage. This is illogical and inconvenient, since oxygen only enters into the very end of the chain of reactions that supply energy and many of them are the same whether oxygen is present or not. Our increased knowledge of the metabolism of the body has now made any extension of the term respiration to include chemical processes both awkward and confusing, since, as has been shown in Chapter 1, and will become even clearer in section 3.14, the reactions that are used in the processes of building up tissues and reserves are inseparable as a class from those that are used in providing energy. It seems best to revert to the older zoological sense of the word, and in this book respiration is taken to mean 'the provision of oxygen and removal of carbon dioxide'. For the wider processes the phrase 'provision of energy' must be used until an acceptable shorter term is invented.

3.1. The Chemistry of the Provision of Energy

Active animals are continually doing work in moving themselves and other objects, in secretion, and to a small extent in building up chemical substances. The energy for all these comes, so far as we know, only from chemical processes. Whether such processes are also necessary for the mere maintenance of life is a matter for largely theoretical argument. Many examples of eggs or other resting stages in which no gas exchange can be detected have been described, perhaps the most striking example being the larva of a Nigerian chironomid (Diptera). When the rock pools in which this animal lives dry up, it shrivels to an apparently lifeless corpse containing sometimes less than 1 per cent. of water. When water returns it swells and swims again within an hour, and the process can be repeated. The general view is that chemical processes must be going on, however slowly, in such dormant stages, and that there may be some uptake of oxygen.

3.11. The Respiratory Quotient

In obtaining their energy most animals and tissues consume oxygen and produce carbon dioxide, and for a preliminary investigation it is usual to measure the volume changes for these two gases. The experiment is easily carried out with some form of manometer. The ratio

$$\frac{\text{volume of carbon dioxide given out in time } t}{\text{volume of oxygen absorbed in time } t}$$

(both being measured under the same conditions) is known as the Respiratory Quotient, usually abbreviated to R.Q.

Since the volume of a gas, under given conditions of temperature and pressure, is proportional to the number of molecules it contains, it is easy to calculate the theoretical values for the chief classes of foodstuffs, assuming complete oxidation to occur. Thus for all carbohydrates the equation is

$$C_x(H_2O)_y + xO_2 = xCO_2 + yH_2O,$$

and it is obvious that the R.Q. is unity. Tristearin, a

common fat, gives

$$2CH_2-OOC-C_{17}H_{35} + 163O_2 \rightarrow 114CO_2 + 110H_2O,$$
$$|$$
$$CH-OOC-C_{17}H_{35}$$
$$|$$
$$CH_2-OOC-C_{17}H_{35}$$

which makes the R.Q. 114/163, or 0·70. Other fats give very similar values, and while the figure for protein is more variable, it is always about 0·8 or a little more. The fact that these values are characteristic provides a simple test for the similarity of two processes. For example, while the respiratory quotient of muscle is 1, that of cilia is 0·8, so that the chemistry of the catabolic processes in the two must therefore be different. It is not possible to argue rigidly from the observed respiratory quotient to the substrate which is being burnt, because a mixture of carbohydrate and fat can obviously give a similar value to protein, and because there is always the possibility of incomplete combustion. The latter is particularly likely where an animal is under peculiar metabolic conditions. In hibernating mammals there is irregular breathing and carbon dioxide is retained for long periods, so that very low values have been obtained for the respiratory quotient. But these are artefacts, the true value being always about 0·7, which agrees with the great loss of fat during the winter sleep. When animals are putting on fat and this substance is being formed from carbohydrate, internal oxygen is made available. (This is evident from an examination of the formulae; in a carbohydrate molecule enough oxygen is present to oxidize all the hydrogen, but in tristearin there is only enough to oxidize about one-ninth of the hydrogen.) Where the food is poor in fat, as in herbivores, this is very noticeable, and in fattening stock the respiratory quotient may be 1·3. The normal respiratory quotient for man is 0·85, which suggests that carbohydrate is an important source of energy, but that either fat or protein or both are used as well. That the last is the case is shown by the fact that the quotient can be altered within limits by eating any one of the three classes of foodstuff in excess.

If oxygen is taken as the unit the energy available is not greatly different for the three foodstuffs. Different compounds give different values, but on the average

1 g of oxygen oxidizes carbohydrate to water plus carbon dioxide giving 3·8 kilocalories,

or fat to water plus carbon dioxide giving 3·2 kcal,

or protein to water plus carbon dioxide giving 3·1 kcal.

But since 1 g of oxygen will oxidize 0·94 g of glucose and only 0·34 g of tristearin, fat is evidently a much more economical form in which to store energy. One gram of fat gives about 9·3 kcal and 1 g of carbohydrate only 4·1 kcal so that a mammal which had its fat replaced by an equivalent amount of glycogen would be very bulky. Both birds and locusts lay down much fat before their migratory flights and the respiratory quotient in flying locusts suggests that 85 per cent. of their energy comes from this. Protein can produce about 4 kcal/g.

An approximate value for the quantity of protein broken down in a given time can be got from the nitrogen excreted in the urine, and if the volumes of oxygen taken up and carbon dioxide produced are known the amounts of these concerned with protein metabolism can be calculated, and so a non-protein respiratory quotient can be obtained if interconversion is neglected. From this, and the volumes of the gases, the quantities of carbohydrate and fat that are oxidized can be calculated. We then have a complete statement of the metabolism, and from this, and the figures given above, the energy production can be calculated, although the only things that have been measured are oxygen, carbon dioxide, and nitrogen.

3.12. Tissue Oxidation

Much energy is released in many of the reactions that have been described in section 1.4 under the heading of intermediate metabolism. Such reactions have two functions in the life of the animal; they provide energy, and they are pathways by which carbohydrates, fats, and proteins, derived ultimately from the food, can be conveyed from place to place and converted into other compounds of the same or a different class. Most of the reactions are reversible, and when they are moving in the catabolic direction there is in general oxidation of the carbon atoms, which is carried out by alternate removal of hydrogen (dehydrogenation) and addition of water (hydration), leading to the net addition of oxygen. In some reactions carbon dioxide is produced (pp. 56–58) and the carbon is then fully oxidized and can give no more energy.

In Chapter 1 we have accounted for the complete oxidation of the carbon of foodstuffs to carbon dioxide, but we have left the hydrogen in combination either with dehydrogenases or with hydrogen acceptors such as coenzyme I (diphosphopyridine nucleotide, DPN for short) or coenzyme II (triphosphopyridine nucleotide, TPN). They are still available for oxidation, and so for the provision of energy, and to the processes by which this takes place the term tissue respiration is sometimes applied.

There are several links in the chain, and at each stage there is formally a transfer of hydrogen atoms and reduction of ferric iron to the ferrous state, but since the hydrogen remains in solution as an ion, it is more correct to think of the reactions as consisting of the transfer of electrons,

$$Fe^{+++} + e^- \rightleftharpoons Fe^{++}$$

At the end the hydrogen ion receives an electron from the ferrous ion (which is thus oxidized), and the atom so produced reacts with molecular oxygen to form water. The commonest pathway is that in which the hydrogen (or electrons) of coenzyme I are transferred to flavine adenine dinucleotide (FAD) and then to a series of cytochromes. The most likely scheme seems to be

$$2 \text{ DPN} \overset{4e^-}{\rightleftharpoons} 2 \text{ FAD} \overset{4e^-}{\rightleftharpoons} 4 \text{ cytochrome b} \overset{4e^-}{\rightleftharpoons} 4 \text{ cytochrome c}$$

$$\overset{4e^-}{\rightleftharpoons} 4 \text{ cytochrome a} \overset{4e^-}{\rightleftharpoons} 4 \text{ cytochrome a}_3$$

and finally

$$4 \text{ cyt. a}_3 \text{ Fe}^{++} + 4\text{H}^+ + \text{O}_2 \rightarrow 4 \text{ cyt. a}_3 \text{ Fe}^{+++} + 2\text{H}_2\text{O}$$

Flavine adenine dinucleotide contains two atoms of reducible iron, and in its active form is combined with protein to form a flavoprotein. Each cytochrome contains the base haem, similar to that present in haemoglobin, attached to a protein. The haem contains only one atom of ferric ion, so that two molecules are reduced by one molecule of flavine adenine dinucleotide. There are specific differences between the cytochromes of different animals, and others, such as a_1 and a_2, are present in other organisms. Cytochrome a_3 may be identical with cytochrome oxidase, which can oxidize cytochrome c and cytochrome b, while cytochrome b is slowly autoxidizable. Since the reactions are reversible, a small supply of the cytochromes can oxidize large amounts of coenzyme I, and so of carbohydrate or fat.

Coenzyme II is oxidized by the same pathway, except that a different flavoprotein is used, while succinic acid is oxidized through succinic dehydrogenase, which appears to be a flavoprotein, and so through the cytochromes.

Cytochromes are found chiefly in mitochondria, which

are therefore the chief site of oxidation in the cell. The oxidation of cytochrome a_3 is stopped by cyanide, which explains why this substance is such a deadly poison. It reduces the oxygen consumption of most animals and tissues to about a tenth of its normal value, so that the cytochrome pathway seems to be important from the Protozoa to the mammals. Some of the oxidation that continues in the presence of cyanide may be carried out by direct oxidation of cytochrome b, which is not very sensitive to the poison, and other enzymes, mainly flavo-proteins, that can take up molecular oxygen *in vitro*, have been extracted from cells. Their relative importance is not known.

Like all chemical reactions, these oxidations increase rapidly with temperature, as the graph for the oxygen consumption of excised guinea-pig muscle shows (Fig. 12). The curve at first rises rapidly, and corresponds to one calculated on the assumption that an increase of 10° C multiplies the rate two and a half times. (The ratio $R_{(t+10)°C}/R_{t°C}$ is called the temperature coefficient or Q_{10}.) At 40° C activity begins to decline, probably owing to damage to enzymes, and at 48° C heat paralysis occurs, but the muscle will recover if cooled. Over the lower part of the range the effect does not differ much from that for any ordinary chemical reaction.

3.13. Anaerobiosis

Of all the energy-giving reactions only a few, and those the last links in the chain, need oxygen, and one would therefore expect that tissues could live and work without oxygen, so long as the necessary enzymes and coenzymes were present in adequate quantity. Any processes by which cells could live without oxygen might be called anaerobic respiration, or anaerobiosis, but these terms are used especially for a set of reactions where it is known that an early supply of oxygen is not needed. During the contrac-

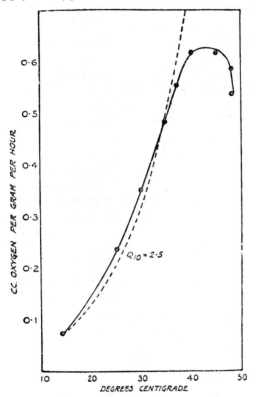

Fig. 12. Effect of alteration of temperature on oxygen usage of plain muscle (guinea-pig uterus).

Abcissae = temperature. Ordinates = c.c. oxygen per gm. per hour. The dotted line represents the theoretical curve if the oxygen intake were increased two and a half times for a rise of 10° C. After Starling.

tion of isolated vertebrate striped muscles in an atmosphere of nitrogen almost the whole of the glycogen is converted to lactic acid by glycolysis (p. 56). During severe exercise also lactic acid accumulates in the intact animal, which shows that the supply of oxygen is not keeping pace with the glycolysis.

The breakdown of glycogen to lactic acid, taken by itself, would be a very wasteful method of providing energy, since much remains unused. If oxygen is present the additional reactions, which have been described in sections 1.43 and 3.12, take place, the foodstuffs are completely oxidized, and the whole process is much more efficient. When oxygen is provided after a period in which a tissue has been without it, these reactions can go on and, as was stated in section 1.43, in voluntary muscle the full oxidation of one-fifth of the lactic acid provides enough energy for the resynthesis of the remaining four-fifths to glycogen. This oxidative recovery may continue long after the muscle has done its work, and indeed it normally does so. After half a minute of severe work the oxygen intake in man remains above the normal for a quarter of an hour or more, and after prolonged exercise the lactic acid in the blood may be above the normal for hours. Effectively, then, the energy for contraction is supplied long after this has actually taken place: the animal is said to put up an oxygen debt. This is paid off later, and, since the blood is continually taking lactic acid away from the working organ, the oxidation goes on in other muscles besides those which are contracting. Man rests his legs by not using his arms.

A beginning has been made in finding out how widespread is this anaerobic means of providing energy. Essentially the same scheme seems to be used in all vertebrate muscles, although the details may be different. Cardiac muscle, for instance, probably never normally works anaerobically. Since the heart never rests it would be very improvident for it to go into oxygen debt. The chemistry of the electric organs of fishes is also in general similar, and so is that of invertebrate muscles. In some active invertebrates very large oxygen debts can be incurred; the bee, for instance, in flight may raise its energy production to more than a thousand times the normal value, whereas in man even in hard exercise the increase is only to twelve times the normal.

Phosphorylating glycolysis is common in other tissues, such as liver and kidney, and is widespread in the animal kingdom as a whole. Cilia and pseudopodia can put up an oxygen debt, but little is known of their chemistry. *Mytilus* cilia can survive in hydrogen for 2 hours, and afterwards beat normally.

It is not surprising that an animal which gets its energy in this way can live for some time without oxygen; earthworms and freshwater snails can survive for 6 days, arthropods, which are more active, for from 2 to 5 hours, and the warm-blooded mammals for a shorter period still. One reason why man can live for only a short time without air is that the nervous system is very sensitive to both lack of oxygen and excess of carbon dioxide. A drowned man who is insensible but not dead cannot revive on restoration to the air unless oxygen is supplied to the body by breathing, and this cannot start until the nerves controlling the respiratory movements receive oxygen. There is therefore a deadlock which can only be resolved by artificial respiration.

It appears that certain tissues may be completely anaerobic. Young chick heart tissue, and certain cancerous cells, can grow *in vitro* completely without oxygen. Skin can live for a week in hydrogen (though without mitosis) and can then recover. Embryonic cartilage uses oxygen at a normal rate, but that of the adult has a consumption that is very low or even zero. Glucose is broken down to lactic acid, and though in some cartilage cytochrome oxidase is present, its action is inhibited. Cartilage is without blood-vessels, so that the value of anaerobiosis is obvious.

3.14. The Energy-Exchange

There are two aspects of the provision of energy by living tissues: the chemical reactions by which it is made available, and the means by which, when released, it is converted to the particular use, such as chemical synthesis, secretion, or muscular contraction, for which it is needed. Of the second little is known, and almost the only generalization that can be made is that no part of the body works as a heat-engine; the energy is in some way transformed directly from chemical potential energy to the form in which it is used, a process that is much more efficient than first converting it into heat.

Anyone reading the chemistry in Chapter 1 must have noticed the frequent formation in metabolism of organic phosphate esters. It is characteristic of many of these that they are easily hydrolysed, and that when this happens a relatively large amount of energy is set free. They are accordingly known as energy-rich compounds, and it is their energy which actually makes possible the processes of life. The energy-rich phosphate group, which is usually written $\sim PO_4$ in formulae, releases about 11·5 kcal or more per gramme-molecule on hydrolysis. One of these energy-rich compounds is adenosine triphosphate (adenyl triphosphate, ATP) and the schemata in Chapter 1 show that several molecules of this are formed, usually by the addition of phosphate to adenosine diphosphate (ADP), in the course of the degradation of one hexose molecule. It is the step-by-step oxidation of the hexose which provides the energy for the formation of the new high-energy phosphates. The subsequent hydrolysis of the ester provides the energy for the activities of the body. In most reactions only one energy-rich group is removed, giving adenosine diphosphate, but occasionally a second is removed also, giving adenosine monophosphate (adenylic acid, AMP). The third phosphate radical is energy-poor, and is not biologically important. It is believed that the three phosphate groups are attached end-to-end, so that the structure of adenosine triphosphate may be indicated by

$$A—O—\overset{\displaystyle O}{\overset{\|}{P}}—O\sim\overset{\displaystyle O}{\overset{\|}{P}}—O\sim\overset{\displaystyle O}{\overset{\|}{P}}—OH$$
$$\underset{OH}{}\quad\underset{OH}{}\quad\underset{OH}{}$$

When the molecule transfers its energy intact to another organic molecule usually only the terminal phosphate group goes over; when two phosphate radicals are lost they usually go as free pyrophosphate.

Adenosine triphosphate is found in most tissues and throughout the animal kingdom, as are enzymes that hydrolyse it. The energy for the contraction of all muscle seems to be given by its hydrolysis to adenosine diphosphate, and it is then restored by phosphate and energy derived from another energy-rich compound called a phosphagen. In vertebrates, and in some invertebrates, notably the ctenophore *Pleurobrachia*, many polychaetes, the Echinoidea and Ophiuroidea, and the protochordate groups Enteropneusta, Cephalochordata, and Tunicata, this is creatine phosphate,

$$HN{=}C\Big\langle {\overset{\displaystyle N(CH_3)\cdot CH_2\cdot COOH}{\underset{NH\sim PO(OH)_2}{}}}$$

In most invertebrates, including platyhelminths, annelids, arthropods, molluscs, echinoderms, and some tunicates and enteropneusts, this is replaced by the related arginine phosphate,

$$HN{=}C\Big\langle {\overset{\displaystyle NH\cdot (CH_2)_3\cdot CH(NH_2)COOH}{\underset{NH\sim PO(OH)_2}{}}}$$

In various polychaetes other compounds, glycocyamine and taurocyamine, are present. The only phosphagen in earthworms (*Lumbricus*) appears to be guanidylethylseryl phosphate. Each phosphagen is accompanied by its appropriate enzyme.

Other important energy-rich phosphorus compounds are the uridine phosphates, glyceric acid-1 : 3-diphosphate, and enol-pyruvic acid phosphate. There are also energy-rich sulphur compounds such as those in which coenzyme A is linked to succinyl or acetyl groups.

According to the reactions described in section 1.43, thirty-eight high-energy phosphate radicals are formed in the oxidation of one molecule of glucose. Our knowledge of metabolic biochemistry is not complete, but this seems to be a minimum number. It seems likely that the energy of all these is available for the life-processes, and if we take the probable value of 12·5 kcal for the energy of a single phosphate, we get 475 kcal as the available energy. Since complete oxidation of a gram-molecule of glucose gives 686 kcal, the minimum efficiency is about 70 per cent. Fat provides energy with about the same efficiency. This is remarkably high for any form of engine. If, however, as has been reported, the increase of free energy on hydrolysis of the phosphate bond of adenosine triphosphate is not 12·5 kcal/mole but only 7, the thermal efficiency is only about 40 per cent., which is only a little better than the best steam power stations, which have a value of 30 per cent.

3.2. Transport of Oxygen

Of two animals of the same activity but of different sizes the larger will need more oxygen, although the consumption of oxygen is not necessarily directly proportional to the size because the bigger animal will generally have a higher proportion of non-active skeletal material in its body. Further, if oxygen can make its way in only by diffusion from the surface, the bigger an animal the lower, under given conditions, will be the concentration of oxygen at its centre. It is obvious that there must be some size at which the concentration becomes too low for activity, and that the animal cannot exceed this size. It is not surprising that all the larger animals have some special means for bringing oxygen to the tissues, although it is impossible to say that such a transport system becomes necessary at a particular size; different animals have different respiratory rates and live in different oxygen concentrations. Isolated frog muscle 4 mm thick can just live without blood-vessels, and most animals larger than this have some mechanism for oxygen transport. The chief exceptions are the coelenterates, which are either inactive or, as in the Scyphomedusae, have a body which is mainly non-living mesogloea. There are two methods of oxygen transport, by tracheae and by a circulatory system.

3.21. Transport by Tracheae

The gaseous oxygen of the air may be carried into the body by tubes called tracheae. These are found in insects, in isopods, in four groups of arachnids (Phalangidae, Pseudoscorpionidae, Solifugae, Araneidae), and in *Peripatus*. It has never been shown that the so-called tracheae of a few coelenterates are respiratory. Those of insects are best known. They arise as ingrowths from the surface, and so are ectodermal however deeply they go in. There is a main longitudinal trunk on each side, which opens to the exterior by spiracles; typically there is on each side one of these between the prothorax and mesothorax, one between the mesothorax and the metathorax, and one on each of the first eight abdominal segments. There are many branches, of which the larger are lined with chitin and the smaller with a protein called trachein. The tracheae typically end in tracheal cells, from which go out fine intracellular tracheoles (Fig. 13). These sometimes form a capillary network amongst the tissues, or they may enter individual cells. They are filled with fluid towards

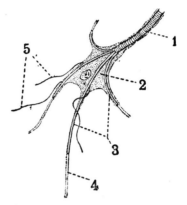

FIG. 13. Detail of tracheal ending.

1, trachea; 2, tracheal cell; 3, main tracheoles containing air; 4, main tracheoles containing liquid; 5, fine tracheoles containing air. After Wigglesworth.

their inner end, and the varying osmotic pressure of the cell causes this to be continually moving up and down, which brings oxygen very efficiently into solution (Fig. 14). Where the tracheoles make a capillary network, oxygen is taken to the cells by the blood, but there is only simple solution and no blood pigment. The tracheae of fully aquatic insect larvae (mayflies, dragonflies, stoneflies) have no open spiracles; oxygen is taken up from the water through the thin walls.

3.22. Transport by a Circulatory System

Elsewhere oxygen is carried round the body in solution. The sea-water in the water-vascular system of echinoderms is respiratory, but in most animals a blood-system not open to the exterior, and containing a special respiratory pigment, is used. A respiratory pigment is a substance which forms a compound with oxygen by means of a reversible reaction, so that it can carry oxygen from regions of high partial pressure of the gas to those where it is low.

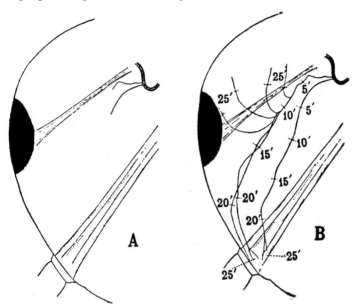

FIG. 14. Effect of asphyxiation on air in tracheoles of a larva of a gnat.

A, larva at rest; B, during asphyxiation. The figures in B show time in minutes, after onset of asphyxiation, at which air reached points indicated, so making the tracheoles visible. After Wigglesworth.

The fact that this substance is always coloured is accidental. Four groups of such pigments are known; they are shown, with some of their chief properties, in Table 2. Haemoglobin consists of a base called protohaem or haematin, which is a ferrous iron porphyrin, united to a protein, globin. It is therefore similar to cytochrome, but in the latter the protein part of the molecule is not a globin, and when oxygen is taken up by haemoglobin there is no change in the valency of the iron. The haemoglobins of different species are slightly different in physical properties, and it is probable that the globin differs in different animals. Even the haemoglobin of one species

TABLE 2

Respiratory Pigments

Pigment	Contained metal	Colour		Occurrence
		Oxygenated	Deoxygenated	
Haemoglobin	Iron	Red	Red	Vertebrates and scattered invertebrates
Chlorocruorin	Iron	Green	Green	Some polychaetes
Haemerythrin	Iron	Red	Colourless	Some annelids
Haemocyanin	Copper	Blue	Colourless	Most molluscs and arthropods

may vary from individual to individual, and that of one individual may be different at different times. The differences are, however, small, and the haemoglobins of species of a genus are usually isomorphic. The red globin pigment of invertebrates differs from the substance in vertebrates in molecular weight, and possibly in other ways, but there is no sharp break between the properties of the two groups, and there seems to be no justification for distinguishing the invertebrate form, as was formerly done, by the special name of erythrocruorin. Chlorocruorin, though similar to haemoglobin in fundamental structure, differs from it both in its protein and in the fact that the base, chlorocruorohaem, contains one atom of oxygen more than protohaem. The molecule of haemocyanin is very large, with a weight of about 2,000,000.

All these pigments work in the same way, which may be illustrated by mammalian haemoglobin. In contact with oxygen this reacts according to the equation

$$Hb + nO_2 \rightleftharpoons HbO_{2n},$$

where Hb stands for a molecule of haemoglobin. This is an ordinary reversible reaction, and can be treated by the methods of physical chemistry. Applying the Law of Mass Action, and using the conventional square brackets to represent concentration, we have,

$$k_1[Hb].[O_2]^n = k_2[HbO_{2n}]$$

or

$$\frac{[Hb]}{[HbO_{2n}]} = \frac{1}{[O_2]^n}\cdot\frac{k_2}{k_1} = \frac{1}{k[O_2]^n};$$

adding one to each side,

$$\frac{[Hb]}{[HbO_{2n}]} + \frac{[HbO_{2n}]}{[HbO_{2n}]} = \frac{1}{k[O_2]^n} + \frac{k[O_2]^n}{k[O_2]^n};$$

reversing,

$$\frac{[HbO_{2n}]}{[Hb]+[HbO_{2n}]} = \frac{k[O_2]^n}{1+k[O_2]^n}$$

Now $[Hb]+[HbO_{2n}]$ is a measure of the total haemoglobin present in whatever state it may be, so that this equation gives us a relation between the proportion of the total which is in the form of oxyhaemoglobin, and the concentration of oxygen with which it is in equilibrium. In practice it is convenient to state the oxyhaemoglobin as a percentage of the total, and to measure the oxygen concentration by its partial pressure in millimetres of mercury. The equation must then be modified to read

$$100\frac{[HbO_{2n}]}{[Hb]+[HbO_{2n}]} = 100\frac{k(cp)^n}{1+k(cp)^n},$$

where p is the partial pressure of oxygen and c is a factor relating this to the concentration in gram-molecules per litre.

The form of the curve given by this equation depends on n, the number of molecules of oxygen which combine with one molecule of haemoglobin, and there is an apparent discrepancy here between the calculated curve and those obtained by direct measurement of the haemoglobin.

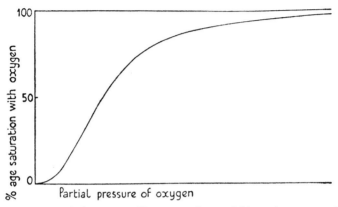

FIG. 15. Dissociation curve of human oxyhaemoglobin under 40 mm of mercury pressure of carbon dioxide at 38° C. After Haldane.

An experimental curve is shown in Fig. 15; it corresponds to a value of n of about 2·5, a figure which can obviously have no physical meaning. The theoretical value of n was determined by ordinary chemical means. Haemoglobin contains iron, and it was fairly easy to find by analysis that 32 g of oxygen react with that weight of haemoglobin which contains 56 g of iron, so that for each atom of iron one molecule of oxygen is added to make oxyhaemoglobin. The next and more difficult step was to find the molecular weight of haemoglobin, and so the number of atoms of iron in one molecule. Direct measurement of the osmotic pressure of a solution suggested that the molecular weight was about 68,000, and this was confirmed by measurement of diffusion rates and more precisely by the rate of sedimentation in the Svedberg ultracentrifuge. In 68,000 g of haemoglobin there are 224 g of iron, so that one molecule contains four atoms of iron and the equation for the reaction with oxygen should be

$$Hb + 4O_2 \rightleftharpoons HbO_8$$

and $n = 4$.

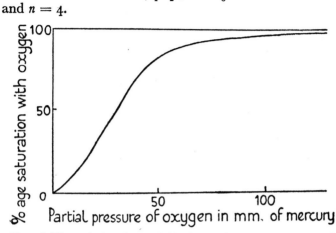

FIG. 16. Theoretical oxyhaemoglobin dissociation curve. See text, and cf. Fig. 15.

The discrepancy cannot be explained without taking into account two other facts. When an experimental dissociation curve is plotted either for a concentrated solution of haemoglobin or for one which is entirely free from the ions normally present in blood-plasma, it is found to be a rectangular hyperbola, for which $n = 1$. This could be easily explained on the assumption that although the gross equation for the oxygenation of haemoglobin involves four molecules of oxygen, these are in fact added on one at a time to make intermediate compounds which have only a transitory existence. There are indeed good reasons for thinking that reactions involving five molecules very seldom take place, owing to the small probability of so many being in collision at once, and careful measurement of the dissociation curves in the ranges 0 to 1 per cent. and 98 to 100 per cent. saturation suggests that this hypothesis is correct, the affinity for the last molecule being much greater than for the others. One more assumption, for which there is some evidence, will bring the ordinary curve into line. Both haemoglobin and oxyhaemoglobin are acids, and as such react with base whenever it is present. In the normal conditions in which they occur, that is in blood, carbonic acid is present as well, and there is not sufficient base present to saturate both this and the haemoglobin, so that an equilibrium is reached which depends on the relative affinities of the base for the different acids present. Now oxyhaemoglobin is a stronger acid than haemoglobin, so that when blood takes up oxygen a new equilibrium is set up and some of the base which was formerly held by carbonic acid is transferred to oxyhaemoglobin. If the further assumption be made that as haemoglobin (or oxyhaemoglobin) takes up base its affinity for oxygen (k, above) increases, the problem is solved, except in small detail. Fig. 16 shows one of many curves which can be constructed on this basis; it is obviously very similar to Fig. 15. When no base is present, or when there is excess so that the haemoglobin is saturated, k cannot alter and the dissociation curve is a normal rectangular hyperbola, as it is found in practice to be.

Whatever be the exact details of the theory, there is no doubt of the validity of the general equation derived above, and it is the practical consequences of this which make it possible for haemoglobin to act as an oxygen-carrier: for the equation means that a given partial pressure of oxygen is in equilibrium with only one definite percentage of oxyhaemoglobin. If, therefore, haemoglobin is brought into a high pressure of oxygen, as it is in the lungs, and then taken to a low pressure, as happens when it is taken by the circulatory system to the tissues, it must take up oxygen in the former place and give it up in the latter. There is no need for vague talk of loose compounds, for the whole matter can be explained in terms of ordinary physical chemistry. The actual position of the curve depends on k, and this varies with the particular haemoglobin used: it can further be altered by other factors in the environment. It is the ratio of the two velocity constants k_1 and k_2, and so will be altered by anything which alters these to different extents. The effect of two important physical factors can be forecast by the application of the principle of Le Chatelier. The reaction $Hb + 4O_2 = HbO_8$ is exothermic. Hence a rise in temperature shifts the equilibrium point of the reaction to the left, k_2 is increased more than k_1 so that k is lowered, and the curve as a whole moves to the right (i.e. a given partial pressure of oxygen is in equilibrium with a lower percentage of oxyhaemoglobin). Oxyhaemoglobin is a stronger acid than haemoglobin, so that an increased hydrogen-ion concentration acts in exactly the same way as a rise in temperature, and dissociates oxyhaemoglobin. This is important in the animal's tissues, because where an organ is active and more oxygen is therefore required, there is usually much carbon dioxide and, in muscle, lactic acid, and so a high acidity. Oxyhaemoglobin therefore dissociates most readily when it is most needed.

The molecular weight of the haemoglobin of lampreys is 17,000, and as would be expected its oxygen saturation curve is hyperbolic, and $n = 1$. It makes an efficient transport system. Some amphibian and reptilian haemoglobins have molecular weights of 150,000 and 290,000, but in spite of this the dissociation curves for these groups are usually nearly hyperbolic. The haemoglobin of birds is very similar to that of mammals. The molecular weights of the haemoglobins of invertebrates range from 17,000 in *Chironomus* to 3,000,000 in *Lumbricus* and *Arenicola*.

Similar curves are given by all the other pigments, but

they are not all affected in the same way by physical factors.

Haemoglobin, chlorocruorin, and haemocyanin form compounds with carbon monoxide. In the case of the first two the action is reversible, but it is nearly complete at very low concentrations of the gas, and the velocity constant for the dissociation is very low. Consequently carbon monoxide is poisonous to animals with either of these pigments. It can be shown by consideration of the reaction between haemoglobin and oxygen and carbon monoxide, when these gases are present together, that a high percentage of oxyhaemoglobin can be formed only if the oxygen concentration is very high. This agrees with the standard method of treating carbon monoxide poisoning, which frequently occurs after coal-mine explosions. The patient is given a mixture of 93 per cent. oxygen and 7 per cent. carbon dioxide; the function of the latter is to raise the heart and respiratory rate.

Oxygenated blood is nearly fully saturated, and venous blood is about half saturated, and it is therefore over this range that the blood works. The pressure of oxygen in equilibrium with blood containing 95 per cent. of its pigment in the oxygenated form, is called the loading tension (t_L), and that in equilibrium with 50 per cent. saturated blood the unloading tension (t_U). A statement of these shows the condition under which the blood will work efficiently. Table 3 shows that the more active animals, and those which live in regions of high oxygen concentrations, have higher values for these functions. This allows for the best possible use of the oxygen supply, for it means that the blood starts to give up its oxygen when the tension in the tissues is only a little below that of the atmosphere. The blood of *Arenicola*, with a loading tension of 5 mm, only starts to provide oxygen at a partial pressure at which mammalian haemoglobin is almost

completely dissociated. The worm lives for part of its time
under conditions of low oxygen tension, and if its pigment
had a high loading tension it would be unable to supply
oxygen when it was most needed. Carp, pike, eels, and

TABLE 3

Loading and Unloading Tensions of Bloods. (Various authors)

Animal	Pigment	Temperature °C	t_U mm Hg	t_L mm Hg
Mammals . .	Haemoglobin	38	c. 27	c. 90
Sea-fish and trout .	,,	17	12–15	30–40
Carp, pike . .	,,	15	2–3	10
Planorbis . .	,,	12	1–2	15
Arenicola marina .	,,	17–20	2	5
Daphnia magna .	,,	17	3	—
Chironomus riparius .	,,	17	0·6	—
Spirographis . .	Chlorocruorin	10 (pH 8)	9	c. 26
,, . .	,,	26 (pH 7·35)	29	c. 50
Crustacea . .	Haemocyanin	15	14	33
Helix . . .	,,	11	4	17

other sluggish fish can live in water which has been saturated with carbon monoxide, so that their haemoglobin is
put out of action. Probably it is only used when they are
swimming fast. Three antarctic species of teleost have
neither erythrocytes nor haemoglobin, and their blood
has the carrying capacity of sea-water.

In the living animal there is a gradient of oxygen tension
from the atmosphere to the blood-plasma, from the plasma
to the pigment, from the pigment back again to the plasma
in the capillaries, and from the plasma to the active tissues.
Oxygen necessarily follows this gradient, the pigment
combining with oxygen at the surface, and dissociating
in the interior of the body. Muscle haemoglobin (myoglobin), with a different chemical composition, is present
in mammals and serves as a short-time oxygen store. It has
a hyperbolic dissociation curve mostly to the left of that
for blood haemoglobin (Fig. 17).

The carrying power, that is the amount of oxygen which a given volume of blood will carry, is quite independent of the dissociation curve. Some typical values are shown

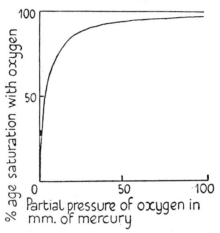

FIG. 17. Dissociation curve of muscle oxyhaemo-globin. Cf. Fig. 15. After R. Hill.

in Table 4. It is noteworthy that in vertebrates, where the pigment is contained in corpuscles, the carrying power is very high. One advantage of the corpuscles is that their walls are impermeable to the pigment, so that this can be present in high concentration. If it were free in the blood to anything like the same extent, it would be inevitably lost through the kidneys.

There is some connexion between the rate of supply of blood and the requirements of the animal for oxygen. In vertebrates the heart has a double innervation, from the depressor branch of the vagus, and from the sympathetic system. Impulses are continually passing down the former, antagonizing the effect of the latter and preventing the heart from racing. In mammals the sympathetic is stimulated and the heart-beat raised both by low external temperatures and by decreased oxygen tension. Hard work in man increases the volume of blood in the lung by 50 per cent. and halves the time which the blood takes to flow through the lung capillaries. In cold-blooded animals such as the frog, *Daphnia*, and the unhatched chick, raising the temperature increases the heart-rate.

TABLE 4

Carrying Power of Bloods. (Various authors)

Fluid	Pigment	Per cent. oxygen by volume when saturated
Sea-water . . .	..	0·7
Human blood . .	Haemoglobin	19·0
Arenicola blood . .	,,	5·7
Spirographis blood .	Chlorocruorin	9·1
Cancer blood . .	Haemocyanin	1·6
Octopus blood . .	,,	4·7

The invertebrate pigments are difficult to interpret. Although in general they are commoner in animals which live in regions of poor oxygen supply than in others, there are many anomalies. *Spirorbis borealis* contains chlorocruorin, *S. corrugatus* haemoglobin, while *S. militaris* has no pigment, yet all three worms live in similar situations. *Serpula vermicularis* and *S. lobiancoi* contain both chlorocruorin and haemoglobin. The low affinities that most invertebrate pigments have for oxygen suggest that only in abnormally bad conditions can they be of any help in oxygen transport. In *Tubifex* and *Lumbricus* (haemoglobin) and in *Sabella* (chlorocruorin) administration of carbon monoxide reduces but does not stop the consumption of oxygen at atmospheric pressure, so that the pigment carries some but not all of the oxygen required; these animals thus resemble the sluggish amphibians and fishes. In the earthworm 23 per cent. of the respired oxygen is carried at 152 mm of mercury, 40 per cent. at 38 mm, 22 per cent. at 19 mm, and 0 per cent. at 8 mm. The pigment is therefore not likely to be of much help in the soil. In other species the pigment can only work at lower partial pressures of oxygen—in *Chironomus* below about 3 mm. The haemoglobin of *Ascaris* does not give up its oxygen even in a vacuum.

It is possible that the haemoglobin of intertidal forms such as *Arenicola* functions as an oxygen store for use when the tide is out, but the experimental evidence is inconclusive. The blood of *Daphnia* develops haemoglobin only when the animal is living in badly aerated water. Under these conditions the pigment increases the survival of starved individuals, increases the feeding rate, and increases the rate of egg-production.

3.3. Transport of Carbon Dioxide

Strictly speaking, the removal of carbon dioxide is a matter of excretion, but it is closely connected with the transport of oxygen, so that it will be dealt with here. Some carbon dioxide undoubtedly finds its way out of the animal by simple diffusion, especially since it can diffuse through vertebrate connective tissue thirty times as fast as does oxygen, and since chitin is fairly permeable to it. Where there is a blood system this seems always to be used as well, and while the following account applies in details to mammals, fishes and reptiles are similar.

Carbon dioxide dissolves in the plasma in the ordinary way and there combines with water to form carbonic acid:

$$CO_2 + H_2O = H_2CO_3 \tag{i}$$

This reaction is slow, so that much carbon dioxide in simple solution diffuses into the red cells. Here carbonic acid is formed very rapidly under the influence of the enzyme carbonic anhydrase. Dissociation into hydrogen and bicarbonate ions occurs immediately and these react with haemoglobin, most of which is present as the potassium salt, also dissociated:

$$H_2CO_3 + KHb = KHCO_3 + HHb \qquad \text{(ii)}$$

The chief ions that are present are therefore

in the plasma Na^+ and Cl^-,

in the corpuscles K^+, HCO_3^-, H^+, and Hb^-.

The walls of the corpuscles are permeable to anions, but not to cations nor to the large haemoglobin ion. Under these circumstances the chloride ions diffuse in and the bicarbonate ions out, to give a Donnan equilibrium (p. 31). The result is that carbon dioxide is carried as sodium bicarbonate in the plasma, and that much more of the gas can be taken up than by mere physical solution or formation of carbonic acid. When the pressure of carbon dioxide is reduced by its diffusion out into the alveoli of the lungs, where the concentration is less than in the plasma, the reactions are reversed; the acid haemoglobin, whose concentration has not altered, drives back reaction (ii), so that bicarbonate enters the cells, and chloride diffuses out. Oxyhaemoglobin is a stronger acid than the reduced form, and so when it is present reaction (ii) does not go so far and less carbon dioxide can be carried; hence oxygen, by forming oxyhaemoglobin, displaces carbon dioxide from the blood.

There are subsidiary phenomena, of which the following are the chief. In the corpuscles, some of the buffering of the carbonic acid is carried out by phosphate,

$$H_2CO_3 + K_2HPO_4 = KHCO_3 + KH_2PO_4 \qquad \text{(iii)}$$

Some carbon dioxide combines directly with haemoglobin to form a carbamino-compound,

$$CO_2 + HbNH_2 = HbNHCOOH \qquad \text{(iv)}$$

and a similar, but less important, reaction takes place with other proteins in the blood.

Of the carbon dioxide added to the blood in the tissues (the arterial-venous difference) about 5 per cent. is carried in simple solution, 30 per cent. as the carbinocompound, and the rest as bicarbonate.

In view of the small size of most invertebrates and the ease of diffusion of carbon dioxide, it is possible that they need no such complicated mechanisms. Carbonic anhydrase is present in the blood of *Chironomus*, and in the tissues, especially the gills, of cephalopods, but not in their blood. There is no evidence that haemocyanin combines directly with carbon dioxide as haemoglobin does.

3.4. Respiratory Organs

The mere possession of a respiratory pigment is not by itself enough to ensure an adequate supply of oxygen to the tissues. There must be some part of the body where oxygen can combine with the pigment. The simplest way is for the animal to make use of its skin, a method used by many small aquatic animals and by those living in damp and protected situations. Examples are numerous. Earthworms obtain all their oxygen through the unspecialized body-surface, and even in polychaetes with well-developed gills 75 per cent. of the gas exchange may take place through the skin. A few Crustacea, such as *Coenobita*, the semi-terrestrial hermit crab which feeds on coco-nuts, have no gills, and there are some Apterygota without tracheae, and a few aquatic insect larvae (*Simulium, Chironomus*) where they are not functional; but for the most part arthropods have some specialized system. The same applies to the molluscs. There are a few scattered cases of fish which breathe through the skin; the mudhopper *Periophthalmus* of the East Indies uses its caudal fin when it is on land, and the eel uses its whole body-surface when it is migrating across country. In the Amphibia the skin is very important. Some Salamandridae have neither gills nor lungs, and the axolotl is not affected by having both cut off. In the edible frog one-third of the total oxygen exchange, and three-quarters of the carbon dioxide exchange, go on through the skin. The amniotes have too thick a covering of scales or fur or feathers for the skin to be used very much, but even in the cat 0.5 per cent. of the gas exchange goes on through it.

The oxygen requirement of an animal depends on its volume, and the rate at which its skin can take up the gas depends on its surface. The larger an animal, the smaller is the ratio of its surface to its volume, so that there is likely to be some size at which the skin is not capable of taking up oxygen fast enough. This point will be reached early when the animal has a poor circulation, or is very active, or has a thick epidermis. Thus the largest animals which use nothing but the unspecialized skin to take up oxygen are the six feet long earthworms of the East, which are sluggish, have no exoskeleton, and have a closed blood system with haemoglobin of low loading tension. Fish, which have thick scales, can seldom use their skin, whereas some of the naked Amphibia, as has been said, use nothing else.

Where the skin is not adequate some special respiratory organ, usually highly vascular, is developed, either from the skin or some other part of the body. If it is used for absorbing the dissolved oxygen of water it is generally called a gill; if it works in air, a lung.

3.41. Gills

From a physiological point of view an organ is not a gill unless it takes up oxygen at a greater rate per unit area than does the rest of the body-surface, and judged in

this way many of the structures which morphologists call
gills do not deserve the name. The gills of lamellibranchs,
for example, are feeding organs, the true respiratory organ
being the mantle, and the anal gills of mosquito and midge
larvae are mainly organs for water exchange, though those
of *Aedes* are probably respiratory. More than half of the
oxygen uptake of the starfish *Asterias rubens* is by the tube-
feet, but this may be merely because in total these organs
have a very large surface area. Good examples of external
gills, that is those which are expansions of the skin, are
found in the marine gastropods and in Crustacea such as
the crayfish. In vertebrates they occur in a few fishes such
as *Polypterus*, and fairly widely in the Amphibia; in all
these they are probably adaptations to low oxygen
tensions.

The aquatic larvae of Trichoptera, Ephemeroptera,
Odonata, a few Lepidoptera, and *Simulium* (Diptera) have
tracheal gills, expansions of the body wall with a network
of fine tracheae, but these do not always absorb oxygen.
In the nymphs of the mayflies their function is connected
with the habitat. In *Ephemera vulgata*, which burrows in
mud, they both absorb oxygen and help by their beating
to ventilate the surface of the body, even at high oxygen
tensions. In *Chloeon*, they do not absorb oxygen, but they
beat actively when the oxygen tension is lowered; in
Baetis, which lives in fast-flowing, and so well aerated,
streams, they seem to be quite functionless.

A good many animals make use of the alimentary canal
instead of the skin. Some polychaetes and aquatic oligochaetes (e.g. *Nais*, common in British waters) have an
ascending ciliary current beginning at the anus, often
assisted by antiperistalsis, and the rectum is similarly used
by many primitive Crustacea such as the water-fleas, and
even to some extent by the crayfish. Dragonflies of the
sub-order Anisoptera have rectal tracheal gills, similar

except in position to those of other aquatic larvae. The Holothuroidea breathe by respiratory trees, which are branched diverticula of the cloaca. Among the vertebrates, some tortoises pump water in and out of the cloaca, while the internal gills of fish are expansions of the pharynx wall which serve also as osmotic regulators (section 8.3).

3.42. Lungs

There are few successful and active terrestrial invertebrates other than the insects, and lungs are correspondingly rare. The mantle, developed to enclose a hollow chamber, is used as such in the snails. Scorpions and spiders have two or more small openings or stigmata, usually on the ventral surface, which lead into chambers into which project several vascular and leaf-like projections of the body wall called lung-books. In some spiders there are also tracheae.

The best-known lung, that of the vertebrates, is, like their gills, developed from the alimentary canal. It is functional and used for taking in air in a few fishes (Dipnoi, Crossopterygii, and Holostei, represented by *Ceratodus*, *Polypterus*, and *Amia* respectively), but in most fish it is replaced by the swim-bladder, which may be closed. It is an important respiratory organ in adult Amphibia, and in the ammiotes is almost the only place where gas-exchange takes place. An increase in efficiency, which goes with an increasing internal surface, can be traced through the vertebrate series. The frog, with simple lungs, uses the roof of its mouth to take up much of its oxygen, and many other amphibians, lizards, and chelonians use the pharynx also. There is often a special blood-supply to the region where oxygen is taken up, which in some lizards is derived partly from the pulmonary arch and partly from the systemic and carotid arches.

3.43. Mechanisms of Breathing

In inactive animals such as the earthworm there is no special arrangement for bringing oxygen to the respiratory surface, but most species have something of this sort, particularly when the respiratory organ is internal. Constant renewal of the layer of air or water immediately in contact with the absorbing surface effectively increases the supply of oxygen, for if the gas can only arrive by diffusion its concentration in the atmosphere immediately adjacent to the surface will rapidly fall to a low value. The polychaetes *Spirographis spallanzanii* and *Sabella pavonina* live in mucin tubes through which they maintain a current of water by rhythmical contractions of the body; a swelling appears at the hind end of the worm, completely filling the tube, and then moves forwards. The result of this is that the worms can live in water of low oxygen concentration, while if they are removed from the tubes they can survive only if the water is well aerated. That no special property of the mucin is involved is shown by the fact that the worms can live in low oxygen concentrations if they are removed from their own tubes and placed in glass ones of the proper size. Presumably the waves of muscular contraction are stimulated by contact with the wall. The beating of the heart in *Daphnia* similarly prevents water from remaining stationary under the carapace.

3.431. Breathing by Gills. In most of the higher Crustacea some of the limbs maintain definite currents over the gills. In the decapods, such as the crayfish and shore-crab, the exopodite of the second maxilla is modified as the scaphognathite, which flaps and draws water forwards through the gill chamber about once a second. Other mouth-parts assist in the process, some of them ensuring that the current actually passes over the gills, and the epipodites of the three maxillipedes brush the surfaces of the gills to prevent the accumulation of foreign matter. The scaphognathite reverses for a few strokes every now and again. The effects of oxygen and carbon dioxide concentration on the beat of the respiratory limbs of several Crustacea have been investigated. They fall into three groups: in the first, represented by the shore-crab (*Carcinus moenas*), the beat is independent of the concentration of the two gases. In the second, of which the amphipods *Gammarus pulex* and *G. locusta* are examples, the beat (in this case of the pleopods) is increased by falling oxygen tension and by increasing carbon dioxide tension. In the third, typified by the crayfish (*Astacus fluviatilis*), the beat is increased by oxygen deficiency but is unaffected by carbon dioxide. The distribution of these three groups certainly does not follow the classification of the Crustacea, and neither does it seem to agree with the habitats or habits of the animals. It appears that the power to regulate the respiratory current in accordance with needs has been independently evolved on several occasions.

In the lamellibranchs the ciliary food currents (see p. 10) also serve to bring in oxygen.

In the selachians each gill pouch is divided into two parts: an inner chamber which is in free communication with the mouth, and an outer which opens to the sea by the externally visible gill slit. These two are separated from one another by the lattice-work of the two hemibranchs. Water passes through the gaps in the lattice by two mechanisms. In the first, which is of the nature of a force-pump, the hypobranchial musculature contracts and lowers the floor of the pharynx, so that water enters through the mouth and spiracles, the external openings of the gill slits being shut. The mouth and spiracles then close, and adductor muscles contract and draw the epi- and cerato-branchials nearer together; the increased pressure in the pharynx forces water through the lattice of the gills into the outer chambers of the gill pouches, and so to the exterior. In the second mechanism, which is a suction pump, the outer gill chambers are first enlarged by the contraction of the adductor muscles and of muscles in the gill septum. While this is happening the external openings of the gill slits are closed, so that water must be drawn through the gills from the inner gill chambers. The outer gill chambers are emptied to the exterior by the contraction of superficial muscles, back-flow into the inner chambers being prevented by the high resistance of the small channels in the gills. By this method breathing can take place with the mouth continuously open. The two mechanisms may work in conjunction with one another, or independently.

In teleosts the same general methods are used but here there is a single outer gill chamber on each side, the operculum covering all the gills. In many species, and perhaps in nearly all, there are two velar folds of tissue in the mouth, which form a valve just behind the front teeth. One, the maxillary, hangs down, and the other, the mandibular, projects up to meet it. In inspiration the folds open and the opercula close, in expiration the folds meet and the opercula are lifted away from the sides of the body. This arrangement enables the fish to breathe with its mouth continuously open. Similar valves are found in the lung-fishes *Polypterus*, *Amia*, and *Lepidosiren*. Artificially reversing the blood-flow through the gill-chamber of the tench reduces the rate of uptake of oxygen, so that probably the counter-current principle, by which the water supplying the oxygen and the blood which is taking it up flow past each other in opposite directions, is important, just as it is in chemical purification.

3.432. Breathing by Lungs. Pulmonate gastropods renew the air in their lung at fairly frequent intervals, since all the gas is expelled when the animal contracts into its shell. The freshwater forms, such as *Planorbis* and *Limnaea*, frequently come to the surface, push the pulmonary aperture into the air, open it, raise the floor of the mantle cavity, and lower it again. This brings in fresh air.

The breathing of the frog, apart from the use of the skin mentioned above, does not seem to be very clearly understood. In the ordinary way air is continually being pumped into and out of the buccal cavity through the nares by the movement of the floor of the mouth by muscles attached to the hyoid. The mouth and the glottis are kept closed. About once a minute the external nares are closed, the glottis opens, and the collapse of the elastic lungs forces the air contained in them into the mouth; it mixes with fresh air there, the floor of the mouth is raised, and so the lungs are refilled. If a frog which has recently been active be watched, it can be seen that the thorax pulsates at the same rate as the floor of the mouth, but slightly out of phase with it, so that the lungs are presumably filled more frequently. One thing that is certain is that if the mouth is held open the thorax ceases to pulsate and the animal shows signs of distress.

Most reptiles also appear to have a pharyngeal type of respiration, in which movement of the hyoid is important, but turtles breathe also by filling their lungs much as mammals do.

In mammals the process of breathing is complicated, but an outline of what happens in man is as follows. In inspiration the diaphragm, which is convex upwards, is contracted; the ribs, normally directed forwards and slightly downwards, are raised; and there is a slight extension of the spinal column. All these movements increase the volume of the thoracic cavity, and so reduce the pressure in it. Atmospheric pressure, therefore, forces air into the lungs, which expand to take up the increased volume of the thorax. If the thoracic wall is punctured, breathing is impossible, for air merely rushes in through the perforation. Expiration is the reverse of inspiration, but it is mainly carried out passively. The lungs are elastic and contract of their own accord as soon as the muscles of the diaphragm and ribs are relaxed. The lungs are never completely emptied, so that the oxygen tension in the alveoli is never equal to that of the atmosphere. It is normally about 102 mm of mercury, about two-thirds that of the air. The respiratory movements are controlled by the central nervous system from the medulla, which in collaboration with impulses arising in the lungs when they are stretched, maintains the normal rhythm. An increased carbon dioxide content or hydrogen ion concentration of the blood reaching the medulla causes it to become more active. Since carbon dioxide is formed when a muscle contracts, it is obvious that exercise should cause an acceleration of breathing, and it is familiar to every one that it does in fact do so. Under ordinary circumstances the oxygen content of the blood does not vary significantly, but in cases of difficult breathing or at high altitudes it may fall sufficiently to have an effect. The receptors for low oxygen content are in the walls of the aorta, and especially of the carotid body. Rapid breathing, and the other symptoms of mountain sickness, only become noticeable at rest at heights above about 14,000 ft, and under these conditions the tension of oxygen in the alveoli of the lungs is only just above half the normal.

In birds breathing is very efficient; air is taken right through the lungs to the thoracic and abdominal air-sacs, and is then forcibly expelled through the alveoli of the lungs. The oxygen tension in contact with the blood is therefore very nearly that of the atmosphere.

Diving mammals and birds, such as seals and ducks, generally have a reflex which produces cessation of breathing (apnoea) when their heads are under water. In ducks it is produced by thermal stimulation of the nares either by hot or by cold water, but not by that between 30° and 40° C. In seals the heart-beat falls from 150 to 10 per min, and the heart is also slowed in penguins. In all the species that have been investigated oxygen is obtained during apnoea from the haemoglobin in the blood and muscles, but the rate at which it is used is reduced, and an oxygen debt is built up, mainly by the lactic acid mechanism.

3.433. Breathing by Tracheae. The replacement of air in the tracheae of insects is surprisingly rapid; if a cockroach is kept in pure oxygen till its tracheae are full of this gas, and then returned to air, it is only a minute before there is 80 per cent. of nitrogen in them. In most insects diffusion is assisted by some sort of pulsation of the abdomen, assisted during flight by movements of the wing muscles. It has been claimed that in grasshoppers a current of air is maintained right through the body, in at the anterior spiracles and out posteriorly, but the experiments involve very unnatural conditions and the conclusion is doubtful. It has been shown that insects suffer easily from water loss, and in most of them at rest the spiracles are closed, presumably to prevent this. When the rat-flea *Xenopsylla cheopis* is at rest, its spiracles open and close rhythmically, but when the muscles are active they remain open. Experimentally they can be induced to do so either by low oxygen concentration or high carbon dioxide concentration.

Those insects which, like mosquito larvae and many of the beetles, live beneath the surface of water but come to the air to breathe, are of some interest. The surface of the stigmata is covered with hydrofuge substances. These have a high angle of contact with water, which is thus prevented from entering, but oil will wet them, so that a film of it spread on the surface will enter as soon as the spiracles touch it. Once the tracheae contain oil no air can go in and so the animal must drown.

Many insects (such as *Dytiscus* and *Notonecta*) carry bubbles of air below the surface with them. This is used directly as a source of oxygen, and it also enables them to extract oxygen from the water in the following way. Oxygen is being used by the animal, so that its partial pressure in the bubble falls, and in time goes below that in the water. But as this happens the partial pressure of the nitrogen in the bubble must necessarily rise and will go above that in the water, for the total pressure in the bubble is determined simply by its depth below the water, and is constant. Equilibrium can be restored either by oxygen entering the bubble or by nitrogen leaving it, but the first goes on three times as fast as the second, so that very little of the latter takes place. *Notonecta* was found to be able to live for 7 hours below water saturated with air, but only 35 min below water saturated with oxygen. In the latter case the nitrogen in the bubble would rapidly dissolve in the water, and the conditions described above would not apply, so that although as much oxygen was present as in the first case, it was not available.

As the bubble of an animal such as *Dytiscus* slowly loses its nitrogen, it shrinks, and so the surface over which oxygen can enter it is reduced, and the rate of diffusion of oxygen inwards falls also. Eventually the bubble disappears, and the animal has to come to the surface to renew it. Some insects do better than this. Their body is covered with a complete layer of air, called the plastron, held by unwettable hairs. The bubble can never disappear, any more than air can disappear from the rigid tracheae of insects with no spiracles, and oxygen is always available if it is present in the water. The bug *Aphelocheirus* forms its gas layer below the skin just before ecdysis, so that when the skin is shed the bubble is complete and in position. If the water is well aerated, as it is in swiftly flowing streams, the bug never needs to come to the surface to breathe. The hairs are about $5\,\mu$ long, and there are two and a half million of them per square millimetre. *Corixa* has a thicker plastron, which is not quite so permanent, so that the animal can survive in oxygen-saturated water for only 40 hours; there is said to be circulation through the tracheae. Plastron respiration is found also in many beetles, in some ichneumons, and possibly in water spiders.

3.44. Comparison of Aquatic and Aerial Respiration

The question is sometimes asked whether aquatic or aerial respiration is the more efficient. The question is probably meaningless, since the conditions which have to be fulfilled are very different for the two. It has been suggested that since the teleost *Erythrinus unitaeniatus,* which can breathe completely through either gills or lungs, has a slightly greater area of the latter, aerial respiration is less efficient, but obviously no conclusions can be drawn unless full information is available as to the activity of the fish. Nevertheless, there is some reason for saying that air-breathing is less efficient. Ultimately all respiration is aquatic, since the first thing the oxygen has to do when it reaches the surface of the lung is to dissolve in the surface film of water. The difference between lungs and gills from a physiological point of view is that the former are covered with a relatively thick surface film of water, while the latter may be swept by a current so that the stationary layer is only a few molecules thick. Although there is more oxygen in the air than in water, it is not so easy for the animal to obtain it. The four species of snail *Littorina littorea*, *L. obtusata*, *L. rudis*, and *L. neritoides* form an ecological series of animals which live in progressively drier situations on the shore. The first lives in rock pools and is only exposed at low tides, but the others may be exposed for several hours. Associated with the habitats is the degree of vascularization of the mantle cavity, which increases in the same order as the dryness of the surroundings.

The rate of diffusion of oxygen in air is 45,000 times that in water, so that unless there were some means for continual renewal of the layer of water in contact with the gill, access of oxygen would be much slower than in air.

Land animals drown largely because their respiratory surfaces become covered with mucus which prevents free access of oxygen. Earthworms can live under well-aerated water. If what has been said above is correct, there seems no reason why aquatic animals should not be able to live in air; that they cannot is probably due to other causes, and in fish the important factor is the haemoglobin. The effective concentration of carbon dioxide in water is not altered by respiration, owing to the presence of bicarbonates. It does not therefore matter that a fish's haemoglobin is very sensitive to carbon dioxide, or, rather, to acidity. In some cases the loading tension in presence of 2 per cent. carbon dioxide is 150 mm of mercury. In air, respiration very greatly raises the carbon dioxide concentration—there is 5 per cent. in the lungs of mammals—so that if the concentration near the gills rises to anything like the same extent, as it probably does when a fish is brought into air, it is not surprising that the animal dies. It is noticeable that many of those fish which do live on land breathe, like the eel, through the skin, so that carbon dioxide is easily carried away.

3.45. Life in Low Oxygen Concentrations

It is sometimes said that parasites live in surroundings devoid of oxygen, but a little consideration will show that this is not generally true. The cells of the host are supplied with oxygen, and a parasite such as *Trichinella* living amongst them must be able to share it. The malarial parasite and others in the blood are very well supplied with oxygen indeed. The only situations where parasites live in which the oxygen concentration is low are the coelom and the gut, and even in these places it will seldom be zero, for there must be diffusion out from the wall, which is supplied, often richly, with blood. Measurements in the small intestine of the rat have shown the pressure of oxygen near the mucosa to range from 19 to 30 mm of mercury; in the sheep, as would be expected with the wider lumen, it is lower, from 4 to 12 mm. The lowest values are likely to be found in the large intestine, where there are usually many Bacteria and much production of other gases. Other habitats where there is likely to be little oxygen are the depths of the sea and mud in ponds and swamps. In these the concentration sometimes falls too low to be measured, but it is not always so.

Most small invertebrates are able to survive for some time without oxygen, but all that have been investigated use oxygen when it is available. *Paramecium*, for instance, normally aerobic, can survive in hydrogen or nitrogen for from 1 to 8 hours, and the ciliate *Balantiophorus minutus*, which lives in dung, for from 5 days to 3 weeks. Most of the mud-living species are inactive forms requiring little oxygen, and probably able to survive for a time by one of the common anaerobic mechanisms which have been discussed in section 3.13. Special attention has been given to the parasitic nematodes. The small forms *Nippostrongylus muris* from the rat, *Haemonchus contortus* from the abomasum of the sheep, and *Nematodirus* from its intestine, all increase their rate of oxygen consumption as its concentration rises. The maximum oxygen consumption corresponds closely to the maximum concentration observed in the intestine. The general course of glycogen breakdown is similar to that of muscle. The larger *Ascaris* uses less oxygen per unit mass than do the smaller forms, but in complete absence of oxygen it produces carbon dioxide at only one-tenth or one-quarter the rate at which it does if oxygen is present. There is still doubt about the chemical mechanism, but there is probably breakdown of glycogen to organic acids. A peculiar dehydrogenase system is present. *Ascaris* and other nematodes have haemoglobin in their body-fluids, but its function is obscure.

Larvae of *Taenia taeniaeformis*, a tapeworm whose hosts are cats and rats, survive longer when oxygen is present than when it is not, and their consumption increases with the concentration. Their respiration is in part cyanide-sensitive, which suggests that cytochrome or some similar substance is used in the oxidation. *Schistosoma* has cytochrome enough to account for only 10 per cent. of its oxygen consumption, but the whole of its oxygen uptake is abolished by cyanide. It can survive and lay eggs when the oxygen uptake is reduced to 20 per cent. of the normal. *Trichinella spiralis* needs oxygen for mobility, but not for survival; it does not possess glycogen and does not produce acids, so presumably the carbon dioxide which it liberates is made from some other storage product.

The symbiotic ciliates of ruminants (p. 29) metabolize carbohydrates anaerobically, producing lactic, acetic, and butyric acids. It has been claimed that some parasitic Protozoa, such as *Nyctotherus* in the rectum of the frog, can live completely anaerobically, but this is based on old work which needs to be repeated, since the difficulty of removing all traces of oxygen was not realized by the early experimenters. The larva of the warble-fly, *Gastrophilus equi*, can live for about three weeks submerged in oil, during which time it converts glycogen to fat, but in life it appears to be an opportunist, seizing bubbles of air which pass down the host's oesophagus and storing the oxygen in haemoglobin. *Chironomus* larvae can also live anaerobically for a time by the breakdown of glycogen.

Terrestrial animals that dive below the surface of the water for more or less lengthy periods have to face a special problem. Insects and the water spider carry air with them. Seals, diving ducks, and penguins have evolved a series of mechanisms which are much alike in the three groups. First, there is a high content of myoglobin in the muscles, so that they carry oxygen with them in the oxygenated form of this. There is enough in the seal *Phoca vitulina* to last for 5 to 10 minutes, and only when it is all used up does anaerobic work start. Secondly, the rate of circulation falls, either by a fall in the rate of heart-beat or by the use of an arteriovenous shunt, so that little carbon dioxide and lactic acid enter the blood from the muscles, and other organs are not affected. This enables a large oxygen-debt to be built up without distress. Thirdly, there is a fall of body-temperature. This saves oxygen by allowing all that is available to be used for swimming, instead of much of it being used merely for heat production.

4

EFFECTOR SYSTEMS

EFFECTOR systems are cells, collections of cells, or parts of cells (using the word in its old and broad sense) by which the organism acts in some way on the environment outside it, and it is by means of them only that an animal can respond to a stimulus or produce any change in its own position or in its own body. Put briefly, in the words of G. H. Parker: 'Effectors are the parts by which animals respond to changes in the world about them.' They are usually classified as follows:

1. Cilia and flagella.
2. Pseudopodia.
3. Muscles.
4. Glands.
5. Electric organs (a specialization of 3).
6. Luminescent organs (a specialization of 4).
7. Nematocysts or urticators.
8. Chromatophores.

In addition, there are some minor types, such as the trichocysts and myonemes of some Protozoa. No animal has all of these, and most possess but three or four. Man, for instance, has only pseudopodia, cilia, glands, and muscles, and of these the last alone have any important connexion with the outside world; all the rest serve only to maintain life inside the animal. Effectors are usually brought into action by stimulation either through the nervous system or by hormones, but there are cases of all classes, except electric organs, where the effector apparently reacts directly to a stimulus. Such an organ is called an independent effector, but its nature and reaction are not affected by the method by which it is activated.

Cilia, flagella, pseudopodia, and muscles are all concerned with movement, and their action is based on an alternation of contraction and extension. It seems that the basic chemistry of the change is always much the same, the contraction depending on the removal of phosphate ions from adenosine triphosphate, or a related compound, with liberation of energy. The restorative processes, by which the energy is ultimately provided, vary widely.

4.1. Cilia and Flagella

Cilia and flagella are contractile outgrowths from a cell, never withdrawn except at reproduction and encystment, and maintaining a shape and size which are nearly constant. Although it is usually easy to decide whether a given structure is a cilium or a flagellum, there are some cases of difficulty. Most cells which have contractile processes that conform to the above description have either a few long ones or many short ones, the former being called flagella and the latter cilia. The doubt arises with animals such as the protozoans *Multicilia* and *Trichonympha*, which have many long processes. It is probable that physiologically these are flagella rather than cilia. In any case the two are probably fundamentally very similar, and the differences may be largely due to necessary mechanical dissimilarities between a short structure and a long. Flagella are found in the Protozoa, in sponges, in some of the endoderm cells of coelenterates, and in the sperms of most animals. Cilia are even more widespread: they form the locomotor organs of a whole class of the Protozoa, of ctenophores, of some planarians, and of rotifers, and of larvae of coelenterates, platyhelminths,

annelids, molluscs, echinoderms, protochordates, and
Amphibia. Internal ciliated cells are present in all Metazoa except Nematoda and Arthropoda; they serve to
maintain currents of water for many purposes: for carrying food (Scyphozoa, lamellibranchs, protochordates), for
carrying out excretory products (all groups with a true
nephridium; see p. 93), for carrying eggs (vertebrates),
or for guiding sperms to the eggs (birds and reptiles).
In the mammals cilia are present chiefly in the respiratory
tract, where they help to keep out dust particles. They
are found in all three germ-layers, and wherever they
occur are very similar in structure and behaviour.

Both cilia and flagella are very thin structures, and
they nearly always appear homogeneous under the light
microscope. In pictures made with the electron microscope a number of filaments can be seen running the
length of the structure, and sections show that these are
arranged with an axial pair and an outer ring of nine.
This arrangement appears to be invariable in all the cilia
and flagella that have been studied, whether they come
from plants, Protozoa, or Metazoa, and is also found in
sperm tails (Fig. 18). Some preparations, for example of
Paramecium and other ciliates, show that each filament
in the outer ring is in fact double, and this may be general.
The bases of the outer filaments fuse or join to form a
continuous collar. The nature and function of these filaments are at present unknown, but a theoretical mechanism to account for the beat has been worked out on the
assumption that the central pair are conducting only,
and those of the ring both conducting and contractile.
The direction of beat is generally perpendicular to the
line joining the central pair. The electron microscope
shows also that some flagella, such as that of *Euglena*, have
a row of short spurs along one side.

Some large cilia, such as the laterofrontals of *Mytilus*

(see p. 11), have been shown to consist of several cilia beating together so that unless their co-ordination is upset they appear as one. In a similar way many undulating membranes consist of a line of cilia beating in order. When

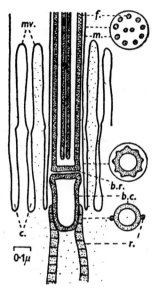

FIG. 18. Reconstruction of basal regions of one *Mytilus* gill cilium, showing 9+2 fibres (*f.*), membrane (*m.*), basal plate or ring (*b.r.*), basal corpuscle (*b.c.*), rootlets (*r.*), microvilli (*mv.*), and crypts (*c.*). Cross-striations have not been clearly observed in these rootlets but they almost certainly exist. After Bradfield.

the rhythm is upset by placing a needle through the apparent membrane, the individual cilia can be seen. There are some authors who consider that all undulating membranes, even that of *Trypanosoma*, are of this nature.

In a preserved cell it is usually possible to see at the base of a flagellum a basal granule, and below the cilia a line of granules, presumably one for each cilium. In living cells of ciliated epithelium there is sometimes a region of slightly higher refractive index corresponding in position to the basal granules. In some fixed cells fibres called rhizoplasts run from the basal granules to the nucleus, and where the granules are remote from the surface there may be an axial filament running from each granule to its flagellum. This is particularly well seen in some of the complicated Mastigophora, such as *Giardia* (Fig. 19). Occasionally it has been possible to peel off the surface layer of cells of ciliated epithelium, and when this has been done it is found that if the basal granules come away with the cilia the latter go on beating normally, but if the region with the granules is left attached to the main part of the cell the cilia are inactive (Fig. 20). These observations suggest that the basal granules are necessary for the functioning of the cilia. A basal granule seems always to be derived from a division centre, but nothing appears to be known as to the way in which it acts.

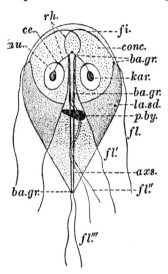

Fig. 19. *Giardia intestinalis*, from the intestine of man. Semi-diagrammatic.

axs., axostyle (axoneme); *ba.gr.*, basal granules; *ce.*, centriole; *conc.*, ventral concavity ('sucker'); *fi.*, fibre around concavity; *fl.*, *fl.'*, *fl."*, *fl."'*, anterolateral, posterolateral, ventral, and caudal flagella; *kar.*, karyosome; *la.sd.*, lateral shield, the thickest part of the body; *nu.*, nucleus; *p.by.*, parabasal body; *rh.*, rhizoplasts. After Borradaile and Potts.

The rate of movement of cilia appears high, but this is because, while velocity has dimensions of one in length and minus one in time, the microscope magnifies length but leaves time unaffected; it therefore magnifies velocity to the same extent as it does length. A cilium $10\,\mu$ long, beating at the normal rate of ten times a second and moving through an arc of π radians, has in its effective beat a velocity of only 1·5 mm/sec at the tip. The speeds produced by cilia correspond to this; *Paramecium* moves at

active cilia ← motionless cilia

basal granules

FIG. 20. Excised strip of lateral epithelium of *Mytilus* (diagrammatic). Note that the cilia are active as long as they are in organic communication with the cells. After Gray.

speeds of the order of 1 mm/sec, and particles placed on ciliated epithelium never move at more than 3 or 4 mm/sec. *Euglena* moves at about 0·2 mm/sec. On account of their slow speed, and because they can only be present on surfaces, which bear a progressively smaller proportion to weight as size increases, cilia can only be used for efficient locomotion if the animal is small and of low density. Thus *Volvox*, with a radius of 0·5 mm and a specific gravity of 1·01, has a maximum velocity at 15° C of 1 mm/sec. At this speed practically all the external work is done against viscosity, and if all the cilia were to stop beating at once the kinetic energy of the animal would only carry it 0·05 mm—one-tenth of its own radius. In the same way full speed is attained almost at once.

The movement of cilia can be studied in three ways: they may be slowed down with drugs such as veratrin; they may be observed with a stroboscope; or they may be photographed with a kinecamera. It is obviously of doubtful legitimacy to argue from a drugged cilium to the normal, so that the first method, though useful, must be supported by others. The principle of the stroboscope is as follows. If a moving object is seen through a rapidly opening and closing diaphragm, it is observed in the positions which it occupies at times o, δt, $2\delta t$, $3\delta t$, and so on, where δt is the interval between successive openings of the shutter. If δt is small enough the eye, owing to persistence of the retinal images, will appear to see continuous movement. If the object is not moving laterally, but is going through a cyclic movement like that of a rotating wheel, and if it takes a time t for one complete cycle, it is in the same position at $t+\delta t$ as it was at δt, the same at $t+2\delta t$ as at $2\delta t$, and more generally in the same position at $t+m\delta t$ as at $m\delta t$. For successive revolutions the same argument holds, and the wheel is in the same position at $2t+m\delta t$ as at $m\delta t$, and more generally in the same position at $nt+m\delta t$ as at $m\delta t$ (where n is a whole number). If, then, the diaphragm is arranged to open at intervals of $t+\delta t$, the object will be seen at times o, $t+\delta t$, $2t+2\delta t$, and so on. It will therefore be observed in exactly the positions that it would have occupied at times o, δt, $2\delta t$, &c., and so will appear to be in continuous movement at much less than its normal speed: how much less will depend on the relative values of t and δt. For investigating ciliary movement the cilium is viewed through a slit in a rotating disk, the rate of revolution of which is adjusted so that the cilium appears to stand still: at this speed the disk rotates once while the cilium goes through one or possibly more exact cycles. The speed of the disk is decreased slightly and the conditions discussed above become operative. The cilium is seen to move slowly. The speed of the disk must be such as to avoid flicker.

The third method consists simply in combining a kinematograph camera with a microscope. It is sometimes convenient to add a stroboscope to this arrangement.

All the methods of investigation agree in showing that the method of beat is that shown in Fig. 21 and Pl. II. There is a rapid effective forward movement which takes (in frog epithelium) about o·02 sec, and a slower limp

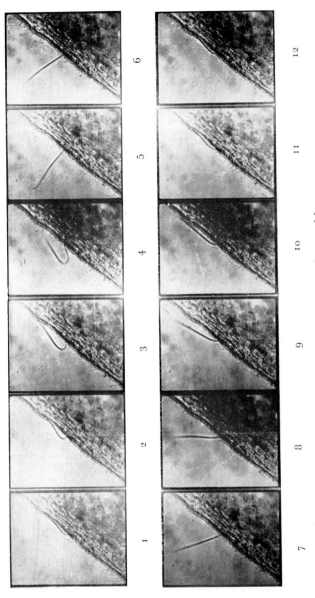

PLATE II. STILLS FROM A FILM OF CILIARY MOVEMENT

Frames 1–5, recovery stroke; 6–12, effective stroke. (Laterofrontal cilium of *Mytilus*; interval 0·05 sec.). After Gray.

recovery which takes about 0·1 sec. During the former the cilium is rigid and can be prevented from moving by a needle placed in its way, but during the recovery stroke it is flexible and simply passes underneath any obstruction

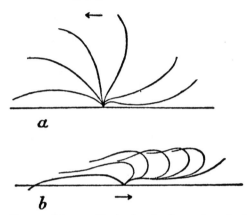

Fig. 21. Diagram illustrating the form of terminal cilia of *Mytilus* during (*a*) the effective, and (*b*) recovery, beats. After Gray.

placed in its path. Either it changes its state from one phase to the next, or it is capable of bending in one direction only, that is in the same direction as its effective stroke. A mechanical model of this sort can be made by gluing a row of small wooden cubes on to a piece of linen. If the cubes are in contact with one another bending is impossible away from the linen-backed side, but it is easy in the opposite direction.

Ciliated surfaces nearly always show metachronal rhythm. This means that the cilia of one cell are slightly out of phase with those of the next, which is again out of phase with the next group by the same amount, and so on. The effect of this is that waves appear to pass over the surface. The direction of the rhythm is always the same for one type of tissue, but all three possibilities are realized in different forms. In ciliated epithelium from the frog and in the frontal cilia of *Mytilus* the waves travel in the same direction as the effective beat of the cilia, which means that each cilium is a little later than the one just behind it. In ctenophores the metachronal waves travel against the beat. In the lateral cilia of *Mytilus* they go across the direction of beat, so that each cilium is in step with those behind and in front of it, but slightly out of step with its neighbours on each side. The rhythm is upset if a needle is placed in the path of some of the cilia so that their beat is disturbed, but starts again when normal conditions are restored. It is the metachronal rhythm of a line of cilia which produces the appearance of an undulating membrane. In Protozoa an injury to the neuromotor centre upsets the rhythm, and in all cases rhythm stops if the rate of beat is brought below a certain value by narcotics or low temperature.

Flagella, owing to their greater length, are somewhat more complicated, and no full account of their mechanics seems possible. It is probable that the wave of contraction always starts at the base, and changes its plane as it moves towards the tip, so that the movement of the whole flagellum is a gyration as well as a lashing. In normal movement long anterior flagella are always recurved, so that they are directed backwards; this would be expected in view of their flexible nature. Much of the backward force which must be produced on the water in order to propel the animal forward is probably mediated by the rotation and gyration of the cell produced as reactions to the contraction of the flagella. When a flagellate organism is confined below a cover-glass, or is otherwise restricted, a long flagellum can sometimes be seen to carry out effective and recovery strokes in one plane, in a very similar manner to cilia, but it is probable that this type of movement is of little or no importance in nature. Anterior flagella used to be called tractella and posterior ones pulsella, but since anterior flagella are probably always trailing when active the distinction is best abandoned.

There is considerable evidence that both cilia and flagella are not inert things wagged from the base, but are living structures liberating energy along their length. For instance, sometimes the tip only of a long flagellum moves, and in most flagellate Protozoa the contraction waves may accelerate.

Cilia and flagella are remarkably free from control by their owner. In the majority of cases they never reverse, and if a piece of epithelium from the roof of the mouth of the frog be cut out, turned through 180°, and regrafted in place, the cilia go on beating in their old way, although they now drive a current down the animal's throat. Reversal does, however, take place in the avoiding reaction of ciliates (see p. 310) and in the food currents of sea-anemones such as *Metridium* (p. 10). The reversal of movement in flagellates like *Euglena* may be brought about by variations in the rate of beat at different parts of the flagellum, without actual reversal. There is only one case on record where cilia can be excited by stimulation of a nerve—in the lip of the mollusc *Physa*—but there are a few cases where nervous stimulation has a depressing influence. If the velar nerve of the veliger larva of the mollusc *Archidoris* is cut or treated with narcotics, the cilia beat continuously instead of intermittently: the nerve must therefore have an inhibitory effect. It is possible that some, but not all, protochordate cilia are under nervous control.

There are some resemblances between the effects of drugs on cilia and those on smooth and cardiac muscle (p. 252). Thus adrenaline and low concentrations of acetylcholine increase the rate of beat of the cilia of the rabbit's trachea, while high concentrations of acetylcholine depress it. Acetylcholine and histamine have been detected in the rabbit's tracheal epithelium, but whether they play any part in the control of the cilia is unknown.

Cilia are dependent on the environment in much the same way as other living structures. The rate of beat increases with temperature, but above a certain value changes occur and finally death ensues. With the cilia of *Mytilus* gill, for example, there is a reversible increase of rate up to 28° C, at 34° C there is a reduced amplitude, at 38° C the rate of beat is reduced, at 40° C the cilia are stationary, at 45° C they contract, and at 47° C there is permanent injury and death. In absence of oxygen cilia will go on beating for 45 min, but after this activity slows down, and if they are kept under anaerobic conditions for 3 or 4 hours recovery on return to oxygen is imperfect or absent. Cyanides, which upset some of the oxidation systems of the cell (p. 120), have a similar effect. Cilia can therefore put up an oxygen debt (p. 122), but they do not normally do so. This is a suitable arrangement for structures which work continuously, and is found also in cardiac muscle (p. 122). The respiratory quotient is 0·8, suggesting that energy is obtained by the oxidation of protein, a supposition which is confirmed by the fact that in the mollusc *Dreissensia* the production of ammonia is proportional to the consumption of oxygen. Both molluscan cilia and *Paramecium*, however, also use glycogen. Increase of acidity slows and finally stops cilia, and decreases the oxygen consumption. A balanced solution of cations (calcium and some alkali metals) is necessary, but this may merely be because they are required to maintain the cell-surface. Absence of calcium ion stops the cilia without affecting their oxygen consumption. These facts may be explained by supposing that some reserve of chemical energy, probably a protein, first becomes changed to an active form, and that acidity prevents this process. The

active substance breaks down anaerobically with liberation of energy. Absence of calcium ion causes this to be
abnormal. Finally, some of the molecules of the breakdown products are resynthesized to the reserve by energy
supplied by the oxidation of the others. The details of the
chemistry are entirely unknown.

The metabolism of mammalian sperms seems to be a
normal glycolysis, and nothing else.

4.2. Pseudopodia and Amoeboid Movement

It is difficult to give an exact definition of pseudopodia,
but the word is generally taken to mean those projections
from a single cell which are of a temporary character and
of not very definite shape. Some of the more extreme
types exist for quite a long time and have something of
the nature of specialized organelles, and all of them are
limited in shape by the cell to which they belong. Pseudopodia are found in the Protozoa, in the cells lining the
gut in some of the coelenterates, in the wandering cells
(phagocytes) of the body fluids of most coelomate animals,
and in similar cells in tissue culture. Those of the Metazoa
are all of the same general type, short and blunt, but those
of the Protozoa can be classified into four groups. Lobo-
podia are rounded blunt structures, the typical locomotor
organs of *Amoeba*. Filopodia are fine and pointed, and are
found in such amoeboid species as *Euglypha*. Rhizopodia
are distinguished by the fact that they anastomose, and
are characteristic of the Foraminifera. Axopodia have an
axial filament, and are therefore at least semi-permanent
in character: probably no satisfactory definition of pseudopodia could be made to include these; they are found in
the Heliozoa. There are no sharp dividing lines between the
classes; pseudopodia may be made more pointed by increasing the hydrogen-ion concentration or the osmotic pressure
of the medium, and blunter by the reverse processes.

It is at least probable that pseudopodia and flagella are fundamentally the same structures. The axial filaments of axopodia suggest this, and it is supported by the case of *Amoeba flagellipoda*, which possesses a single long thin pseudopodium which moves round in a spiral, like a slowly acting flagellum, once every 3 seconds. In moribund specimens of the flagellate *Trichomonas* the undulating membrane appears to be replaced by pseudopodium-like projections which move rapidly over the surface. Pseudopodia are often assumed to be primitive, largely because they appear to be unspecialized and because it is traditional to regard *Amoeba* as the lowliest of animals. But pseudopodial formation is certainly not simple, and most protozoologists now regard *Amoeba* as a degenerate probably descended from the Mastigophora, so that flagella are more primitive than, and possible ancestral to, pseudopodia.

A cell may bear one or many pseudopodia, and they are used for two chief purposes: for ingesting foreign particles and for locomotion. The particles ingested may be food, as in the Rhizopoda, coelenterates, and lamellibranchs; excretory matter in annelids; Bacteria in vertebrates; and tissues of the body which are digested and carried elsewhere during the metamorphosis of Amphibia. The different methods of ingestion of food particles in Rhizopoda are mentioned in section 1.22. When pseudopodia are used for locomotion it is generally only a single cell which is moved, and the expression 'amoeboid movement' may then be used to describe what happens; occasionally, however, as in *Hydra* and some other of the Hydrozoa, a larger animal is slowly carried by the pseudopodia of the cells of its base. Amoeboid movement has been studied chiefly in the Protozoa, and has been classified into five groups.

The first is that found in the Mycetozoa, which appear

merely to flow over a surface as a liquid film of protoplasm, no well-defined pseudopodia being formed. The
second is that exemplified by the normal movement of
Amoeba, which has been much studied. The chief species

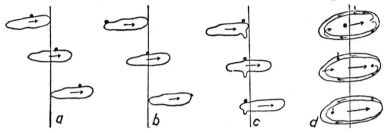

Fig. 22. Motion of *Amoeba* relative to the substratum and to an attached
particle.

In *a* the particle is moving at the same speed as the organism; in *b* the particle is moving
forward over the surface of the amoeba, e.g. *A. discoides*; in *c* the particle is stationary relative
to the substratum, and is moving backwards relative to the surface of the organism; this
occurs when attached particles are heavy; *d*, movement of ectoplasm in an amoeba suspended
in a jelly. The vertical lines represent a fixed point in the environment. After Schaeffer.

which experimenters have used is the marine *Amoeba limax*,
which has the great advantage that it forms only one
pseudopodium at a time, but other species have been
worked with as well. The accounts differ so much that it
is possible there is more than one type of movement. To
study the movement of the surface of the animal small
particles have been dropped on to the upper surface, and
then watched. They have been seen to behave in three
different ways (Fig. 22): sometimes they maintain their
original position relative to the ground, which means that
they gradually move to the posterior end of the amoeba;
sometimes they maintain their position on the animal, so
moving forward at the same speed; and lastly they sometimes move slowly to the front end of the pseudopodium.
In this last case they may collect at the front end or they
may return along the ventral surface, so that the amoeba
has been described as 'rolling like a bag of oats'. The
speed of *Amoeba* is of the order of 1 μ/sec.

The third type is that in which pseudopodia are formed, not in contact with a surface. This happens chiefly when an animal like *Amoeba* is suspended in water. Pseudopodia are put out in all directions, and when one of them touches anything solid it attaches itself and the whole mass of protoplasm is drawn into it. Instead of the pseudopodium being withdrawn into the animal, the animal is withdrawn into the pseudopodium. Sometimes *Amoeba* moves by a looping movement; one pseudopodium is put out, and after it has stuck to a surface the whole animal moves after it.

The fourth type is found in some species such as *Difflugia* and *Polystomella* in which the pseudopodia become attached by their tips and then contract; when the animal has been drawn up somewhat the same pseudopodia are extended again. This possibly differs in degree rather than in kind from the third type.

The fifth type is the Catherine-wheeling of the Heliozoa. Successive pseudopodia are put out, attached, and contracted, so that the animal rolls on a succession of spokes which it makes for itself. This is the quickest type of amoeboid movement, giving a speed about ten times as fast as that of *Amoeba*.

The effect of temperature on amoeboid movement is similar to that on all biological reactions. The rate increases up to a maximum, and then falls off rapidly until death occurs. The maximum depends on the normal environment of the animal—it was 40° C for an amoeba from the Tortugas, but only 20° C for a very similar species from the English Channel. The maximum is to some extent an artefact, since it becomes lower if the duration of the experiment is increased. Amoeboid movement in the marine *Amoeba limax* is inhibited reversibly at pH 6 and irreversibly at pH 9. As with cilia, a balanced solution of cations is essential. Lack of oxygen does not at first stop movement, but finally it does, and up to a point there is recovery on readmission of oxygen.

These facts point to some chemical basis for amoeboid movement of the same general type as those occurring in cilia and muscles, that is to say of an anaerobic breakdown of reserve materials followed by an oxidative recovery. But pseudopodia differ from cilia and muscle-fibres in that they are labile structures, dependent for their very existence on a suitable environment, and much thought has been given to the possible physical processes involved in their formation. One thing that can be said with confidence is that complete satisfaction is given by none of the purely mechanical hypotheses which make pseudopodia the necessary consequences of contact between protoplasm and water of particular viscosity and surface tension. Some chemical reaction is obviously involved, and since oxygen is necessary it is probably of a nature in general similar to other biological processes. The better of the existing theories are all based on the observations that the endoplasm is in active streaming movement, and that at the anterior end of a pseudopodium there is change of endoplasm to ectoplasm. *Amoeba* consists of three layers. On the outside there is a thin plasmalemma, which can be lifted off with needles and is of a dough-like consistency. Inside this is the plasmagel, which is solid, and includes the classical ectoplasm and some endoplasm; inside this again is liquid plasmasol. The theory of movement is as follows (Fig. 23): at one place the plasmagel becomes weakened and disappears, and since the rest of the plasmagel is contractile and under tension, plasmasol is forced out at this point. As it comes in contact with the external medium it gelates and so forms a tube of plasmagel. Since plasmagel does not collect at the posterior end, at that point there must be solation to plasmasol. The changes of state of the protoplasm are probably fundamentally changes in the configuration of protein molecules, solation consisting in the folding of a chain-molecule into the globular form and gelation of the reverse. Although pseudopodia may be formed at any point on the surface, the 'tail', where solation occurs, is fixed, being the region where the cell was

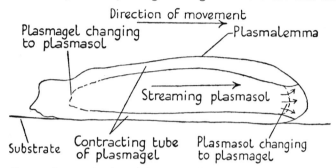

FIG. 23. Locomotion in *Amoeba limax*. Slightly modified from Pantin.

separated from its sibling in the fission which gave rise to it. This suggests that the initiation of movement occurs at the tail by solation of plasmagel, and that local influences determine where pseudopodia are formed by the weakening of the plasmagel. Adenosine triphosphate (p. 124), injected in the tail, raises the speed of movement, but injected at the anterior end it causes reversal, so that probably the tail acts by producing this substance or something like it. The respiration of *Amoeba* is cyanide-sensitive.

For locomotion to take place, there must be, in addition to the changes of state, attachment to the substrate, and this is the function of the plasmalemma. The movement is rather like what would take place in an imaginary tube of toothpaste which could squeeze itself out and convert paste to aluminium at the open end and aluminium to paste at the closed end while it did so. This theory does not go greatly beyond observation: gelation at the anterior end can be seen, and sometimes the plasmagel at the end of a pseudopodium is missing, sometimes it is merely thin. If the animal is turgid it is to be expected that slight local alterations in external conditions would be able to produce new pseudopodia by weakening the plasmagel, and this is found to be the case. The direction of movement can be reversed by pressure and other things (cf. section 6.1). The different directions of movement of a particle dropped on the surface can be explained on the assumption that the plasmalemma has differing relations to the underlying plasmagel. In the typical case it would be expected to be in rigid contact with this, and so particles in contact with it would remain stationary relative to the substrate but move to the posterior end of the animal.

The theory does not pretend to be complete, since fine pseudopodia may be formed from ectoplasm only.

4.3. Muscles

Muscles are made up of individual elongated structures called muscle-fibres, which when stimulated contract in length and increase in girth so that their volume is little altered. All muscle-fibres seem to be built on the same general plan of a number of myofibrils consisting largely of the protein myosin and embedded in a fluid sarcoplasm, the whole surrounded by a sheath or sarcolemma. There are many histological variants of this. Muscles may be formed from any germ layer, but they are found predominantly in the mesoderm.

4.31. Vertebrate Skeletal Muscle

Vertebrate skeletal muscle is by far the best known of all contractile tissues. It is sometimes called striped muscle, from its characteristic appearance, and sometimes voluntary muscle, since in man it is, or appears to be, normally under the control of the will. (It is quite obvious that under experimental conditions it is not.) It is innervated directly from the cranial and spinal nerves. Most of the work has been done on the frog, but enough has been done on mammalian tissue to show that it is very similar.

Unlike pseudopodia and cilia, skeletal muscle does not contract unless it receives some definite stimulus, either directly or through its nerve. It may react to pressure, chemicals, or to change of temperature, but by far the most convenient stimulus to use is an electric one: its intensity is easily measured and reproduced and varied, and it is easy to record the exact time of its application. The first things to be said about the working of muscle are therefore concerned with the results of electrical stimulation.

A very weak electrical shock does not cause any response, and the threshold for excitation depends on the strength and duration of the current that is applied. The less the strength the longer will be its duration before a response occurs. For short durations the product of strength and duration is constant, so that a minimum quantity of electricity must pass for the muscle to contract. If current is plotted against time for threshold excitation in this region, a rectangular hyperbola is obtained, but for longer durations, and so smaller currents, the product of the two increases, and the simple relationship is lost. The smallest current that will produce a response, however long it passes, is called the rheobase, and the duration necessary for a response to be produced by a current of twice the rheobase is the chronaxie. These properties may be used to define the excitability of a tissue. In practical work it is most convenient to use a strong current of very short duration. Successive stimuli, each below the threshold, may cause a contraction, a phenomenon called summation of stimuli.

It is easy to show the contraction of a muscle by removing the gastrocnemius (or calf) muscle from a pithed frog, together with the bone to which it is attached, a piece of its tendon and a length of the sciatic nerve. The bone is pinned down, an electric shock is applied to the nerve, and the muscle responds; if the tendon is tied to a strong spring or to a heavy weight hanging over a pulley, the muscle cannot in fact shorten, but the response is conventionally known as an isometric contraction; if a lighter weight is used the muscle will lift it, and the contraction is called isotonic. With a single shock the response is short, and the muscle quickly goes back to approximately its original length. The whole cycle is called a twitch. Repeated shocks give repeated twitches, and if the shocks are close enough together the twitches are superimposed on each other, so that the contraction is three or four times as great as in one twitch, and is maintained so long as the repeated stimuli continue. This summation of contraction is called tetanus. An incompletely fused series of twitches is called clonus. Two threshold stimuli very close together have no more effect than one by itself, so that there must be a time after a stimulus has had its effect in which the muscle does not respond; this is called the refractory period. Tetanus, clonus, and the refractory period apply to a single fibre just as to a whole muscle. The graded responses given by a whole muscle to stimuli of different intensities are mainly produced by the varying numbers of fibres which respond. The greater the stimulus, the more fibres contract, though the degree of contraction in each of them is, under given conditions of experiment, much the same. This relative constancy of contraction of individual fibres is sometimes raised to the status of a rule—the 'all-or-nothing' rule.

The same things may be shown more elaborately with smoked drums, which purport to record the time relations of the response, and examples of traces obtained with them are given in Figs. 24 and 25. What, in fact, they show are chiefly the elastic properties of string and the inertia of levers. More precise instruments show that the mechanical properties of the muscle begin to change very soon after the stimulus is received—about 3 msec (= thousandths of

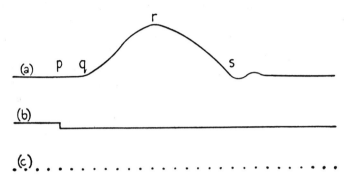

FIG. 24. Tracings of an isotonic contraction of gastrocnemius muscle of toad.

(a) Curve of contraction of muscle; the deflexion below the base line at the end and the subsequent rise are due to the imperfections of the recording apparatus.

(b) Shows point of application of the stimulus.

(c) Shows intervals of 0·02 sec.

pq, latent period; qr, contraction; rs, relaxation.

a second) at 0° C. Tension begins at about 12 msec, and isotonic shortening at full speed at 20 msec. There then follows a plateau of activity lasting 40 msec, and a very rapid decline of activity during which the muscle relaxes or returns to its original condition. At higher temperatures these times are reduced, the plateau lasting only 10 msec at 20° C. A muscle-fibre has, in addition to its active part, an elastic component which resists change of shape; this is in part accounted for by the sarcolemma.

In addition to the mechanical changes, an electrical change can be detected in the muscle during the twitch. It is very similar to that which occurs in nerve (p. 243) and consists in a lowering or reversal of the potential difference

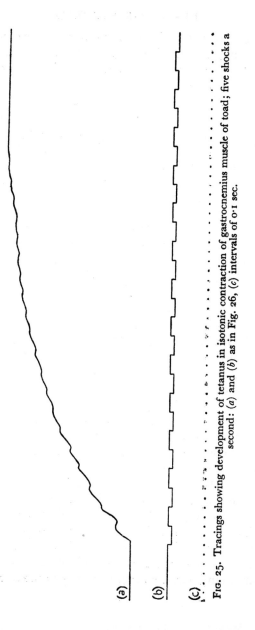

(a)

(b)

(c) ·

FIG. 25. Tracings showing development of tetanus in isotonic contraction of gastrocnemius muscle of toad; five shocks a second: (a) and (b) as in Fig. 26, (c) intervals of 0·1 sec.

across the surface membrane, the outer surface of which is, in the resting state, positive to the inner, with a difference of potential of 50 to 100 mV. If two points a and b on a muscle are connected to a sensitive galvanometer or an oscillograph, it is found that on stimulation of the muscle a current flows in the circuit first in one direction and then in the other; in other words the instrument records a diphasic wave. The direction of the current is such that a, which is the electrode nearer the point of stimulation, first becomes negative to b, and then b becomes negative to a. Since it does not matter where a and b are, so long as they are on the muscle, this can only be an expression of the fact that a wave of negativity passes down the muscle in the same direction as the wave of contraction. As each point becomes negative to the rest of the muscle a current flows to it in the outer circuit. The electrical change slightly precedes the mechanical change, but the gap between the two is certainly largely, and may be entirely, due to the inertia of the recording instruments for the latter. The better the instruments the smaller it is, and some workers have claimed that it is as little as 0·4 msec. Diphasic waves are a general characteristic of propagated electrical disturbances, and will be further considered in the chapter on nerve.

The wave of negativity that passes over the muscle-surface normally begins when acetylcholine is produced at the motor end-plate of the nerve (p. 252). The electron microscope shows that the muscle-fibre has a three-layered membrane which is 400 to 700 Å thick, but probably only one of these layers is concerned in the electrical change, since the electrical evidence suggests that it need not be more than 100 Å thick. The impulse is probably conducted into the fibres by the Z membrane (Fig. 26A).

In a few slowly contracting tonic muscles of the frog there are many scattered motor nerve-endings, and action potentials are not conducted. These muscles respond to trains of impulses by progressive contraction.

Fatigue is the phenomenon of a muscle refusing to react to a stimulus which normally causes contraction. Complete fatigue is preceded by an increase in the duration of the twitch, and a diminution in the amount of work done. It is necessary to distinguish between fatigue of the muscle and fatigue of the stimulating system, since both are theoretically possible.

The contraction of human voluntary muscle under ordinary circumstances is of the same general type as that of isolated experimental material. For weak contraction increasing strength is brought about by the use of more fibres, i.e. by quantal summation, but for strong contractions tetanus develops, so that there is fusion of successive contractions of the same fibres, or wave summation. It now seems that when a muscle is moved voluntarily until it can be moved no more, true muscular fatigue has developed, which cannot be abolished even though strong stimulation be given to the efferent nerve or to the muscle itself; an intact blood supply is necessary for recovery. The old experiments that claimed to show the contrary presumably dealt with more than one muscle or set of fibres, not all of which were fatigued. All intact skeletal muscle maintains a certain degree of tension or tonus or tone. This is due to a few fibres contracting for a time, and then relaxing and being replaced by others, so that the tension may be kept up permanently, but none of the fibres ever becomes fatigued. Tonus is caused by nervous stimulation: it is abolished if either the tendon or the motor nerve of the muscle be cut, and is increased by increasing the pull on the tendon. This behaviour is called the stretch reflex, and is very important in some types of locomotion (p. 263). The sense organ concerned in maintaining tone is the muscle-spindle, which is a modified muscle-cell. It is stimulated by being stretched, and through the central nervous system it stimulates a group of muscle-fibres to contract. To give an explanation of tone it may be assumed that this contraction releases the strain on the particular muscle-spindle concerned in the reflex, but increases that on others. The first group of fibres will, after their twitch is over, relax again, but by this time other groups will have been stimulated to contract. The muscle-spindle also contains contractile elements, the intrafusal muscle-fibres, in series with the sensory region. They are innervated by small motor nerve-fibres, separate from the large motor fibres that run to the extrafusal muscle-fibres that make up the rest of the working part of the muscle. An increase in the activity of the small motor fibres leads to a greater contraction of the intrafusal fibres, and so stretches the sensory region. The stretch reflex then results in contraction of the extrafusal fibres, and this reduces again the tension on the spindle. This reduction will not, however, be complete, and the tonus of the muscle will depend on the level of activity in the small nerve-fibres. Thus accurately graded and maintained contractions can result reflexly from activity of the small fibres, and direct stimulation of the large fibres by the central nervous system is found only in sudden and strong contractions.

More is known of the chemistry of voluntary muscle than of any other tissue, but the matter is complicated and in part still obscure. Ultimately the energy usually comes from carbohydrate, by one of the pathways described in Chapters 1 and 3. As the glucose in the muscle, and so in the blood, is reduced, more is provided, by the breakdown of glycogen in the liver, or, in severe exercise, by gluconeogenesis from aminoacids. In severe exercise the liver also oxidizes fatty acids to form acetoacetic acid, which enters into the tricarboxylic acid cycle in the muscle. Fat and protein are also broken down in the muscle itself to provide energy. Contraction of muscle is possible without the breakdown of carbohydrate, and so far as is at present known the only reaction that is necessary is the hydrolysis of adenosine triphosphate, for which myosin itself acts as the enzyme. In the normal muscle adenosine triphosphate is immediately restored by phosphate and energy supplied by the breakdown of creatine phosphate, and the restoration of this depends on the energy from glycolysis. In many of the fibres of the breast muscles of some birds, such as the pigeon, there is little glycogen, and fat appears to be the source of energy.

Although we cannot yet be certain what produces contraction, the reaction between adenosine triphosphate and myosin must be very important. They react in such a way that the former is hydrolysed and phosphate ions and energy are liberated, and at the same time there are changes in the viscosity and other properties of the myosin. Since isolated fibrils contract violently when adenosine triphosphate is added to them in a concentration no more than that present in relaxed muscle, there must be an inhibitor which prevents the reaction from taking place except on stimulation. A substance of unknown composition which has this property has been extracted from sarcoplasm. It appears to act by binding magnesium ions, which are necessary for contraction. In the presence of this inhibitor, or relaxing factor, adenosine triphosphate seems to break the linkages that join the two proteins of muscle, actin and myosin, to make actomyosin, so that it has a plasticizing effect on muscle in addition to its more dramatic effect in providing energy for contraction.

The chemical processes agree with the heat production. The heat produced by the breakdown of adenosine triphosphate, and that part of the energy liberated by phosphagen breakdown which is not immediately used for resynthesis of adenosine triphosphate, make up the heat of activation and heat of shortening. The glycogen breakdown produces the 'delayed anaerobic heat' which is formed after the muscle has relaxed, and (in the frog) if oxygen is present the oxidation of lactic acid accounts for the 'delayed aerobic heat' or 'recovery heat'. The third of these may go on for a long time after contraction.

It is now possible to relate all these aspects of contraction to molecular changes in the muscle. A single striated fibre consists of alternate light and dark bands, which are further subdivided as shown in Fig. 26A. The dark A bands are anisotropic (doubly refracting) and the I bands isotropic, that is their refraction does not depend on the plane of polarization of the light transmitted through them. Further detail can be made out with the electron microscope. Each myofibril consists of two types of rod, one much thicker than the other, both embedded in sarcoplasm and arranged in hexagons in such a way that every thick rod is surrounded by six other thick ones and six thin ones, and every thin one by three other thin ones and three thick ones (Fig. 26c). The thick rods consist of myosin, a protein of unit weight about 425,000, and the thin ones of actin, a protein of unit weight 74,000. Under certain conditions these two can combine to form actomyosin. The rods are not continuous, but overlap as shown in Fig. 26B, so that the I bands have actin rods only, the H bands myosin rods only, and the rest of the A bands have both. In contraction, down to 85 per cent. of resting length, both H and I bands shorten; at this length the H bands have disappeared. What has happened is that the actin rods have slid into the spaces between the myosin rods. Further contraction is accompanied by further shortening of the I bands, during which the actin filaments fold or coil, until at 65 per cent. of the resting length the I bands are obliterated. If there is further contraction still, the A bands shorten, and the myosin rods coil. The shortening probably takes place by a step-wise formation

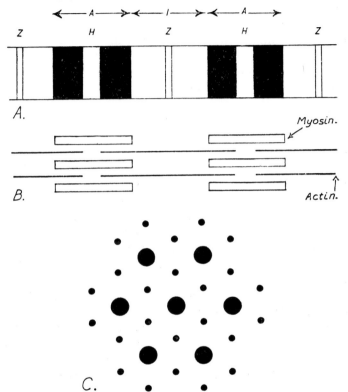

FIG. 26. Diagrams of the structure of voluntary muscle, based on A. F. Huxley.

A, longitudinal section, showing A and I bands, and H and Z lines.
B, longitudinal section (electron microscope), showing actin and myosin filaments corresponding to the bands and lines in *A*.
C, transverse section (electron microscope), showing the large filaments of myosin and small ones of actin.

of actomyosin through cross-linkages, and the folding or crumpling is presumably caused by some sort of contraction and folding of the protein molecules, although the

X-ray pictures have not given any certain evidence on this. The immediate effect of a stimulus is the removal or inhibition of the inhibitor, so that adenosine triphosphate can react with myosin. Injection of calcium ions into a resting myofibril causes contraction, and it may be that the effect of a nerve impulse is to increase their concentration in the sarcoplasm, so releasing the magnesium ions that are bound by the inhibitor.

4.32. Vertebrate Plain Muscle

Plain, smooth, unstriated or involuntary muscle occurs chiefly in the internal organs such as the gut, arteries, bladder, and urinary and genital ducts. It has certain histological differences from skeletal muscle, such as the absence of any syncytium, but they are not clearly connected with the physiological differences. The chief of these is that smooth muscle possesses a much greater intrinsic irritability of its own, and with this is correlated its double innervation, one set of nerve-fibres inciting the tissue to contraction, and the other inhibiting it. Between these two types of stimulus smooth muscle carries out the details of its movements automatically, using this word in its strict sense. The motor nerve-fibres which supply smooth muscle are all autonomic (that is their cell bodies are all outside the central nervous system) and they terminate in a plexus in which the inhibitory and excitatory fibres are probably mixed. The two types of fibre have a separate origin as nerves in the central nervous system, the first usually being sympathetic and the second parasympathetic, although the correlation is not absolute.

For experimental purposes nerve-muscle preparations may be made with smooth muscle just as with skeletal muscle. The contraction curves for the two are very similar, but the time relations of smooth muscle are very much slower. The apparent latent period, during which the ordinary arrangement of levers shows no change in the muscle, is from 0·2 sec to 2 sec, and even the electrical changes do not start till 40 msec after the stimulation. Contraction itself may last for minutes, and the refractory period is long. Corresponding to this is a high chronaxie, which means that high voltages of short duration, such as are given by induction shocks, are sometimes insufficient to excite. In these cases the make or break of a constant current must be used. The phenomena of summation of stimuli and summation of contractions are shown. Different effects are naturally produced according to the nerve which is stimulated, but it is not a simple case of excitation from one nerve and inhibition from the other, for the type of stimulus may alter the result obtained. Isolated smooth muscle is very sensitive to other forms of stimulation, such as chemicals, temperature, and mechanical changes. In general it contracts with increased alkalinity, low temperature, and stretching, but effects vary greatly according to the origin of the muscle, its past history, and the mode of application of the stimulus. With some muscles, some kinds of chemical, electrical, and mechanical stimuli, which excite when the tissue is relaxed, cause relaxation when it is already contracted. This is perhaps connected with the double innervation, and may be explained if activity alters the relative excitability of the two types of nerve-endings.

When a stimulus is applied directly to one point of smooth muscle, the contraction may spread over the whole tissue, a result which is very different from the highly individual contractions of fibres of skeletal muscle. Whether the conduction is carried out through the medium of protoplasmic continuity between the fibres, or whether it is merely the nerve plexus that is used, is unknown.

Smooth muscle, whether isolated or in the intact animal, differs from skeletal muscle in that it continually maintains activity of two types. It possesses a certain amount of tonus, and it shows rhythmical contractions superimposed on this: in different places one or the other phenomenon predominates, and occasionally one of them may be absent. They can be explained in terms of the ordinary muscle twitch. Passive stretch is known to be a stimulus for contraction, and the refractory period is known to be long; tonus will be caused by a synchronous contraction, only a few fibres being active at one time. When these active fibres begin to relax all the other fibres are stretched, but only those which have emerged from their refractory period can respond, and they take over the work of maintaining the tonic contraction. This can go on indefinitely, a few fibres being in activity at any moment, and the rest in a refractory state and waiting to function in their turn. Rhythm may be assumed to be caused by synchronous contraction determined by the nerve net, or by a stimulus carried directly from one muscle-fibre to another where (as in the segmentation movements of the intestine, p. 35) no nervous tissue is present.

The chemistry of smooth muscle, like that of striped muscle, is based on adenosine triphosphate and the breakdown of glycogen to lactic acid. The actual contraction presumably depends on a change of state in the actomyosin, but there is clearly not the neat arrangement of molecules that has been shown to exist in striped muscle. Electron microscopy generally shows some internal structure, so that a similar sliding mechanism to that in striated muscle is possible, but the details are unknown.

4.33. Vertebrate Cardiac Muscle

Like the other types, cardiac muscle is made up histologically of fibres. Here they are cross-striped, and each consists of several cells placed end to end. Cardiac muscle differs, however, from the other two types in that its fibres are connected to one another by branches; this fact means that the fibre is not the effective unit, and accounts for many of the physiological peculiarities of heart muscle. The all-or-nothing rule applies to the heart as a whole, so that if any part of the intact organ contracts, the whole does.

For experimental purposes a complete heart, or a strip from some part of the heart such as the ventricle, may be used. The curve for contraction is similar in general form to that of skeletal muscle, but the reaction is slower. The response of the mammalian ventricle lasts 0·3 sec, that of the frog 0·5 sec. Rise of temperature quickens the response, a correct hydrogen-ion concentration must be maintained, and the heart is very sensitive to the other ions present in the medium. The refractory period is exceptionally long. The absolute refractory period lasts as long as the contraction, and this is followed by a period of subnormal sensitivity while the muscle relaxes. There is a short period of supernormal sensitivity before the normal state is reached. The effect of the long refractory period is that heart muscle cannot be tetanized, which is obviously of great value physiologically. The phenomenon of summation of stimulus is shown, repeated subminimal shocks finally causing a contraction.

The excised heart, whether of the frog or the mammal, will under appropriate conditions go on beating rhythmically for hours, although it is receiving no obvious stimulus. (The correct temperature must be maintained, and in the mammal oxygenated Locke's fluid must be perfused through the coronary blood-vessels which supply the heart.) It seems, then, that there must be some source of stimulation within the heart itself. The situation of this has been investigated by making cuts or ligatures which functionally separate the various parts of the heart. If the sinus of the frog be thus separated from the (auricles plus ventricle), it goes on beating rhythmically, but the auricles and ventricle stop for a time and then start again at less than the normal rate. If a ligature be applied between auricles and ventricle, the first continue beating but the second stops, and either never beats again or does so only very slowly. There is thus a gradient of excitability and of speed of rhythm, which shows that in the normal heart the sinus must act as a pacemaker; the more slowly moving auricles and ventricle are quite unable to beat in their own rhythm, because they are in physiological continuity with the sinus and so are compelled to beat at the pace of this. The rhythm is entirely independent of nervous origin, for it goes on when the nerves are poisoned by drugs, and it starts in the embryonic chick before any nervous tissue is formed. Isolated cells of heart muscle grown in tissue culture beat rhythmically, so that rhythm seems to be a fundamental feature of cardiac tissue.

The mammalian heart likewise has an automatic rhythm, which is more rapid at the venous end than in the ventricles. In addition to the complete separation of the pulmonary and systemic circulations there are certain anatomical modifications as well (Fig. 27): in particular the muscles of the auricles and ventricles are not in general histological continuity. The pacemaker is the sinu-auricular node, which is a piece of tissue lying between the right superior vena cava and the right auricle, and representing part of the sinus venosus. From this the contraction spreads over the auricles. At the bottom of the auricular septum is another piece of tissue, the auriculo-ventricular node, which also represents part of the sinus venosus. From this starts a band of muscle-fibres known as the bundle of His, or the auriculo-ventricular bundle. It runs in the interventricular septum, and divides into right and left branches for the two papillary muscles. Each branch subdivides so that its fibres are distributed to nearly the whole of the ventricular muscle. It is this bundle which provides the continuity between auricle and ventricle along which the wave of excitation can pass. The rate of conduction is ten times as fast in the bundle as in ordinary muscle, which

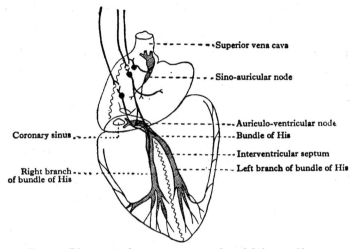

Fig. 27. Diagram to show arrangement of special tissues of heart.
After Wiggers.

means that the whole of the ventricle contracts practically simultaneously. There is a similar arrangement of special fibres in birds, but in cold-blooded vertebrates the conduction is carried out by the ordinary fibres.

The strength of the beat increases with distension of the heart because as in skeletal muscle the energy of contraction depends on the length of the fibres. The efficiency is about the same as in voluntary muscle, that is, about 25 per cent.

The chemistry of the contraction of cardiac muscle is not known so well as that of skeletal muscle, but there is evidence that in the frog it is somewhat similar. The respiratory quotient of the aerobic heart is 0·85, which suggests that fat or protein or both are used in addition to carbohydrate. The heart will go on beating in nitrogen for hours, although it is then much more sensitive to neutral or acid concentrations of hydrogen ion. Under these conditions the concentration of glycogen is reduced and that of lactic acid increases. In the aerobic heart, on the other hand, glycogen disappears only slowly. It seems therefore that when it is beating anaerobically the frog heart gets its energy as does skeletal muscle by glycolysis, but that under normal conditions there is some other source as well. This is confirmed by the action of iodo-acetic acid, which would undoubtedly stop lactic acid formation. If oxygen is present when this reagent is added the heart goes on beating normally, but in its absence activity only lasts for a short time, about twenty beats. The details of the carbohydrate metabolism of the heart are quite unknown, and they may be different from those in skeletal muscle.

Creatine phosphate and adenosine triphosphate occur in cardiac muscle, though not in such high concentrations as in skeletal muscle, and it is at least possible that they act in the same way in the two situations. The small amount of phosphagen present would explain the short time for which the anaerobic heart can beat when iodoacetic acid is present.

Events in the mammalian heart may be similar, but judging from the effects of lack of oxygen it is unlikely that it ever beats anaerobically in the living animal.

4.34. Invertebrate Muscle

The muscles of invertebrates are much less well known than those of vertebrates, and since the term invertebrate covers several phyla which may be as widely separated from each other as they are from the vertebrates, there is no reason other than that of convenience for grouping them together. Generalization from one phylum is therefore illegitimate, but enough investigation has been carried out to show that in several groups muscular contraction is fundamentally similar to what it is in vertebrates. The contraction curve varies enormously from muscle to muscle; in the anemone *Metridium senile* the contraction may last for 6 sec, and in *Holothuria nigra* for 3 sec, but in the wing muscles of the wasp it is complete in 5 msec and in some flies in less than 1 msec. The rapidly moving muscles, such as those of the limbs of arthropods and the swimming muscles of cephalopods, approximate to vertebrate skeletal muscle, while the slower ones, such as the intestinal muscle of arthropods and most of those of molluscs, are more like vertebrate smooth muscle. Striations similar to those of vertebrate striped muscle are found in medusae, molluscs, and arthropods, and these are in general the faster-acting forms, though there are exceptions.

Many invertebrates can maintain many of their muscles in a contracted state for a very long time. Sea-anemones and molluscs of the intertidal zone normally remain contracted for the whole of the time during which they are not covered by water, while the oyster and some other bivalves can remain closed for as long as 30 days. The muscles of molluscs may be taken as an example. When a lamellibranch with open valves is touched, the two halves of the shell are drawn together by the adductor muscles, and remain tightly closed until the animal spontaneously opens them again. If a solid object is placed between the valves before stimulation, they shut on this, and if it is gently removed they remain set until they open again or receive another closing stimulus. The tension necessary to open the valves forcibly when they are thus set is much greater than that which will just prevent closure; in other words the adductor muscles can support a weight which they cannot raise. Each adductor muscle contains two bands of fibres of different sorts. These can be separated, and it is found that their properties are very different. In *Pecten*, the one which is striated works at the same speed as frog muscle, and is used for the quick closing of the shell and for flapping the valves in swimming. The other band is much slower in its reaction, having in *Pecten* a relaxation period of about thirty seconds and in the oyster of from a quarter to one hour: it is this which maintains the tension. It may be regarded as acting in the same way as vertebrate smooth muscle which is maintaining tonus, but the tensions reached are very much greater. Some of the slowing-down of contraction and relaxation is probably due to the deformation of the accompanying connective tissue.

In other muscles, such as the anterior retractor of the byssus of *Mytilus*, there is no separation of the fibres, but the two types of contraction are produced by different types of stimulation. A short shock produces an ordinary fast twitch, which is caused by synchronous contraction of many fibres. Sometimes, especially with stimulation by direct current, there is a slowly-relaxing tonic response. During this the muscle is electrically active in short bursts of variable intensity, the larger ones corresponding to minute contractions of the muscle, and this goes on even though all the nerve-supply is removed. Presumably the muscle continues to be automatically active, small groups of fibres contracting in turn. This hypothesis is strengthened by the observation that at some points on the surface of the muscle no electrical activity can be detected, and that if records are taken simultaneously from more than one site there is no correspondence between them. There are special inhibitory nerves from the pedal ganglion, stimulation of which hastens the relaxation of tonus, and abolishes the electrical activity associated with it. The tonic contraction of molluscan muscle thus appears to be very similar to that of smooth muscle in vertebrates.

Contraction spreads much less readily in invertebrate muscles than it does in vertebrates. Each fibre in a crustacean has many nerve-endings, and all of them must be

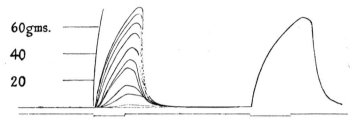

FIG. 28. Superimposed contractions of flexor of dactylopodite of leg of crab *Carcinus*. Frequencies of stimulation/sec: 250, 185, 137, 103, 94, 79, 67, 51, 44, 33. Vertical scale: isometric contraction developed. After Pantin.

stimulated for the fibre to contract as a unit; if only one is stimulated there is only local contraction. This grading of response is achieved by varying the frequency of the nervous discharge and by facilitation. One nervous impulse has no effect, but it enhances the influence of a subsequent impulse, and if impulses follow rapidly enough there is response, and the higher the frequency the more complete the contraction (Fig. 28). Facilitation occurs in coelenterates (where the frequencies are low), in crustaceans (where they may be hundreds per second) and probably in insects, molluscs, annelids, and echinoderms. It is complicated in crustaceans by double and triple innervation, one set of fibres being inhibitory. There may be, as in the claws of *Astacus*, a motor system which produces a quick twitch without facilitation (see section 5.32).

The tensions which can be produced in apparently weak invertebrate muscles are often high; the sea-anemone *Metridium senile*, for instance, can exert 40 kg. cm.$^{-2}$, which compares with only 3·5 kg. cm.$^{-2}$ in the frog sartorious, and the leg muscles of the locust in tetanus exert 20,000 gm. wt./gm, against 1,000 in the frog and 2,000 in man.

The hearts of molluscs have a myogenic pacemaker which, like that of cold-blooded vertebrates, is part of the contractile system. In arthropods the pacemaker is neurogenic.

Of the chemistry of invertebrate muscle little is known. Adenosine triphosphate is widespread and probably universal, and its dephosphorylation to adenosine diphosphate is probably always the first chemical change in the provision of energy for contraction. The phosphagens that restore the triphosphate have been mentioned in section 3.14. The ultimate source of energy is probably usually some form of glycolysis, but the details are unlikely to be the same as in vertebrates. Flying *Drosophila* rapidly use glycogen, and flies flown to exhaustion can be made to fly again if they are given sugar solutions. Their fat reserves are used in starvation, but are mobilized too slowly to be used in continuous flight. Migratory locusts, which normally fly for longer periods without resting than does *Drosophila*, can use their fat reserves during flight.

4.4. Glands

Glands are organs which secrete, and secretion means the preparation of a material and its extrusion from the cell. As to the properties and purposes of such materials, each gland must be considered separately, and an account of the functions of a good many of them is found here and there in this book, particularly in Chapters 1 and 5. Yet there remains something common to all of them which must be considered here, for glands are very important effectors.

The formation of material goes on inside cells, and all observations on the early stages of secretion are essentially cytological ones. The first phase is the reception of material, and of this little can be said; it is similar to other cases of passage through a living membrane, and at least at times requires energy. Next comes the actual chemical process of formation of the material. It is assumed that this is aided by enzymes, and there is much circumstantial evidence that both the mitochondria and Golgi bodies are used in the process. The Golgi apparatus increases in size during secretion in glands of many different types, as well as in the cells of the intestinal epithelium during the resynthesis of fats. In the cells of the pancreas the secretion appears as granules, so that its formation can be watched. If the mitochondria are destroyed by X-rays, as they can be without any other apparent damage being done to the cell, no more secretion is formed until they reappear, which is not until a few hours after radiation. Many enzymes, particularly those concerned in oxidation, have been shown to be concentrated in mitochondria, but enzymes also occur free in the cytoplasm and there are no means of determining their exact point of origin. Possibly the importance of mitochondria lies in the large area of surface which they provide, since they have been shown with the electron microscope to have inpushings of their walls which must greatly increase this.

The nucleus also seems to be necessary for metabolic processes such as secretion, for while separated parts of Protozoa without nuclei can move and ingest food, they cannot digest it, and their oxygen consumption is reduced; enucleated plant protoplasm cannot form cellulose, nor can adult mammalian erythrocytes make haemoglobin. The nucleus in gland cells is often found to be near the part of the cytoplasm which is most active, and sometimes it shrinks and shrivels during secretion, which suggests that substances pass out from it.

In vertebrate salivary glands and some others it has been shown that there is an increased oxygen consumption and a rise of temperature during activity.

Extrusion, which may be brought about by a stimulus given by nerve or hormone, is accompanied not only by rise of oxygen consumption and heat production, but by electrical changes as well. It takes a number of different forms. The granules of secretion may be dissolved and go out in bursting vacuoles, as in the pancreas, or as much as half the cytoplasm may be lost with the granules. This happens in the mucus-secreting cells of the intestine of Amphibia, in the midgut and salivary gland of the snail, and in sweat and lacrimal glands. The nucleus and sometimes parts of the Golgi apparatus and mitochondria remain. In some extreme cases, as in the midgut of the crayfish and in sebaceous glands, whole cells may be lost, so that each cell secretes but once, and the gland is only maintained by rapid mitosis. Secretion is a cyclical process which goes on without any apparent outside stimulus, but when the cells are exhausted by repeated stimulation the formation of material takes place more rapidly than usual.

4.5. Electric Organs

Electric organs are sufficiently described by their name. They are found only in fishes, and are particularly well developed in the three species *Gymnotus* (= *Electrophorus*) *electricus* (the electric eel), *Malopterurus electricus* (the electric catfish), and *Torpedo marmorata* (the torpedo or electric ray). While small electric changes are accompaniments of almost all biological reactions, it is only in electric organs that the production of a relatively big potential difference is an important function.

In all cases the organ is made up of a number of disks or compartments, which in *Malopterurus* are modified skin glands, but which in all the other species are derived from striped muscle. They are so arranged that the voltages due to the separate disks are largely summed; in short, most of the disks are in series and some in parallel. The voltage for each compartment varies, but is about 0·04 to 0·1, which gives a total potential difference for the whole organ of 200 V in *Malopterurus*, 300 in *Gymnotus*, and 30 in *Torpedo*. The motor nerve to the organ has a number of branches which supply each disk individually. The arborization of the nerve occurs always on one side only of the disk, and the current in the organ flows from this side to the other. The nervous side is therefore the negative pole. (The direction of the current in *Malopterurus* is exceptional.)

Nerve-organ preparations, similar to the common nerve-muscle preparations, have been used for experimental study, and the results obtained are in a general way similar to those for muscle. An electric organ responds with difficulty to chemical reagents, but easily to mechanical shock. For electrical stimulation the rheobasic current is about one hundred times that for the frog's gastrocnemius. There is a latent period of about 10 msec at 5° C and 3 msec at 30° C. The preparation can be fatigued, but is relatively indifferent to drugs such as curari and atropine. There is no spread of excitation from one disk to the next other than by nerves, but each discharge is rhythmical, because the current produced by the first discharge excites the nerve and so stimulates a second discharge, and so on. There is thus, for one primary stimulation, a series of successive discharges at a frequency which varies with the temperature but is of the order of 100 per sec. There is, however, a decrement in successive discharges, and the whole series seldom lasts more than half a second.

The ordinary reflex discharge in the intact fish is also a rhythmical one, but the rhythm here is due to the stimulus from the central nervous system, for its frequency depends not on the temperature of the organ, but on that of the ganglion from which the nerve starts. The reflex discharge, which in *Gymnotus* lasts 2 msec, is given on the receipt of various sensory stimuli by the fish, particularly by mechanical pressure on the skin. *Gymnotus* is stimulated to discharge when live fish are placed in the same tank; some of them are stunned, and the eel, which swims only slowly, is able to catch and eat them. Electric fish are themselves relatively insensitive to electric shocks, so that they are not adversely affected either by the voltage from their own organs, or from other fish in their vicinity.

Gymnarcinus niloticus and some other species have an electric organ in the tail, from which they send out a continuous electric pulse. If this is fed back into the water the fish finds the electrodes and attacks them. A bent copper wire placed in the water causes escape reactions. It thus seems that in these species the function of the electric organ is to enable the fish to perceive other individuals, and possibly to avoid obstacles, although it seems unlikely that enough conductors are present in the environment for this to be of much importance.

Of the details of the physiology of the organs little is known. The time relations are by no means clear, for while it is obvious that if the voltages of the separate plates of tissue are to be summed, as in fact they are, discharge in all of them must be simultaneous, it is impossible to see how the time of receipt of the stimulus can be the same for all of them, when the organ may be as much as 30 cm long and the nerve enters at one end. There is some evidence that the organ acts as a concentration cell, which agrees with its high efficiency: an average value in *Torpedo* is 60 per cent. The chemistry of the energy production in *Gymnotos* is fundamentally similar to that in muscle. Creatine phosphate is broken down, acetylcholine being formed at the same time, and there is subsequent formation of lactic acid.

4.6. Luminescent Organs

It is possible that a good many of the chemical processes which help to make up the phenomena of life are accompanied by a fortuitous emission of invisible electromagnetic radiation, but in spite of many claims made in the nineteen-twenties and thirties there is no evidence that this, if it occurs at all, is of any strength or of any importance. Light which is within the range of wave-lengths to which the human retina is sensitive is produced by representatives of about forty orders of animals, distributed through nearly all the phyla. It is found in the Protozoa (Radiolaria and Dinoflagellata); in all three classes of Coelenterata and in the Ctenophora; in Polychaeta and Oligochaeta; in the Ophiuroidea; in four classes of Crustacea, in the Chilopoda, and in many orders of Insecta; in the three main classes of Mollusca; in the Hemichordata and Urochordata, and in both Elasmobranchii and Teleostei. It is noticeable that all the forms which possess it, except for one glow-worm, are either marine or terrestrial, but the significance of this is unknown.

Animals differ from the light-producing Bacteria and Fungi in that only a few fish and one beetle luminesce continuously, and these are not truly exceptions because it is not the animal itself which produces the light, but symbiotic Bacteria. All the others start glowing or flashing only when they receive some stimulus, which experimentally may be almost anything which is strong enough to disturb the animal. In the polychaete *Chaetopterus* the best stimulus is tension or pressure on segment 12. Fireflies (Coleoptera of the genera *Photinus* and *Photurus*) begin flashing when the general light intensity falls below a certain value. Control is generally by nerves, but in some fish the slowness of the response suggests hormones, and injected adrenaline induces flashing. In *Chaetopterus* luminescence is often local, but it spreads if the intensity or frequency of stimulation is raised, so that there may be facilitation in the central nervous system. Acetylcholine is weakly excitatory, even on pieces of tissue with no nerve supply, so that the nerves probably act by liberating this substance at their ends (p. 252). The form of the control is various: in the ostracod *Cypridina* and others granules of one of the chemicals concerned are extruded from the cells by muscles; in the boring bivalve *Pholas* and many worms active secretion by the cells is initiated; and in many shrimps, squids, fish, and fireflies the luminescence which is started is intracellular.

The uses of the light vary with the species emitting it. In the planktonic forms such as the dinoflagellate *Noctiluca* no function can be assigned to it, and it is probably merely a useless but necessary accompaniment of a chemical reaction which goes on for other purposes. In many others, such as the fireflies and the glow-worm (a beetle called *Lampyris*), and some worms and fishes, the light is produced chiefly or only in the breeding season. From this fact, and from the behaviour of the animals, it seems clear that the light is used as a sex signal, and is thus of the same sort of use as the bright colours of birds or the scent produced by many female moths. Luminous animals living in the deep sea (fish, squids, and shrimps) often have complex organs with reflectors and lenses which throw the light in a beam. Here it seems likely that the animal is providing its own artificial light in a region where there is no daylight.

The intensity of the light is low, the steady glow of the fireflies being about $1/50,000$ candle and their brightest flashes only $\frac{1}{50}$ candle. As the area of luminescence is small the brightness of the surface is relatively high, ranging in various species of firefly from 0·3 to 45 millilamberts. This compares with the brightness of the blue sky of one lambert and of white paper suitably lit for reading of 4 millilamberts. The colours range from red to blue, and have usually short continuous spectra. Some fireflies can produce more than one colour. The reaction is very efficient, from 20 per cent. to 90 per cent. of the total radiation being luminous.

All animal light disappears irreversibly when the tissues are boiled, so that it seems that an enzyme reaction is involved, and it has been shown, following the original observations of Robert Boyle, that oxygen is generally necessary. It is not needed by Radiolaria, ctenophores, and some medusae. As a general scheme for most animals it may be said that light is produced by an enzyme oxidation. The substrate is called luciferin and the enzyme luciferase. Since these are not the same in all animals the words should be regarded as generic names and may be used in the plural. The luciferin is almost always manufactured by living cells in the form of granules which may either be oxidized within the cell as in insects and most fishes, or may be extruded as a secretion, as in most Crustacea and annelids. More is known of the latter type, particularly in the ostracod *Cypridina*. In this the granules dissolve in the sea-water and the light is emitted from the resulting colloidal solution. In others, such as the fish *Malacocephalus*, the granules do not dissolve, so that under the microscope discrete points of light can be seen.

Luciferin and luciferase have not been demonstrated in all the groups of luminous animals, but they have been found in the worm *Odontosyllis*, in *Cypridina*, in a decapod, in fireflies and beetles, in the lamellibranch *Pholas dactylis*, and in *Malacocephalus*. The luciferases are non-specific, but only within a fairly narrow range; those of the fireflies and other beetles are active with the luciferins of each other, but not with that of *Cypridina*, which is a member of the same phylum. *Cypridina* luciferase is non-dialysable, is destroyed by trypsin, and is insoluble in fat solvents but soluble in water, from which it is precipitated by saturated ammonium sulphate but not sodium chloride. In other words it has the properties of an albumen. Luciferin from the same animal is dialysable, is not destroyed by trypsin, is insoluble in ordinary fat solvents, but is soluble in alcohol as well as water. Its nature is unknown, but it does not appear to be a protein. In alkaline solution in the air it readily oxidizes spontaneously, but in the absence of oxygen it has been kept stable for 10 years.

In general, the production of the light is concerned both with the luciferase and with the luciferin, for usually when the latter is oxidized in other ways or when the former reacts with other substances, no light is emitted. When luciferase and luciferin from different species are mixed, the spectrum of the light is that characteristic of the animal supplying the enzyme. Free oxygen is also necessary, for when luciferin is oxidized by luciferase in presence of potassium ferricyanide but in absence of oxygen, no light is produced. The total amount of light produced is proportional to the quantity of luciferin present at the beginning so that it must be used up in the reaction.

On these and other facts the following theory of the reaction is based: luciferin (LH_2) forms a complex with luciferase (A) and this rapidly takes up molecular oxygen;

$$A + LH_2 = ALH_2$$

$$ALH_2 + \tfrac{1}{2}O_2 = ALH_2O$$

This decomposes, leaving luciferin in the oxidized form and the luciferase in an excited state;

$$ALH_2O = A' + L + H_2O,$$

and the luciferase rapidly returns to its normal state, giving out its excess energy in the form of radiation,

$$A' = A + h\nu.$$

Such a reaction is known as a sensitized photochemical reaction. The spectrum of *Cypridina* has a maximum at $\lambda = 4,800$ Ångströms and is a broad band, which fits the theory of this type of reaction. Quantitative studies on the reaction show that molecules of oxygen to the order of one hundred must react to give one quantum of light energy, which means that only one collision in a hundred is effective in producing the necessary active state.

4.7. Nematocysts

The nematocysts of coelenterates are peculiar effectors which are produced in special cells called cnidoblasts, but which are not themselves living. When fully formed, a nematocyst consists of an ovoid sac or capsule which has a tough wall which at one pole is invaginated to form a tube; the latter has a wide basal portion, and then a longer coiled narrow part. The inside of both parts of the tube usually bears spines, arranged in whorls of three at different levels. The base of the tube, where it is continuous with the walls of the capsule, is closed off from the outside by an operculum. The capsule is filled with liquid. After the nematocyst has been discharged its structure is not essentially altered, but the operculum has burst and the tube has been evaginated, so that it projects into the surrounding medium and its spines are now on the outside. In an average nematocyst the tube is $700\,\mu$ long, but there is much variation. Seventeen different varieties based on this general plan have been recognized, and of these four are present in *Hydra*. In the first type, which is large, the tube has a well-defined basal portion which is dilated at its base; spines are restricted to the upper part of the wide tube, and the three lower ones are much longer than the others; the tube is open at its end. Two of the other types are small and have a tube which is iso-diametric along its whole length and open at the end, and differ only in that the one bears spines uniformly to its end while the other has none. The fourth type has much reduced spines, and the tube evaginates in the form of a corkscrew and is closed at the end.

The cnidocil is a short projection at the side of or on top of the operculum, but it is often absent. The base of the cnidoblast is elongated and rests on the mesogloea, but there is no evidence that it is attached to a nerve-cell. The cnidoblast may start in either ectoderm or endoderm or as an interstitial cell, according to the species, and undergoes a complicated migration before it comes to rest in its definitive position. In some cases it even passes through the enteron, being carried by the flagella of the cells lining that cavity. The wall of the capsule is made of a mucoprotein, and its contents include protein and a phenolic compound.

The process of discharge is always an evagination, and takes from 1 to 3 sec. It can be slowed down and observed under the action of chemicals, and a kinematographic record of it has been made. The appearance of the wall of the capsule does not change and its volume, although it usually alters slightly, does not change in any regular way. The tube, on the other hand, increases in size, some-times to double its resting diameter and length. The spines may remain attached or they may fall off, and several may stick together as they fall, forming a sort of harpoon. In some cases the contents of the capsule can be stained with neutral red, and the discharge, which is then slowed down, can be watched under the microscope. No liquid comes out of the tube until evagination is complete, but before this the contents, both of capsule and tube, break up into coloured and colourless drops. Liquid then comes slowly out of the end of the tube; the colourless parts immediately disappear in the water, but the coloured drops run together and dissolve only slowly. The volume of liquid which goes out is greater than that of the original capsule, and some coloured liquid remains inside. In those nematocysts which have a blind tube no liquid leaves it, but the capsule swells on discharge.

There seems little doubt that discharge takes place through the absorption of water by the capsular contents, with consequent increase in pressure and bursting of the operculum; the wall then contracts and evaginates the tube and forces out the liquid contents. Experimentally a hypotonic solution, a strong reagent such as an acid or base, or a surface-active agent such as detergents or bile salts followed by a touch, are adequate stimuli. The normal stimulus seems to be akin to the last—some chemical, which is not protein or carbohydrate, but may be a lipoid, followed by contact. High concentrations of the chemical, or heavy blows, may cause a discharge by themselves. It is possible that the small spineless nematocysts of *Hydra*, which are used for attachment of the tentacles in walking, discharge on continued contact of at least ten seconds only. How the capsular contents come to absorb water, and whether the process is osmotic or not, are unknown. Since there is no connexion with nerve-cells, and since isolated nematocysts discharge perfectly well, there is no evidence for nervous control. It has been suggested that the cnidocil is a chemoreceptor, reacting to chemicals in the medium, but as it is often absent it cannot be a necessary structure. There is no evidence that contractile fibres help in the discharge except that in some cases they may assist in breaking the operculum.

The precise function of the nematocyst also remains uncertain. Cnidaria are surely on the whole able to sting, but the stinging properties of jellyfish as judged subjectively by man seem to be quite independent of the discharge of nematocysts, and it is at least possible that the poison is not produced by these effectors at all. Some animals are

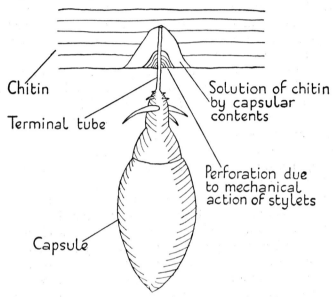

Chitin

Terminal tube

Solution of chitin by capsular contents

Perforation due to mechanical action of stylets

Capsule

FIG. 29. Nematocyst of *Hydra* with the tube perforating the chitin of an arthropod. After Toppe.

quite immune to the attacks of coelenterates and even feed on them, but it is not known whether this is true chemical immunity or whether these animals just do not stimulate the cells to discharge. In a few cases, notably for the large nematocysts of *Hydra*, it has been shown that the spines pierce chitin mechanically, and that the tube enters the perforation which is enlarged by solution (Fig. 29). The corkscrew type and the small form with spines possibly assist in holding the prey and the small spineless type is used for attachment of the tentacles when the animal walks. Release in all types is produced by the discharge of the nematocyst from its cell. Some types of nematocyst, with a closed tube and no spines, have been said to have no conceivable function whatever.

4.8. Chromatophores

It is convenient to include under the name of chromatophore all cells near the surface of an animal by which it can make temporary changes in the colour or shade of its skin. Such cells are found in molluscs, Crustacea, and all classes of cold-blooded vertebrates. The word is not applied where a colour change is caused, as in blushing, by changes in blood-content of the superficial vessels, nor where a prolonged change such as the tanning of the skin on exposure to the sun is brought about by the development of fresh pigment. A chromatophore is a cell which contains a quantity of pigment which varies in its disposition. Where the pigment is black the name melanophore is often used, and corresponding words derived from the Greek have been used for other colours.

A chromatophore of a cephalopod consists of a pigmented cell, to the outside of which are attached several radiating muscle-fibres which are in the plane of the surface of the body. When these contract, the cell is drawn out to its maximum size, and if all the chromatophores in one part of the skin are in the same state the area will have the colour of the pigment. When the muscles relax, the cell by its own elasticity contracts to a point, and the pigment therefore contributes little to the colour of the skin as a whole. Differently coloured cells may be present, and, by the independent action of these, very varied colours are produced. The system is one of muscle controlled by nerves and hormones, and calls for no special comment.

The typical chromatophore is found in polychaete larvae, leeches, echinoderms, Crustacea (almost exclusively the Malacostraca), and vertebrates. In all of these it is a cell (or sometimes a syncytium) with branched processes, and it is the movement of the pigment into and out of these which causes the colour change (Fig. 30). As in the

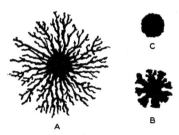

FIG. 30. Melanophores of *Fundulus* with pigment in three stages.
A, fully dispersed; B, stellate; C, fully concentrated, punctate.
After Parker.

molluscs, dispersion of the pigment produces colour or a dark condition of the skin, and its concentration produces pallor. Chromatophores of different animals differ widely in the way in which they react to stimuli, and above all in the way in which they are controlled. Most of them need a stimulus for both dispersion and concentration, so that it is impossible to say what is their resting and what their active state. Only when the particles are moving do they show Brownian movement, so that perhaps this condition is the active one, and any state where the particles are stationary is passive. There is no reason for regarding chromatophores of this type as being modified smooth muscle.

In the shrimp *Crangon* (= *Crago*) there are four different pigments, brown, white, yellow, and red, which are distributed amongst the chromatophores in all possible ways except that brown is always present. By appropriate movements of the pigment the animal matches itself to any background which comes towards the red end of the spectrum, and *Palaemonetes* does even better. Other Crustacea, such as some crabs and isopods, are similar, but not so complicated. If both eyes of one of these animals are excised there is no response to a changed background, the chromatophores remaining permanently in dispersion, so that the eye is clearly the organ which receives the stimulus. In these and other Crustacea the movement of the pigments is controlled by hormones which are formed in various parts of the nervous system and stored in the sinus gland and elsewhere. It is impossible to give any simple account of the matter, because no two genera seem to be quite alike. In general, antagonistic dispersing and concentrating hormones are present, but any one of these may have different effects on different pigments and different effects on the same pigment in different types of chromatophore. Investigation is difficult because there is often a daily rhythm which persists throughout the experiments and because some chromatophores seem to be able to respond directly to illumination, concentrating their pigment in bright light. In this they may be acting as independent effectors, but more probably they are merely made more sensitive to the hormones.

The few chromatophores of insects, for example *Carausius*, the stick-insect, are also controlled by hormones.

Many fish possess chromatophores, and their colour changes range from a mere passage from white through grey to black, to an ability to take up almost any colour of the spectrum. In some species chromatophores with different pigments have been found, and it is likely that such occur wherever there is a real change of colour as opposed to a mere change of intensity. In the teleosts, as in the Crustacea, excising the eyes or covering them inhibits the response. It is interesting that when the fish is on a dark background it is dark, but when it is in complete darkness it is pale, so that being in the dark and seeing black are not the same thing. The chromatophores have been shown by histological preparations to have a good nerve-supply, and if the nerves to an area are cut in such a way as not to hinder the blood-supply, the skin of this part maintains a uniform grey colour, while the rest of the body may change and become lighter or darker according to the background. Both dispersion and concentration are, then, under nervous control. In *Fundulus*, which has yellow xanthophores as well as melanophores, the two types of cell are under independent control, so that on a yellow background the xanthophores are in dispersion and the melanophores in concentration. It seems likely that a similar explanation would account for the more complicated colour changes of other fish, but this has not actually been shown to be the case. Some fish assimilate their body to a mottled background with considerable success, and even make a fair attempt to copy an artificial chessboard pattern on which they may be placed. The response is here a complex one involving independent behaviour of chromatophores in different parts of the skin. There is evidence that in *Fundulus* there is double innervation of the cells, and dispersion may perhaps be parasympathetic and concentration sympathetic, but in the elasmobranchs the neurohumour which produces pallor seems not to be adrenaline but an unidentified lipoid-soluble substance called selachine. Fish chromatophores do, however, concentrate with adrenaline and disperse with acetylcholine. The nerves probably act on the chromatophores by secreting a substance which acts directly on them (see section 5.32).

In some bony fish, and in all the elasmobranchs which have been studied, hormones are used as well, apparently the same B- and W-substances as are found in Amphibia (see below). In the eel *Anguilla vulgaris*, the stickleback *Gasterosteus aculeatus*, and some others the humoral control works alongside that by nerves. In the dogfish *Mustelus canis* pallor alone is caused by stimulation of nerve-fibres, darkening by a hormone. The catfish *Ameiurus* behaves like *Fundulus*, with double innervation, but at the same time dispersion is normally produced by the action of the pituitary. Three species of *Raja* and two of *Scyllium*, including the common roughhound, go even farther than *Mustelus*, for their chromatophores have no nervous control, but are probably regulated entirely by hormones. In the cyclostome *Lampetra planeri* there is a single hormone from the pituitary, which causes darkening, and light stimuli received by the pineal and parapineal in the larva, and by these and the lateral eyes in the adult, inhibit the pituitary and cause pallor.

Many of the Amphibia change the colour of their skin, just as do fishes, so that it resembles the background, but at the same time they react to other stimuli as well (Pl. I). In general, pallor is produced by a light background, dryness, or a relatively high temperature, and darkening by a dark background, moisture, and a low temperature. Being in the dark has the same effect as being on a dark background. Where two of these stimuli are in opposition to one another, one may be preponderant or a balance may be struck; so that the eight possible combinations give, in the common toad, the following order of decreasing blackness:

> Cold wet on black background
> Cold dry on black background
> { Cold wet on white background
> { Hot wet on black background
> Hot dry on black background
> Cold dry on white background
> { Hot wet on white background
> { Hot dry on white background.

Cold means on ice; hot, at about 20° C: wet is in a closed

vessel containing water; dry, in a closed vessel containing calcium chloride. The actual chromatophores are similar to those of the fishes, and the changes in colour are produced by actual migration of pigment; cells of two different colours may be present. A further point of similarity is that response to light is nearly, but not quite, abolished when the animal is blinded. It must therefore be admitted that although the eyes are the chief sense organs involved, yet the Amphibia also possess photoreceptors in their skin. These may be the chromatophores themselves which will then be independent effectors.

No nerve-supply to amphibian chromatophores has ever been demonstrated, and experiments on nerve-cutting have shown that nervous control has scarcely any effect on them; it certainly has no part in the ordinary colour responses of the animal. On the other hand it has been conclusively shown that control is by the pituitary gland; if this gland, or its posterior part, is extirpated the frog becomes uniformly pale under whatever conditions it may be placed; and if extract of pituitary be injected into such an animal the pigment of the chromatophores gradually disperses. The dispersion is, however, only temporary, so that either concentration is the resting state of the cells, or more probably another hormone is at work. Further more detailed investigation has shown that at least three influences co-operate in determining the colour of Amphibia. There is first a primary response in which the chromatophores react directly to light by dispersion. This is generally subordinate to the other two influences, but in a few genera such as *Necturus* it is predominant. The secondary response is the co-ordinated one which, as seen in the common frog, generally assimilates the animal to its background and which is worked through the eyes. It is carried out by two pituitary hormones; the B-substance (= intermedin), produced by the pars intermedia, causes darkening, and the W-substance, probably formed in the pars tuberalis, causes pallor. Adrenaline also can cause pallor, but whether it ever acts in the natural state is unknown. The hormonic control, which is necessarily generalized, adequately explains why the colour change is slower than in fish, and why the Amphibia cannot imitate a chessboard pattern.

But few reptiles can change their colour, and those which can belong mainly to the Lacertilia. The chameleon is proverbial for the many colours which it can take up, but it does not ordinarily resemble its background. Reptilian chromatophores are in general similar to those of other vertebrates, but in addition they act in part by covering or uncovering stationary masses of pigment in underlying tissue. The physiology of the response has been worked out in only a few species, but in general, bright illumination and low temperature produce pallor, while darkness and high temperature cause the pigment to disperse. In addition, any noxious stimulus produces pallor, and the animal is lighter on a white background than on a dark one. As before, the eye is the receptor for the response to light, but there is direct action on the skin as well. In the chameleon the melanophores are under direct nervous control, since electrical stimulation of the roof of the mouth induces pallor only in those parts of the skin to which the nerve-supply is intact, but no fully satisfactory mechanism for this animal has been worked out. In *Phrynosoma* (miscalled the horned toad) there is double control, pallor being produced either through the nervous system or by the liberation of adrenaline into the bloodstream, and darkening by intermedin.

In the lizard *Anolis* there is no nervous control, and adrenaline does not produce pallor; control seems to be by the single dispersing hormone, intermedin. The only chelonian known to change its colour appears to be similar.

No other effector shows such a varied and complicated type of control as does the chromatophore. Sometimes it is humoral, sometimes nervous, and it is noteworthy that in the vertebrates nervous control seems to have been given up in the Amphibia and regained in the reptiles. (It must be remembered that none of the existing orders of Amphibia is anywhere near the presumed ancestry of the reptiles.) Where the control is humoral there is little specificity, extract of the pars nervosa and pars intermedia of mammals being potent in causing dispersion in Amphibia, and mammalian adrenaline causing concentration in both reptiles and amphibians. It has even been shown that extract of the eye-stalks of prawns will induce concentration of the melanophores of plaice, and that the pigmentary hormone of *Dixippus* disperses the pigment of Amphibia. Although the essence of a chromatophore is that it works by the movement of pigment, in many species prolonged exposure to a dark background causes an increase in the number of melanophores and in the amount of pigment present, and probably exposure to a light background causes their decrease. These are changes comparable to those which occur in the stationary pigment cells of man.

5

CO-ORDINATION OF FUNCTION

I T has been pointed out on p. 158 that most effectors need to be stimulated into activity by some influence which they receive from elsewhere. If this were not so, if all effectors were independent, no co-ordination would be possible: each small part of the body would act solely in accordance with the stimuli which itself received. The mechanism which conveys the stimulus from the receptor which picks it up to the effector which reacts to it, and so ensures concerted action by different regions of the body, is called a co-ordinating system. There are three types of this, but it is possible that all three are really developments of the same fundamental method.

5.1. Hormones

Almost everything that an animal does is initiated, or has its rate determined, by substances produced within the body. The ability of a muscle to contract repeatedly depends on an adequate supply of glucose, digestion depends on enzymes, and the rate of breathing is affected by the concentration of carbon dioxide in the blood. These and many similar instances have been known for a long time, and they are not usually thought of as examples of co-ordination. The substances concerned may be put in four groups: the substrates of metabolism, such as glucose; excretory products, such as carbon dioxide; enzymes carrying out metabolic processes; and secretions passed by a duct to the gut or to the exterior. In addition to these we now know of many substances which are produced for the special purpose of initiating or controlling some process in the body; their action is thought of as chemical co-ordination, and they are called hormones. Their delimitation from enzymes, other than those passed to the gut or the exterior, is difficult and in part arbitrary. In part also it depends on the history of their discovery, for while enzymes were discovered as substances taking part in chemical reactions, hormones were discovered as substances which affect the response of a muscle or other effector, and only a few of them are known to act by taking part in a reaction as an enzyme does. The fact that hormones are produced in the body distinguishes them, just as it does enzymes, from vitamins, but it does not separate them. When ascorbic acid is produced by the tissues it is a hormone; when it is obtained in the food it is a vitamin. At least some of the effect of young grass in stimulating milk-production in cows is due to oestrogenic substances which it contains. An androgen secreted in the breeding season as a sex hormone by the male bitterling is also excreted into the surrounding water, where it causes the growth of the ovipositor of his mate. Since it is apparently not eaten by her it cannot be called a vitamin, nor, by the usual definition, is it for her a hormone, but physiologically it is doing the work of one or the other of these.

Some hormones act close to the place where they are formed, as do the evocating substances produced in vertebrate embryos and the neurohumours liberated at the end of motor nerves, but the typical hormones are made in glands that are remote from the point of application. They are carried in the blood-stream, and have been certainly proved to exist in all the main phyla in which a vascular system is present, that is in annelids, arthropods, molluscs, and chordates. The earliest known example, that of the stimulation of the pancreas by secretin (p. 37), was described by Bayliss and Starling in 1902, and since our knowledge of the physiology of invertebrates other than insects is still very small, it is not impossible that hormones may yet be found to be present, in some form, in other phyla.

The glands that make hormones may have no other function, as the adrenal (though one gland may make more than one hormone), or they may also produce secretions which pass down a duct in the ordinary way; there is then generally separation of the tissues within the gland, as with the islet tissue of the pancreas which produces insulin and glucagon. A gland that produces a hormone is called an endocrine gland, and hormones are sometimes called internal secretions and autacoids. No generalization about the chemical nature of hormones is possible.

The normal way of testing for endocrine action is, first, to remove the suspected organ from an animal and observe the effects. Extracts of the organ are then injected into the blood; if they restore the animal to normal, endocrine action may be taken as proved. Where removal of the organ is impossible other tests may be used; extracts may produce overdose effects, it may be possible to demonstrate an increased concentration of an active principle in the blood leaving the organ, the concentration of some substance in the blood may depend on the condition of an organ, or effects may be produced by the grafting of an organ from another animal. That an effector is under endocrine control may be assumed when it continues to act and to respond to stimuli when all its nervous connexions have been cut. Endocrine glands are themselves under control, usually of the nervous system, and there is thus a double link between the stimulus and its response. The stimulus activates a receptor, which initiates an impulse which travels via the central nervous system to the gland, which is caused to produce or release a hormone into the blood-stream, by which it travels to the effector.

From the nature of their action it is possible to make some generalizations about the properties which hormones must possess if they are to be effective. They must be soluble in water, or they could not be readily carried by the blood or pass into the tissues, although a few, which have been distinguished as lipohumours, may be fat-soluble and of purely local effect. They must diffuse readily through protoplasm, or they would not be able to escape fast enough from the blood-vessels or reach all the cells on which they act; this means that they must be of relatively low molecular weight. If they were not fairly rapidly removed, their effects would be permanent, and so their value as co-ordinating agents would be lost; their removal might be by excretion, or by oxidation, or by digestion, and examples of all of these are known. There might also be specific inhibitors, or anti-hormones, but although these are certainly formed in some circumstances it is not certain that they have any natural function.

The effects of hormones range from determining the fate of cells once for all, as in embryos, through general influences on the rate of a process which never stops, as the thyroid secretion raises basal metabolic rate, to brief action on individual effectors, as in the control of amphibian melanophores by the pituitary. It is possible that the first is the most primitive, and that it developed from the general chemical control which the nucleus has over the cytoplasm. The most likely way in which the genes could act would be by the production of chemicals which diffuse into the cytoplasm, and there is evidence that a few genes do act by producing particular enzymes, or, as they would be better called, hormones. That the cytoplasm behaves in a similar way is suggested by the fact that the control by the nucleus is not absolute. From this general power of protoplasm to produce chemical substances would seem to have developed the various types of hormone now known. Their primitive and fundamental nature is shown by their lack of specificity. In general they act on a tissue or cell-type rather than on an organ. Each hormone seems to be chemically almost or exactly the same throughout the vertebrate classes, and there are some hormones which have similar effects in invertebrates and vertebrates.

5.11. Hormones in Invertebrates

Until 1928 no clear case of the existence of a hormone in an invertebrate was known, but in that year it was shown that contraction of the chromatophores of the shrimp is caused by a substance formed in the eye-stalks. This is now known to be general for those Crustacea which can change colour, and the subject is more fully treated on pp. 210–11. Since then it has gradually been shown that hormones play as important a part in the life of Crustacea as they do in that of vertebrates. The endocrine organs are small and of different forms in different groups, and there has been some confusion of nomenclature, but the most important of them are specializations of nervous tissue. The best known are situated in the eye-stalks (where there are two distinct structures, both called X-organs), the post-oesophageal commissure, and the pericardial wall. The sinus gland, formed from the epineurium which encloses the ganglia of the eye-stalk, is the most potent source of many hormones, but it probably does not make them. They are passed into it along axon fibres which run from the neurosecretory cells and end in club-shaped swellings. Besides the hormones which affect the chromatophores the sinus gland contains several which control the movements of the pigments of the retina, and a diabeto-genic principle which keeps the blood sugar above a minimum. It has also at least three moult-hormones; one inhibits the onset of the preparatory changes of the premoult period, and another accelerates and controls the premoult once it has begun, while both of these cause the production of a third hormone which is necessary for the moult itself. These hormones are also present in other parts of the body.

The pericardial organs contain a substance which accelerates the heart-beat. The growth of the ovary and testis is hormonally controlled, and certainly in male amphipods and probably more generally the development of secondary sexual characters is dependent on hormones. Other processes in which hormones are possibly or probably concerned are respiration, the metabolism of fat, protein, and calcium, the control of water balance, and the formation of chitin.

Work on the chemical separation of the hormones has been begun, and it has been shown that at least one of those involved in colour change contains peptide links which are essential for its activity.

The best-known hormones in insects are those which control growth and moulting. A part of the brain called the pars intercerebralis produces a hormone which activates the thoracic gland. This structure takes various forms in different orders, and is known as prothoracic, peritracheal, pericardial, and so on according to its position. Its hormone stimulates the growth and mitosis of epidermal cells and the secretion of a new cuticle. It therefore induces moulting. It is not specific, is non-nitrogenous, but is normally carried by a protein. The thoracic gland atrophies in the adult and so moulting does not occur. Where, as in the Thysanura, the gland persists, moulting continues two or three times a year throughout life, and moulting has been induced in adults of the bug *Rhodnius* by grafting them on to nymphs and by the implantation of thoracic glands.

In young stages (up to the fourth nymphal instar in *Rhodnius*) a juvenile hormone, which has been called neotenin, is also present. It is formed in another gland in the head, called the corpus allatum, and actively promotes juvenile characters and suppresses imaginal ones. There is some development of adult characters, or metamorphosis, at each moult, but their full development waits on the reduction of juvenile hormone. Whether this is gradual, or in two well-marked stages, determines the absence or presence of a pupa.

In some insects the corpora allata of the adult female produce a hormone which is necessary for yolk formation; it may be identical with the juvenile hormone. The chromatophores of insects are controlled by hormones, and the gonads may produce sex-hormones. The queen bee produces a queen-substance which, licked from her body by the workers, inhibits the development of their ovaries and the building of queen-cells; but it is difficult to bring this within the definition of a hormone. There is some evidence that it is the same as the ovary-inhibiting substance produced by the eye-stalks of Crustacea. In some insects, and perhaps in all, the arrest of growth known as diapause, which occurs at various stages from the egg onwards, is under humoral control. In the silk-worm (*Bombyx mori*) dispause occurs in the embryo if the mother's suboesophageal ganglion produces the appropriate hormone. The synthesis, or perhaps the release, of this is determined by nervous stimuli from the brain, so that diapause is facultative. In the giant silk-moth (*Platysamia cecropia*) diapause occurs in the pupa because of a failure of the pars intercerebralis–prothoracic gland system which also controls metamorphosis. A period of low temperature is necessary to stimulate the pars inter-cerebralis, and when this is activated development continues and leads to metamorphosis.

There is histological evidence that a substance produced in the brain of the cockroach *Leucophaea* passes along axons into the corpus cardiacum. Extracts of this body in *Periplaneta* are widely active physiologically; they induce or accelerate contraction of the hind gut, Malpighian tubules, and heart, and they affect the chromatophores of insects and crustaceans. Chromatographic analysis suggests that the principle which is active on the heart is an orthodiphenol, similar to, but not identical with, adrenaline. It is therefore not surprising that the insect heart is affected by adrenaline (and acetylcholine). There is some evidence that the effect of extracts of corpus cardiacum on chromatophores is due to a different substance. Extracts of the corpus cardiacum of *Rhodnius* and of mealworm larvae (*Tenebrio*) have similar but weaker effects. It seems likely that while the chromatophore-principle may be produced in the brain and transferred to the corpus cardiacum, the heart-stimulating principle is made in the gland itself.

The neurosecretory cells of crustaceans and insects stain in the same way as those of vertebrates. There is a remarkable analogy between the sinus gland, the corpus cardiacum, and the neurohypophysis (section 5.1264), all of which receive and store hormones produced in the nervous system; but the similarities, except that they are based on the fundamental properties of nervous tissue, cannot have any significance.

Neurosecretory cells have also been recognized in poly-clads, polychaetes, oligochaetes, scaphopods, opisthobranchs, prosobranchs, and cephalopods. In the polychaetes the supraoesophageal ganglion produces a hormone which appears in the blood and controls the sexual development; in the oligochaetes regeneration cannot take place without a hormone produced by the central nervous system. Hormones control the chromatophores of cephalopods, and possibly the development of the genital ducts in gastropods.

5.12. Hormones in Vertebrates

In vertebrates many endocrine glands and many hormones are known, their interrelationships with each other and with the nervous system being often very complex. A list of them, with a brief account of their properties, follows. The neurohumours, secreted at synapses and nerve-endings, are dealt with in section 5.32.

5.121. The Mucosa of the Gut

The action of this in co-ordinating digestion is described on pp. 36–37.

5.122. The Pancreas

The islets of Langerhans in this gland produce two hormones, insulin and glucagon, which affect the metabolism of sugar (p. 60). Both are polypeptides, of unit molecular weight about 12,000, or possibly half this, and there are slight differences in the aminoacids present in hormones from different species. Insulin is produced by the β-cells of the pancreas, and glucagon presumably by the α-cells.

5.123. The Thyroid

The mammalian thyroid consists of two masses lying one on each side of the trachea just behind the thyroid cartilage. The division into two parts is secondary, and in the rabbit and many other animals the two halves are joined by a ventral strand across the trachea. The gland starts as a single diverticulum from the pharynx, and its position and mode of development show that it is probably homologous with the endostyle of *Branchiostoma* and lampreys. It is made up of closed vesicles with a wall of cubical epithelium, the cells of which have a brush border. In the frog the thyroid consists of a small reddish body on each external jugular vein, and in the dogfish of a pear-shaped structure just below the fork of the ventral aorta, while in adult cyclostomes and many teleosts it consists of groups of follicles scattered about the region of the ventral aorta.

The effects of thyroidectomy can be counteracted by a number of substances, both natural and artificial, all of which contain iodine, and it seems that the important part of the molecule is a substituted benzene ring, thus,

The gland takes up iodine or iodide from the food, oxidizes it, and incorporates it in a protein, thyroglobulin, of molecular weight about 700,000. This is stored in the vesicles of the gland, and then split by a proteolytic enzyme to form the circulating hormone, which is thyroxine,

$-CH_2 \cdot CH \cdot NH_2 \cdot COOH.$

Triiodothyromine, which has only one iodine atom in the left-hand ring, is also present in the blood in small amounts, and since it seems to have more powerful effects than thyroxine is perhaps the active form. The release of thyroxine from thyroglobulin is brought about by a hormone from the anterior pituitary. Thyroxine is unique among hormones in that it is not easily digested, and so can be successfully administered by the mouth.

Over-activity of the gland produces the disease known as exophthalmic goitre, and under-activity myxoedema in adults and cretinism in children, but an account of these belongs to pathology rather than physiology. Their symptoms, however, suggest that the chief normal function of the thyroid is probably the regulation of the growth and activity of the animal. In particular it controls basal metabolism (p. 8), which in myxoedema may be 25 per cent. below normal and in goitre 100 per cent. up. The rise of temperature and increased metabolism in fevers are possibly caused by over-secretion by the thyroid, and it may be that the increased metabolism produced by low temperatures is brought about in the same way. The latter is the only case where it is likely that the thyroid normally varies in its activity during life so as to co-ordinate any other processes in the body. For the rest, it maintains a general control over certain aspects of metabolism, and is particularly important during the time when growth is going on; for example, the bones of cretins cease growing at an early age, and their mental powers never develop.

Thyroxine was early shown to increase the oxygen consumption of many tissues, and more recently it has been shown to accelerate several enzyme reactions, including some of those involved in protein breakdown and phospholipid synthesis and other metabolic processes, mostly oxidative. Which, if any, of these is fundamental, and which are side-effects, is unknown, but many of them involve cytochrome. Thyroxine has also been claimed to stimulate spermatogenesis and sexual activity generally.

The effects on birds, so far as they have been studied, seem to be generally similar to those on mammals, but in addition the thyroid seems to be in some way responsible for moulting, since this can be induced by thyroxine; however, thyroidectomy does not prevent moulting in ducks nor does thiouracil (which prevents the gland from utilizing iodine) in hens, so that there must be some other control. The 'silky' state of feathers, in which the barbules are absent, can be induced by thyroidectomy or thiouracil, and a nearly normal feather structure can be induced in genotypically silky birds by thyroxine.

The functions of the thyroid seem to be somewhat different in cold-blooded vertebrates. The most striking is that it controls the metamorphosis of Amphibia, for if it be extirpated in tadpoles they grow far beyond their normal size and never change into frogs or newts as they should. Thyroxine, or even elemental iodine, will make such thyroidectomized tadpoles develop normally. Conversely, feeding normal tadpoles with thyroid makes them metamorphose at an early age—at 6 weeks instead of 3 years in the extreme case of *Rana catesbiana*—and the axolotl larva of *Amblystoma mexicanum*, which normally never metamorphoses, can be induced to do so.

The deficiency in this species lies not in the thyroid itself, but in the pituitary, for if an anterior pituitary gland from the related *A. tigrinum*, which does metamorphose, is grafted on to it, metamorphosis occurs. By contrast, the perennibranchiate amphibians have normal thyroids and normal pituitaries, but their tissues are unresponsive. There is a little evidence that the thyroid may control the metamorphosis of a few teleosts, notably the change from parr to smolt in the rainbow trout of North America. It appears to control the sloughing of the skin in reptiles.

Most experiments suggest that thyroid hormones affect neither growth nor oxygen consumption in cold blooded vertebrates. Thiourea (another substance which prevents the formation of thyroglobulin) reduces the onset of spermatogenesis and external sexual characters in the male minnow, and has comparable but less striking effects in the female. The influence of the pituitary on the thyroid of teleosts seems to be of the same form as in mammals.

5.124. The Parathyroids

The parathyroids lie on the surface of, or embedded in, the thyroid, and consist of two pairs of bodies derived from the third and fourth branchial pouches. Their secretion, which has not been obtained pure, is called parathormone or parathymin and appears to be a protein of about the same molecular weight as insulin. Its action is obscure, but injection of it raises the level of calcium in the blood, lowers that of phosphate, and increases the excretion of both; there is some evidence that the effects on calcium and phosphate are caused by two different hormones. Its effects on these ions explains why activity of the gland interferes with bone formation, and, since altering the ionic balance affects the muscle proteins and nervous system, its removal causes tetany. The exact way in which parathormone controls the calcium and phosphate metabolism is unknown, but it acts in a very different way from vitamin D (p. 77), for it ionizes the calcium phosphate of bone and so brings it into solution. Extract of parathyroid is said also to retard growth in rodents and Amphibia, and removal of the gland to impair lactation in rats. No parathyroids are known in fish.

5.125. The Thymus

The thymus has long been suspected as an endocrine gland, but although some evidence for its action has been published little seems to be known of what it does. It consists in mammals of two masses in the space (the mediastinum) in front of the heart. They are derived from the epithelium of the gill slits. In the frog there is a small lobe at each angle of the jaw, and in the dogfish a small mass above each gill cleft. It is largest in young animals, and in man is at its maximum at 2 years, while in adults it is very variable in size. It becomes smaller when the body is subject to stress or disease, so that it is often small after death. This at once suggests that its function is connected with growth, and it has been claimed that if extract of thymus be injected into rats greatly accelerated development follows. In particular the time of descent of the testes or opening of the vagina (the sign of sexual maturity) is reached much earlier. This effect on the reproductive organs has been confirmed in mice, but in these animals no general effect on growth was found.

5.126. The Pituitary

The pituitary is a complex gland, consisting in mammals of four parts, the pars anterior (or distalis), pars tuberalis, pars intermedia, and pars nervosa (Fig. 31). The first three are formed from the hypophysis, which is an upgrowth from the roof of the mouth homologous with the preoral pit of *Branchiostoma*. The pars nervosa is developed from the infundibulum, which grows down from the floor of the third ventricle. The pars anterior is known as the anterior lobe, in which the pars tuberalis and pars intermedia are sometimes included; the others make up the posterior or neuro-intermediate lobe.

The same four parts can generally be recognized in other vertebrates, though their disposition may be somewhat different. The gland has a double blood supply, by arteries from the internal carotid and by portal vessels which come from the venous drainage of the hypothalamus and break up into capillaries in the pars distalis.

The exact number of hormones produced by the pituitary is still not certain, partly because it is not easy to know how many of the several undoubted functions of the gland can be ascribed to a single substance. Each part is probably best regarded as a separate gland, and the account that

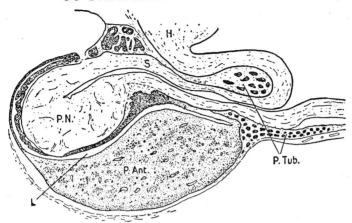

FIG. 31. Pituitary body of cat.

P. Ant., pars anterior; *P. Tub.*, pars tuberalis; *P.N.*, pars nervosa; *I.*, pars intermedia (darkly staining tissue enveloping *P.N.*); *L.*, cleft separating *P. Ant.* from *I.* (this is the residual lumen of Rathke's pouch); *S.*, stalk (infundibulum), showing cleft which is continuous with third ventricle; *H.*, hypothalamus. From a drawing by Dr. J. H. Woodger.

follows attempts to list their known hormones and effects as simply as possible, no doubt with some loss of accuracy.

5.1261. Pars distalis, 'Anterior Pituitary'

The active substances that have been extracted from the anterior pituitary of mammals are all proteins of relatively low molecular weight. They can be put in five main groups, but the number of hormones produced in life may be more or less than this. The same, or similar, hormones probably occur in birds, although the first of those listed below, the growth hormone, has not been demonstrated. In cold-blooded vertebrates sexual hormones are certainly present, but less is known of the others. Both in mammals and in birds the secretion of the anterior pituitary is controlled by exteroceptive factors through the nervous system, as described in sections 7.22 and 7.23, but as it has no nerve supply the mechanism was for long unknown. There is now good evidence that in birds control is by a hormone secreted by the hypothalamus and passed along the hypophyseal portal vessels, and there is some evidence, and a strong probability, that the same is true of mammals.

5.12611. Growth Hormone. It has long been known that hypertrophy of the pituitary leads to gigantism and the disease called acromegaly, in which hands, feet, and lower jaw are of unusual size, and that deficiency produces dwarfing. The former effects can be produced by a relatively pure substance called growth hormone (GH) or somatotrophic hormone (STH). It has also effects on the metabolism of carbohydrates (p. 61), protein and fat; and probably the 'diabetogenic hormone' and 'ketogenic hormone' that have been described were simply impure preparations of it. Both in man and the rat it is not necessary for growth in early life, but it becomes important in man at the age of two to four years. Injection of it increases growth in all classes of vertebrates. It appears to be able to increase, but not to initiate, milk secretion in cows.

5.12612. Thyrotropin. The action of the pituitary in stimulating the thyroid has been described in section 5.123. The hormone concerned is called thyrotropin, or thyroid-stimulating hormone (TSH).

5.12613. Corticotropin. Two substances that stimulate the adrenal cortex to produce its hormones have been extracted from the gland, but it is simplest to assume that they are derivatives of a single hormone, which is called corticotropin, or adrenocorticotropic hormone (ACTH). It is probable that its production is increased by hormones from the hypothalamus in the portal system and by adrenaline in the blood, and decreased by circulating cortical steroids (section 5.1272), so that there is some automatic control of the latter. Corticotropin raises the oxygen consumption of the cortex, and has what may be side-effects in lowering blood sugar and mobilizing depot-fat. It, or more probably impurities associated with it, has the same effects on amphibian melanophores as does intermedin (p. 214).

5.12614. Gonadotropins. The action of follicle-stimulating hormone (FSH), luteinizing hormone (LH), and prolactin or luteotropic hormone (LTH), collectively known as gonadotropins, in controlling the sexual cycle will be described in section 7.22. Luteinizing hormone is identical with the interstitial cell stimulating hormone (ICSH) of males. Prolactin not only initiates milk secretion in mammals, but also that of the functionally similar 'pigeons' milk' produced by the crop-gland of those birds. It also induces broodiness in female birds and causes the development of brood patches, areas of the abdomen from which the feathers fall off at incubation. Pigeons' milk, and in some species brood patches, are present in both sexes, so that here what in mammals appears to be a characteristically female hormone is active in the male.

5.1262. Pars tuberalis

The only hormone known certainly to be produced by the pars tuberalis is the W-substance that concentrates the pigment of amphibian melanophores and of those of some fish (p. 215).

5.1263. Pars intermedia

Likewise, the pars intermedia is known to be active only in poikilotherms. It produces intermedin which causes the dispersion of pigment in the chromatophores of Amphibia and of some fish and reptiles, and possibly induces the synthesis of more melanin. Intermedin can be extracted from the pituitary of birds and mammals, but has no known function in them.

5.1264. Pars nervosa, 'Posterior Pituitary'

Two hormones have been extracted from the pars nervosa, pitressin and pitocin (or oxytocin), but it is not certain that they are not fragments of a single hormone. Pitressin causes constriction of nearly all blood-vessels, but in mammals does not affect those of the kidney. It, or possibly a third hormone, also causes a reduced production of urine in most vertebrates, but its precise effects are different in the different classes. In mammals there is increased tubular resorption, in crocodiles decreased filtration, in birds and frogs both occur, and in fish neither has been found. The general effect seems to be an influence on permeability which drives potassium out of the cells and sodium and water in. This antidiuretic effect is controlled by cells in the hypothalamus which respond to the concentration of chloride or other solutes in the blood. The same, or perhaps another hormone, increases the uptake of water through the skin of Amphibia, especially the more terrestrial forms.

Pitocin causes contraction of the smooth muscle of the uterus and of the mammary gland, and possibly in other places. It is the normal initiator of the 'let-down' of milk in suckling, but its function in the control of the uterus is more doubtful. It may initiate labour, and may be responsible for the uterine contractions that accompany copulation and, in some species, such as the cow, are important in the transport of sperms.

The pars nervosa may not be an endocrine gland at all, but merely a storage organ for hormones produced elsewhere. It has a good nerve supply by a tract from the supraoptic and paraventricular nuclei of the hypothalamus, and there is now some evidence that substances produced in the brain pass down these nerve fibres to be stored in the pituitary. There is here a remarkable parallel with what occurs in arthropods (p. 224).

5.127. The Suprarenals or Adrenals

The suprarenals or adrenals consist in mammals of two small bodies, one in front of each kidney. Each has two parts, an inner medulla and an outer cortex. The former, the suprarenal proper, is derived from the same set of cells as the sympathetic system, while the cortex has its origin in that part of the mesoblast which gives rise to the mesonephros. The functions of the two are quite distinct, and their association is probably an accident, for in some fishes they are quite separate. In the dogfish, for instance, the interrenal, representing the cortex, lies between the kidneys, and the suprarenals, representing the medulla, consist of small masses on the sympathetic chains. The adrenals of the frog lie on the ventral surface of the kidneys and are yellowish in colour. In some animals patches of tissue which is histologically similar to medulla or cortex are found detached from them.

5.1271. The Adrenal Medulla

The medulla produces a substance, adrenaline or epinephrin, the formula of which is

$$HO-C_6H_3(OH)-CH(OH)-CH_2-NH-CH_3$$

This, when injected into the blood, produces almost exactly the effects of stimulation of the sympathetic nervous system: it raises blood-pressure by arterial constriction; it causes contraction or relaxation of smooth muscle according to its origin and previous condition, dilatation of the pupil, erection of hairs by contraction of their muscles; it breaks down liver glycogen and muscle glycogen to lactic acid; it induces secretion of saliva; and it causes dilatation of the arterioles of the muscles and heart and contraction of those of the skin and most viscera. In addition it causes contraction of amphibian and reptilian chromatophores. Its exact function in the normal animal is obscure, but its most probable role is as follows. It is continually being produced in small amounts, but not in sufficient quantity to have any great effect. On the stimulation of cold, lack of oxygen, or the emotional states of fear and anger, its output is greatly increased, so that the characteristic effects of injection of adrenaline, which are also those of these emotions, follow. The external stimuli act through the splanchnic nerves, which release acetylcholine and so cause the medulla to discharge its secretion.

The medulla also produces smaller quantities of noradrenaline, which lacks the terminal methyl group but has similar effects to adrenaline. It is the substance produced at sympathetic nerve-endings.

5.1272. The Adrenal Cortex

Removal of the adrenal cortex lowers the concentration of sugar and sodium in the blood, and leads to death within a few weeks. These effects can be avoided by the administration of an extract of the gland called cortin, and it is now clear that the active substances are one or more steroids, of the general structure

The length of the side-chain attached to carbon atom 17 varies. A score and a half of these compounds are now known, and possibly three or four of them, such as corticosterone and cortisone (11-dehydro-17-hydroxycorticosterone) are active in life. Aldosterone appears to be an especially important regulator of sodium and potassium balance in man and the dog. It is still disputed whether the effects of cortin can only be produced by mixtures, or whether a single substance is all that is needed. Possibly there are specific differences, for the same steroid may not have the same effect on all animals.

In general the steroids increase the formation of carbohydrate from protein and fat, acting mainly on the liver, and increase the excretion of nitrogen. There is a fall in the sodium of blood and intercellular spaces, and a rise in intracellular potassium. Presumably all these effects arise from an influence on an enzyme reaction, possibly one that maintains the properties of the cell membrane.

The general effect of cortical steroids in life seems to be to enable the body to meet stress, whether coming from cold, heavy exercise, or infection, for any of these causes a discharge of the hormones into the blood, the immediate cause being the liberation of corticotropin from the pituitary. Prolonged stress causes hypertrophy of the gland. Conversely, removal of the adrenals lowers the capacity of the animal to meet conditions such as cold, low oxygen supply, or infection. The output of the hormones is also directly affected by the intake of electrolytes.

The corticosteroids are closely related to those of the gonads (section 7.22), and there is some indication that they may be able to substitute for these in controlling the oestrous cycle. Some types of precocious sexual development in boys, and masculine features in women, are due to overactivity of the adrenal cortex.

5.128. The Pineal

The pineal, which in the earliest vertebrates was an eye on the top of the head, is only a very doubtful endocrine gland. There are some clinical indications that it is concerned with sexual development. Its extract causes contraction of anuran melanophores, but not of those of urodeles, and it does not appear to be normally important in this way.

5.129. The Gonads and Related Structures

The hormones that control the sexual cycle are described in section 7.22. It has long been suspected, as a result of the effects of castration and disease, that the interstitial cells of the gonads also control the secondary sexual characteristics and the development of the accessory organs, and this is now known to be generally true.

The sex of the gonad rudiment, originally undifferentiated, is normally genetically determined, and as it develops into one sex or the other it produces something that may induce like development in other rudiments of the opposite sex grafted near it. This effect has been shown in amphibia, birds, and mammals, and in some species the male is dominant, in others the female. In general the Müllerian duct develops without hormonal control, but if a testis is present it is suppressed; conversely, the Wolffian duct does not develop unless a testis is present. Whether these effects are due to the adult hormones, or whether they are produced by special ones, is not known.

All the secondary sexual characters that have been tested can be maintained in male castrates by injection of testosterone, which may therefore be the only hormone concerned in their production. For example, castrated deer do not grow antlers, and the fructose normally added to the semen of the rabbit and bull by the accessory glands is not formed after castration, but both antlers and fructose are restored by testosterone.

The secondary effects of oestrogen are not so clear. Injected into castrate adolescent kangaroos it causes the scrotum (which is in front of the penis in marsupials) to change into the typical female pouch. Low circulating levels of oestrogen activate both the initiation and the maintenance of milk-production, while high levels inhibit them. The skeletal adjustments of the sacrum and the pubic symphysis that occur in the female mammal are brought about by a hormone from the ovary and other parts of the reproductive tract that has been called relaxin.

Finally, both androgens and oestrogens play some part, though exactly what is not clear, in the general psychic and emotional life of both mammals and birds. Androsterone probably raises and oestrogen lowers the position of birds and chimpanzees in the social hierarchy. The evaluation of the function of these hormones is made more difficult by the fact that both occur to some extent in both sexes.

5.2. Neuroid Transmission

Where there is no cellular structure there can be neither conduction by nerves nor conduction by fluids in blood-vessels. Where under such circumstances stimuli are nevertheless carried from one part of the cell to another their transmission is called neuroid. This name is also applied to conduction in cellular structures where no nerves or blood-vessels by which co-ordination could be effected are demonstrable. The word is little more than a name for our ignorance. There is well-defined conduction of impulses in the Protozoa; an amoeba, touched at its forward end, very soon starts forming pseudopodia at other points. In ciliates the co-ordination of the cilia is only maintained so long as the neuromotor system is intact (Fig. 32). When the fibres of this are cut the cilia beat at random. Similar fibres have been found in cells of ciliated epithelium, where the cilia are kept in a rhythm by conducted waves which do not necessarily travel in the same direction as the beat of the cilia (p. 165). The conduction of stimulus cannot therefore be mechanical. When sperms are allowed to come together and clump, the beating of their tails may become synchronized; if this is not an example of forced vibrations, in which the most strongly beating tail imposes its rhythm on the others, it suggests that neuroid transmission takes place by the gradual diffusion of secreted substances, for in this case there is not likely to be any protoplasmic continuity. The same explanation might account for the fact that the cells of a sponge react to a stimulus received as far as a centimetre away from them.

5.3. The Nervous System

From an evolutionary point of view the nerve net, such as is found in coelenterates and echinoderms, is the most primitive type of nervous system. Little, however, is known of its physiology, and it is more convenient to start with the nerve-cell or neurone as it is found in higher animals and particularly in vertebrates. The functional unit here is the reflex arc. One nerve-cell called a receptor picks up a stimulus, and as a result transmits an impulse along a sensory or afferent fibre to a synapse; this is a junction at which the impulse is transferred to another fibre, called motor or efferent, along which it is conveyed to the effector. By this mechanism it is possible for one effector to be specifically joined to one receptor. More usually the case is not quite so simple: intercalated between the sensory and motor neurones are one or more association or internuncial nerve-cells, and each synapse is a complex junction in which the afferent neurone is connected with more than one efferent, or vice versa. The effect of this is that while there is still localization of response, one small part of the body responding to a stimulus received on another small part, yet an effector can respond to impulses received from more than one receptor, and the same receptor can influence many effectors. Any aggregation of nervous tissue consisting of the synapses and adjacent parts of the nerve-cells, or of complete association

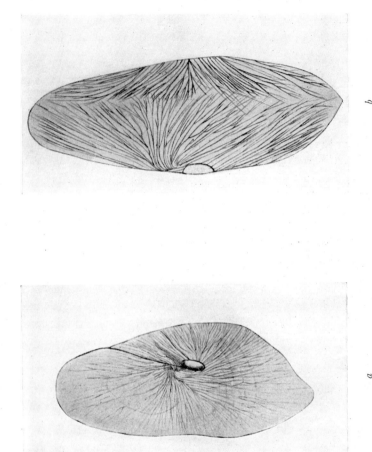

a

b

FIG. 32. Neuromotor system of *Paramecium*: (*a*) oral view showing the oral whorl of fibres ramifying out from the neuromotor centre or motorium; (*b*) view of the left side, showing the ends of the fibres of both the oral and aboral whorls. After Rees.

neurones, is called a central nervous system. The remaining parts of the nerve-cells, mostly collected together into nerves, constitute the peripheral system.

5.31. Propagation of the Nervous Impulse

A nerve may be stimulated by almost any sudden change in its environment—by pressure, by heating, or by the application of chemicals—but in life sensory nerves are usually particularly sensitive to one form of stimulus. That the impulse passed along the nerve is independent of the type of stimulus is suggested by a simple experiment. The right eye is shut, and turned as far to the left as possible, and the eyeball is then pressed sharply with the finger at the outer (temporal) corner of the lids. A flash of light is seen, apparently just above the nose. A little consideration will show that an object in this position would produce an image on the retina at about the spot where pressure has been applied, and the obvious explanation is that pressure and light both have the same effect on the retina, but that the brain is accustomed to appreciate all stimuli received there as light.

For experimental work electrical stimulation is generally employed, on account of the ease with which it can be controlled and measured. After one impulse has passed there is a refractory period during which a second stimulus is ineffective: the period for the frog's sciatic nerve is about 1 msec at 20° C and longer at lower temperatures; in *Carcinus* it is 2 msec. After the absolute refractory period there is a relatively refractory one, and this is followed by a time in which the nerve is abnormally sensitive. Even if a stimulus be inadequate, it is still followed by a refractory period, so that if stimuli are very frequent and correctly spaced (about 1,000 per sec in the frog) none but the first one has any effect. The immediate effect of an inadequate stimulus must be to make the nerve supersensitive, for if another inadequate one follows within 0·5 msec a response follows, so that there has been summation. The relationship between strength of stimulus and duration of application, and the conceptions of rheobase and chronaxie (p. 176) are the same for nerve as for muscle. The two tissues are similar also in that the make stimulus starts from the cathode, and in their other electrical relations. Cooling the nerve greatly increases its excitability, and it is found that the effect is entirely on the rheobase; the chronaxie, as with muscle, is actually increased. Excitation and conduction are only possible within certain limits of temperature, which depend on the animal. Frog nerve at 2° C is very sensitive, but mammalian nerve is inactive below 5° C. It is found that the larger the chronaxie the smaller is the fibre size and the greater the velocity of conduction.

The impulse takes a certain time to travel along the nerve, and this is fairly readily demonstrable with an ordinary nerve-muscle preparation with a long piece of sciatic nerve. Two tracings are obtained, with the electrodes first as near the muscle as possible, and then near the cut end of the nerve; the muscle is later in responding in the second case. More elaborate methods are necessary to get good values for the velocity of transmission in individual fibres. It is found that the larger the fibre the more rapidly it conducts, and that medullated fibres conduct more rapidly than non-medullated. In mammals the fastest fibres are those of the motor and some sensory nerves with a velocity of 100 m/sec, but there are others which range down to 0·3 m/sec. A high value for the frog is 40 m/sec, for Crustacea 15 m/sec, and for the squid *Loligo* 22 m/sec. The temperature coefficient for conduction is about 1·7. When the velocity of conduction is measured crudely for a whole nerve the value obtained is obviously that for the fastest fibres present.

The propagation of the nervous impulse is accompanied

by a wave of electrical change, each part in turn becoming negative to the rest. It is by means of this change that the rate of propagation is usually determined. It has been shown with the cathode-ray oscillograph that the wave which passes down such a nerve as the frog's sciatic is complex, and its peculiar shape is due to the fact that the nerve consists of a bundle of fibres which produce different potentials and in which the impulse travels at different rates. The tracing of a wave in a single fibre is difficult, and the properties of single fibres are therefore obtained in part by inference. The largest fibres produce the highest potential and conduct the wave at the highest rate—about 3,000 μV and 42 m/sec in the frog—and other fibres range down to 25 μV and 0·3 m/sec. The conduction rate in medullated fibres varies approximately as the diameter, while in non-medullated fibres it varies as the square root of the diameter. This means that the smaller nerves conduct faster if non-medullated, the larger nerves faster if medullated. The change-over occurs at a diameter of 1 to 2 μ, which is exactly the size at which all mammalian fibres acquire their sheaths. There thus seems to have been selection for maximum conduction velocity. Work on single fibres has shown that after the action potential or spike (so called because of its shape on the tracing) there is a negative after-potential (i.e. one of the same sign as the spike) which may be as high as 25 μV, and then a positive after-potential of not more than 10 μV. The negative after-potential corresponds to the supersensitive period, and the positive to the sub-normal period.

The quicker fibres are also the more easily stimulated, so that a weak shock given to the whole nerve produces a wave from which the slowly moving low potentials are missing. The threshold for a fibre varies from moment to moment, and the size of stimulus which excites in 50 per cent. of cases is taken as the official value. The induction shock given to a nerve may last for 0·04 msec, but response does not begin for up to 0·4 msec. This is not true latency, for if during this interval another shock of opposite sign is put in, the nerve does not respond, which means that the first shock cannot have got through to the essential part of the nerve. If there is a period of true latency, that is a period during which the stimulus has been fully received but response has not begun, it is certainly less than 0·1 msec.

The electrical wave travels in both directions from the point of stimulation, and there is physiological evidence that this can be the case with ordinary stimulation during life: normally, however, nerve-fibres are stimulated only at one end, so that they never get a chance to conduct in more than one direction; fibres are either sensory or motor. When a nerve is kept excited by continuous stimulation, as by pressure on the skin or light on the eye, it is found that a succession of separate waves is passing along it. The individual impulses are all of the same size, but the more powerful the stimulus the more frequent they are. The upper limit to the number which can pass in a second is determined by the refractory period. Experimentally, rates as high as 450 or more per sec have been obtained, but the rates in life are normally lower, anything between 5 and 50 per sec being a fair value for both sensory and motor nerve.

If a stretch of nerve be narcotized, the action potential is lowered as it passes along this, but when it emerges into the unharmed part of the fibres it rises to its normal value again. This implies that the energy for the nerve current is provided by the nerve itself. This agrees with what little is known of the chemistry and heat production. The general relations of nerve to oxygen are similar to those of muscle. Oxygen is absorbed, carbon dioxide is liberated, and the process is more rapid when the nerve is stimulated. In the absence of oxygen lactic acid accumulates, but when oxygen is admitted it is removed with increased usage of the gas. If a nerve be deprived of oxygen for long, it loses its irritability, and the loss is more rapid if the nerve be repeatedly stimulated. Readmission of oxygen restores the sensitivity of the nerve. Stimulated nerve also produces ammonia and inorganic phosphate.

In oxygen, frog's nerve at rest gives off 7×10^{-5} cal/gm/sec, and about one-quarter of this amount in nitrogen. When an action current passes along a nerve the heat production rises above normal in three phases. There is an initial heat of about 5×10^{-6} cal/gm/sec followed by a short rapid-recovery heat of about the same size, and a delayed-recovery heat lasting for up to an hour and about thirty times as large as the initial heat. The delayed heat is associated with the after-potentials.

The general phenomena of nervous conduction appear to be very similar in vertebrate nerves and in the giant fibres which mediate the quick responses of annelids, arthropods, and cephalopods. There are some differences, for example in the giant fibres of the earthworm there is facilitation of conduction, successive impulses up to the fifth increasing in velocity. Little is known of the smaller invertebrate fibres.

It is now possible to explain much of what is known of the nervous impulse in electrical and chemical terms. The surface of the axon at rest is polarized, with a layer of positive ions on the outer surface and one of negative ions inside. This state is brought about partly by the differential permeability of the membrane, which lets potassium and chloride ions through fairly readily but opposes the passage of sodium ions, and also by some metabolic mechanism, called the sodium pump, which actively extrudes sodium, so that the final result is that the concentration of sodium in the external fluid is from three to ten times as great as within the fibre, and that of potassium from twenty to sixty times as great within the fibre as outside. The absolute concentration of sodium inside is greater than that of potassium outside. As a result of the polarization there is a difference of potential across the membrane, the outside being about 60 to 80 mV positive to the inside.

The passage of the nervous impulse appears as a wave of depolarization, which can be accounted for in terms of changes in permeability. On stimulation the nerve becomes locally permeable to sodium, so that, under the concentration gradient, there is an inrush of sodium ions to the extent of 3×10^{-12} mol. cm^{-2} for one impulse. Calculations show that this cannot be accounted for merely by cessation of the sodium pump. The effect of this movement of ions is that there is a local current, which is enough to affect and depolarize adjacent regions of the nerve, and so the impulse is propagated. This can happen only if the inward movement of sodium is greater than the outward movement of potassium, which must start as soon as the equilibrium is disturbed, so that there is a threshold. The potential difference is abolished and reversed, and generally reaches about -30 to -50 mV, and it is this which appears as the action potential in the usual electrical recording of nervous action. The increase in permeability to sodium is brief, but it is followed by an increased permeability to potassium which lasts longer. During this, potassium ions pass out, and the polarization is restored. The changes are shown diagrammatically in Fig. 33. The interchange of sodium and potassium provides the immediate energy for the impulse, but the ultimate source must be the metabolism of the sodium pump, which slowly restores the ionic distribution to what it was before. The sodium pump seems to depend on the splitting of thiamine, and the recovery of this on glycolysis. The recovery heat is probably enough to account for the metabolism, but no very precise agreement has been obtained.

At high frequencies (above 200 per sec in the frog) the total heat per impulse falls off, which suggests that the metabolism is lagging behind and sodium is accumulating in the axon. In *Sepia* this accumulation has been

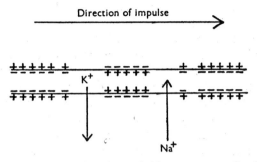

Fig. 33. Diagram illustrating the probable movements of sodium and potassium during a propagated action potential. After Hodgkin.

chemically proved. Decline of heat per impulse occurs in crabs at quite low frequencies, about 4 per sec, an interesting example of the relative emancipation of the vertebrates. The actual ionic changes are very small; the giant axon of the squid *Loligo* loses only one-millionth of its potassium in one impulse, so that restoration could be slow, as the small increase of metabolism on stimulation suggests that it is.

There is no satisfactory explanation of the initial change in permeability on stimulation, but it may be connected with the production of acetylcholine (see section 5.32). The mechanism of the ionic transport is also unknown, but it seems unlikely that such great differences between the permeabilities for ions so similar as those of potassium and sodium could be maintained unless they moved in association with other particles. It is possible that they form different organometallic complexes which are lipoid-soluble, and calcium ions seem also to be involved.

The sodium-potassium theory is supported by many measurements of the concentrations and movements of these ions, and by the effects of an excess of potassium in the medium in preventing the passage of an impulse. It holds for the nerves of vertebrates, cephalopods, and crustaceans, but is not necessarily universal. Insects appear to be different, since some of them have only traces of sodium in their body fluids and many of them have much potassium in their haemolymph. Conduction in vertebrate myelinated fibres appears to be saltatory, sodium entering only at the nodes of Ranvier, and the internodes being depolarized only by local circuit action. Potassium probably goes out all along the nerve. This arrangement is very efficient, since very much less sodium is transported during the passage of an impulse than when it enters along the whole length of the nerve.

It has been suggested that the neurofibrils in the axon are important in the act of conduction, but there is evidence that this is not so. It is possible in the nerves to the tentacle of *Carcinus* to remove the bodies of the nerve-cells, and so to interrupt the fibrils. Impulses are nevertheless still able to pass, which implies that the fibrils are not necessary for activity. This and similar experiments on vertebrates also show that the body of the neurone is not essential to its activity except in so far as it contains the nucleus, so that isolated parts of the axon sooner or later die. The same thing is shown by the activity of the ordinary nerve-muscle preparation, in which no nerve-cell body is present. In fact the flow of current in the nerve-fibre seems comparable to that in a uniform ionic liquid, such as Ringer.

5.32. The Synapse and Nerve-Muscle Junction

Although, as has been said above, the impulse in a nerve-fibre travels in both directions from its point of origin, stimuli in the animal pass only in one direction—from sense organ to effector. This must be because the impulse can pass across the junction from fibre to fibre (or from fibre to effector) in one direction only. The synapse or nerve-muscle junction acts like a valve, so that in the central nervous system it allows an impulse to pass from axon to dendrites, but not in the opposite direction. The synapse therefore appears to be an important part of the system.

Between the application of a stimulus to a nerve and the response of the effector, there is a distinct delay, the latent time. This may be made up of a number of parts: first, there is the latent period of the effector itself. Then there is the time taken for the impulse to be transferred from nerve to effector, which is easily measured by the difference between the latent period for direct stimulation and that when the nerve is stimulated as close to the effector as possible. Thirdly, there is the time taken for the impulse to travel along the nerve, which can be calculated from the known rate of propagation of the wave and the length of nerve. When these three together are subtracted from the total latent time for a given reflex, there is obtained the reduced reflex time. It seems that this can only be the time taken for the impulse to pass the synapses involved in the reflex. When the leg of a frog was stimulated the reduced reflex time for the contraction of the gastro-cnemius of the same side was found to be 8 msec, but for the contraction of the gastrocnemius of the opposite side it was 12 msec. The simple interpretation of this is that the crossed reflex added one more synaptic junction, so that the time for an impulse to pass a synapse is 4 msec, and two synapses are involved in the simple reflex. Of course, two extra synapses might be involved in the crossed reflex, in which case the time for one would be 2 msec, and four would be used in the simple reflex There is reason to think that the usual synaptic time in vertebrate ganglia is about 2 to 4 msec, but that it is only about a quarter of this in the brain.

It is characteristic of the nervous system of the higher animals that there is localization of response, and this is not abolished by the interpolation of association neurones, for these merely allow one effector to be connected to more than one afferent nerve, and vice versa. In normal reflex action, for instance, a muscle may be caused to contract by stimuli received by several different sensory nerves. But when one such nerve is stimulated it will not cause anything like as great a tension in the muscle as direct stimulation of the motor nerve, a phenomenon termed fractionation. The interpretation of this is that the afferent nerve which has been stimulated is connected with only a limited number of the fibres which make up the muscle. When two afferent nerves are stimulated together the tension developed is usually less than the sum of the tensions got by stimulating the two nerves separately. This phenomenon, known as occlusion, suggests that the group of muscle-fibres to which the first nerve is connected to some extent overlaps that connected with the second. In other words, one effector unit (here a muscle-fibre) is connected, through the association neurones, to two nerve-cells.

The account of reflex action contained in the last paragraph does not seem to agree with what can be observed of the histological structure of the central nervous system. The cells have so many processes, and so many connexions with other cells, that one would expect that an impulse entering at a point could spread to every cell in the central nervous system and so to every motor neurone. This condition, although never normal, is observed in animals poisoned with strychnine, for in this state a touch on the skin causes vigorous contraction of every muscle in the body. In the normal animal there must be some mechanism which prevents this and maintains localization, and it is probably to be found in the varying resistances of the synapses; probably the impulse travels only along a few lines where the synaptic resistance is low. Increase in strength of the stimulus will cause the impulse to travel along more pathways and across other synapses, but it is only under the influence of strychnine that all synaptic resistances are broken down so that response is general and uncoordinated.

Although the frequent passage of impulses along a path leads to fatigue, a less frequent use of the pathway makes it easier for subsequent impulses to travel along it, so that a response may now be elicited by a smaller stimulus than formerly. This is known as facilitation, and has the important effect that a strong stimulus, which often affects the sense organs as would a volley of stimuli, may travel farther, and cause a more vigorous reaction, than a weak one, because a number of impulses is sent along the nerve, and each of them weakens the synaptic resistance and aids the passage of its successor.

A third characteristic of the synapse in addition to facilitation and resistance is its ability to block other synapses, the phenomenon known as inhibition. If two stimuli, which by themselves would produce two different reflex actions, are applied simultaneously, in general the response for only one of them is obtained. The passage of the one impulse increases the block on nearby synapses, so that the pathway for the second impulse is closed.

Both histologically and in its ease of fatigue and valve-like action the synapse resembles the nerve-muscle junction. The two are physiologically very similar, and in both the nervous impulse is transmitted by the liberation of a chemical substance.

A heart can be kept going for a long time with an artificial fluid circulating through it, and it is found that if such a perfused heart be depressed by stimulation of the vagus, and the perfusion liquid be passed through a second heart, the latter also is slowed. The obvious interpretation of this is that the vagus, in acting on the heart-muscle, liberates some substance into it. This substance has been identified as acetylcholine,

$$(CH_3)_3N(OH)CH_2CH_2OOCCH_3,$$

and there is abundant evidence that in vertebrates the voluntary nerves and the parasympathetic system act on their effectors by liberation of this base. Such nerves are said to be cholinergic. Most tissues contain an esterase which rapidly destroys acetylcholine, so that it does not accumulate. Stimulation of sympathetic nerves produces a substance called sympathin, which acts in the same way. It is similar in most of its properties to adrenaline (p. 235), but is not identical with this. In the cat it appears to be the closely related substance noradrenaline. Nerves of this class are called adrenergic. The distribution of the two classes of nerve is shown in Fig. 34. The nerves which control the chromatophores of fishes are said to produce unidentified substances which are fat-soluble and slowly diffuse through the tissues to affect the colour cells. They have been called lipohumours to distinguish them from the water-soluble hydrohumours which include the hormones of the ductless glands and both sympathin and acetylcholine. All these substances formed by the nerves as part of their ordinary function are called neurohumours.

It seems that a muscle that is supplied by a cholinergic nerve is continually bombarded by minute quantities of acetylcholine, which are released spontaneously and at random by the nerve-ending. These quanta of acetylcholine are nearly constant in size, consisting of some thousands of molecules, and each causes a minute change of potential in the surface of the muscle. This does not spread, presumably because it is below the threshold necessary to propagate the change in permeability (see section 5.31; the spread of excitation over the surface of muscle is, like that in nerve, by entry of sodium ions and loss of potassium). When a normal motor impulse reaches

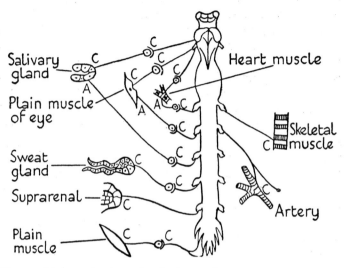

Fig. 34. Diagram showing points in the vertebrate nervous system where there is evidence of cholinergic transmission (C) and adrenergic transmission (A). On the left, sympathetic and parasympathetic fibres and their ganglia; on the right a motor fibre and a sensory fibre with a peripheral axon branch. Slightly modified from Dale.

the end of the axon some hundreds of quanta of acetylcholine are liberated, the end-plate potential rises above the threshold, and the muscle-fibre contracts over its whole length. Facilitation and summation of stimuli are due to a build-up of the necessary size of end-plate potential by the accumulation of acetylcholine. Fatigue could be due to a temporary exhaustion of the substances from which acetylcholine is formed. The spread of a wave of depolarization over the surface has been found in all vertebrate muscles that have been thoroughly investigated. In rhythmically contracting muscles, such as those of the heart and gut, it occurs spontaneously without nervous stimulation. Direct application of acetylcholine to a muscle causes depolarization, and the region of the end-plate is one thousand times as sensitive as the general surface.

There can be little doubt that the nerves of invertebrates act in the same sort of way, but most of the investigations have been disappointing. Acetylcholine is widespread, but it has been shown to be the effective neuro-humour only in the motor nerves of leeches (and possibly some other annelids), and of holothurians, and probably in lamellibranchs. Adrenergic nerves are possibly present in leeches and molluscs, and other transmitter substances possibly exist, such as 5-hydroxytryptamine in molluscs and 5-6-dihydroxytryptamine in crabs.

Many invertebrates have different systems of innervation from the vertebrates, and these differences appear to be connected with their physiology. The limb muscles of decapod Crustacea have three types of motor nerve. One appears to act in much the same way as vertebrate nerves, giving a large end-plate potential and propagated depolarization and contraction, while the second gives a small end-plate potential which causes only local contraction of the muscle-fibre, which may, however, be enough for slow movement and accounts for much of the normal functioning of the limbs. These small end-plate potentials may, on repeated stimulation of the nerve, build up to a threshold and give a propagated contraction. The third type of nerve is inhibitory, and acts to prevent response to the other two. Schema 6 shows these actions in diagrammatic form, and compares them with the vertebrate system. The action of the slow crustacean system is very similar to that of the vertebrate when drugged with curare. It is tempting to suppose that the three types of crustacean nerve act by liberating three different chemical substances, but there is no evidence for this.

'Fast' and 'slow' motor fibres which act in a similar sort of way are found in annelids, molluscs, and insects. The inhibitory nerves of the byssus-retractor of *Mytilus* (section 4.34) probably act by the liberation of a neuro-humour. The leg muscles of locusts have one set of axons which branch to give multiple innervation of every fibre. A single impulse produces depolarization at every point of innervation and a twitch follows. Repeated impulses give tetanus. This system is used in hopping and jumping. Another nerve, which supplies only 30 per cent. of the muscle-fibres, and gives ordinary end-plate potentials and a long lasting depolarization of low value, is used in walk-ing and tonic contraction. A third small nerve gives long-lasting hyperpolarizations which perhaps prepare the muscle for the quick contractions.

It is easy to suppose that synaptic transmission is similar to that across the nerve-muscle junction. The relaying of impulses in both sympathetic and parasympathetic ganglia of vertebrates is due to the liberation of acetylcholine, and other ganglia can produce it. Fatigue might be caused by a local exhaustion of the sources from which the neuro-humour is produced; resistance would be merely a measure of the time for an adequate concentration of the substance to be produced, and summation and facilitation would be caused by successive formation of small amounts of it. The one-way conduction at the synapse would be due to the fact that the active substance could only be produced at the one end of the nerve. There are, however, some facts which are not yet explained, and there may be more than one transmitter.

Invertebrates have synapses of more than one type; those between the cercal sensory fibres of the cockroach and the ascending giant fibres probably act by the liberation

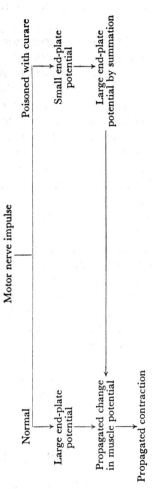

SCHEMA 6A. Amphibian nerve-muscle system (modified from Katz)

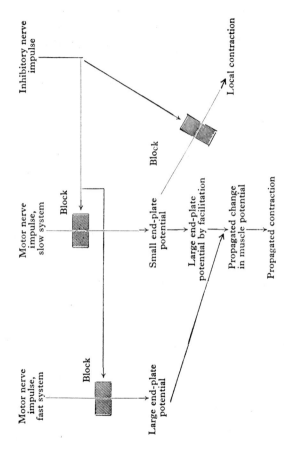

SCHEMA 6в. Crustacean nerve-muscle system (modified from Katz)

of acetylcholine, but the comparable synapses in the crayfish are unaffected by this substance. The synapses between some giant fibres, such as those of the earthworm, transmit in both directions, and impose little or no delay on the passage of an impulse—certainly less than 0·1 msec. They have been called macrosynapses, and are clearly of a different nature from the normal polarized type.

5.33. The Central Nervous System

So far as it has been possible to study them, the internuncial neurones of the central nervous system have been found to behave in a somewhat similar way to ordinary nerve-fibres, but they have their peculiarities. The duration of their positive after-potentials is much longer, and they are able to lengthen or repeat the impulses which they receive. The impulse given to an internuncial neurone by an afferent nerve lasts for not more than 1 msec, but that which is received from the spinal cord by a motor neurone may be as long as 25 msec.

The grey matter of the central nervous system, which consists chiefly of cell bodies and synapses, is somewhat different in its metabolism from nerve-fibres. Its resting oxygen consumption is about five times as great, and it ceases to function normally as soon as the oxygen concentration falls below a certain value. At the same time it needs a continual supply of organic food, while nerve-fibres and muscles continue to live actively in plain Ringer solution, and go on using oxygen. The consumption of oxygen by grey matter begins to fall as soon as it is placed in Ringer, and can only be kept up if glucose or certain other substances be present in the perfusion fluid. In the living animal the case is similar, except that glucose, fructose and mannose (which are readily converted to glucose by the liver) are the only substances effective. These results imply that the central nervous system requires more energy than it can get by anaerobic respiration, and that it carries no reserves of substrate. We do not know to what part of the nerve-cell this chiefly applies, but it is possible, in view of their great importance, that it is the synapses.

There is no reason to think that the mechanism of nervous action in the central nervous system is different in principle from that in nerves, but direct evidence is scanty. The rate of production of acetylcholine in some parts appears to be two to three times as great, which would agree with the large number of synapses that are present, but in others, such as the cerebellum, cholinesterase cannot be detected, so that acetylcholine is probably absent from them.

The central nervous system is probably important as a co-ordinating and dominating mechanism in all animals that possess it, and in many there is some degree of concentration of the central tissue into a brain. Removal of the cerebral ganglia from turbellarians interferes with their locomotion and other activities, and the effect is greater in polyclads than in triclads. Earthworms, with their receptors scattered over the surface of the body, suffer relatively little from the removal of the supraoesophageal ganglia; they can crawl normally, eat, and burrow slowly. *Nereis*, on the other hand, which has its chemoreceptors effectively confined to the palps and tentacles and has eyes instead of scattered photoreceptors, is strongly affected by the removal; it is over-active and neither feeds nor burrows. More complex animals show an increasing degree of dependence on the brain, but even many insects, with their high degree of cephalization, can carry out activities such as copulation when headless. This is perhaps connected with the presence of chemoreceptors on the legs.

5.34. The Nerve Net

The bare nature of a nerve net is adequately described by its name; it is a nervous system in which one cell connects with many others, so that localization seems impossible. It is the only type found in the coelenterates, is conspicuous, though not the dominant system of control, in the echinoderms, and is found in some other places such as the small intestine of vertebrates and on the foot and labial palps of mussels. The central nervous system of vertebrates is a network of nerve-cells, but differs from the others in that it consists almost entirely of association neurones which have no direct connexion with any effector or sense organ. The cells of the nerve net in the usual sense of the word supply both effectors and receptors, so that there are no motor or sensory nerves and no necessary similarity to the central nervous system. In coelenterates no central nervous system is present at all.

Most of the more recent work has been done on sea-anemones, and it is to these that the following account chiefly applies, although Scyphomedusae are basically similar. The best histological work indicates that there is no direct connexion between two nerve-cells, so that the junction is a synapse just as it is in vertebrates. This means that there is no need to expect the behaviour of the net to be greatly different from that of an ordinary nervous system, and this is in fact the case. The nervous impulse travels with a finite velocity, but one which is much less than that for vertebrate nerve; for the general nerve net of *Calliactis* it is from 0·1 to 0·2 m/sec as compared with a minimum of 0·3 in the frog. But the values for the frog are those for the velocity in a single nerve-fibre, and, as has been pointed out above, a finite time appears to be taken for an impulse to pass each synapse. The nerve net contains very many synapses, and it is to be expected that the velocity of conduction in it would be slow. In some parts of the sea-anemone, such as the mesenteries, where there are specialized conducting tracts, it is over 1 m/sec. In *Calliactis* the refractory period is from 40 to 60 msec and the chronaxie from 2 to 4 msec.

In most cases the conduction is diffuse, with a complete absence of polarity. A stimulus applied at one point spreads equally in all directions, and reaches any other given point in the animal by the shortest possible path. Considerable cuts may be made in the tissue, and provided the nerve net still has any continuity the stimulus can reach any part of the body. A jellyfish may be cut into a spiral strip, and the nervous impulse will travel right along it. The impulse apparently behaves like an electric current in a network, a result which is to be expected from the structure of the nerve net. There is no distinction of motor and sensory nerves, and stimuli can be transmitted in both directions across the nerve-cell junctions; the latter are therefore slightly different physiologically from the synapses of higher animals. In some places, for example on the tentacles of anemones, there is a certain amount of polarity, which appears to be of two sorts. Centripetally, that is from the tentacle into the mesentery, conduction is always much easier than anywhere else, which suggests that there is some anatomical peculiarity of the cells allowing this. Centrifugally, that is from mesentery to tentacle, the polarity is physiological; when repeated stimuli are given facilitation occurs much more readily in this direction than in any other. This presumably means that facilitation is easier in one direction across a nerve-junction than in the other—perhaps a foreshadowing of the coelomate synapse, which conducts in one way only.

In two important points the nerve net appears to be greatly different from a localized nervous system, but they can be satisfactorily explained in terms of the properties of all nervous tissue. As an impulse spreads out from its point of origin its response becomes weaker and weaker, so that there appears to be conduction with a decrement, which is quite unknown in ordinary nerve-fibres. Secondly, there is graded response; a light touch on a tentacle of *Hydra* will cause that tentacle alone to contract, a stronger will cause other tentacles to do so, and a very strong one will cause the whole animal to respond. These two phenomena are basically the same, and both can be explained in terms of facilitation. The usual stimulus, whether mechanical or not, is really compound, and consists of a succession of impulses presumably relayed to the nervous system by the sense organs. A weak stimulus means a low frequency of impulses, a stronger one a higher frequency. The greater the frequency, up to a limit set by the refractory period, the easier will be facilitation. In most cases in anemones the important junction where facilitation takes place is that between nerve and muscle, but in some that between nerve-cells is involved. In both types a stronger stimulus activates more muscles or travels farther than a weak because it in reality consists of a more rapid succession of unitary impulses. The nature of facilitation is unknown, but its effect persists much longer at lower temperatures—three times as long for a fall of 10° C. This would be compatible with the suggestion made above that facilitation consists in the liberation of a chemical substance: the rate of destruction of this would naturally be lowered by a fall in temperature.

The more active movements of the arms and tube-feet of starfish are controlled through tracts of nerve-fibres which behave much like those of vertebrates, but the local responses of the pedicellariae and spines show decremental conduction and facilitation like those of the anemones, and are probably controlled by the nerve net of the dorsal integument. It is probable also that strong stimuli may affect the tube-feet through the net.

5.4. Mechanical Co-ordination

The co-ordination of the tube-feet of the starfish is helped also by a purely mechanical principle, for if an arm is merely sewn on to a disk its tube-feet point in the proper direction. This mechanical co-ordination is of great importance in many segmented animals. The ordinary locomotion of the earthworm is effected by alternate contraction of the circular and longitudinal muscles so that the body is alternately extended and contracted. The segments contract successively from the front backwards, and the resulting wave, assisted by a differential coefficient of friction in the two directions along the body, causes the body to move forward. If all the tissue but the nerve-cord be removed from one segment, locomotion can still continue, and the same is true if up to six adjacent segments are similarly treated. But if the nerve-cord be left as the sole connexion for a greater length than this, the part behind the operation becomes inactive. The nervous system alone is not adequate to co-ordinate movement. The explanation lies in the fact that contraction of one segment causes a mechanical stretching of the next. This stimulates proprioceptors in the muscles of that segment, which send an impulse via the central nervous system back to the muscles to cause them to contract. The process is then repeated for the next segment. The central nervous system is thus necessary but by itself inadequate for co-ordination.

A similar explanation holds for the swimming of *Nereis* and of the eel and other fishes, as well as for the walking of Amphibia and probably of the dog. In all these cases the brain acts as an inhibitor of a locomotory rhythm which would otherwise continue unchecked. A *Nereis* without a head swims continuously because there is nothing to stop the rhythm, and if a decerebrate dog be suspended with its legs off the ground, the weight of its legs stretches the muscles and so causes the animal to perform running movements.

5.5. Sense Organs

It is a truism that an animal cannot respond to a stimulus unless the latter is first picked up by a receptor or, in more general language, a sense organ. On the subject of sensation, physiology becomes even more intimately connected with psychology than it does on behaviour, for strictly speaking all sensation is subjective. Nevertheless, something is known about the means by which an event outside the animal becomes the starting-point for an event inside it, and it is with this that the present section is concerned.

The traditional statement that there are five senses is inadequate biologically for two reasons: first, even in man there are certainly more—the temperature sense is an obvious one left out of the usual list; secondly, and more important, the list is compiled not from observed reactions, but from subjective feelings which are not applicable to animals other than man. An amoeba reacts to light, but it would be over-bold to conclude that it sees or has the sensation of sight. The rational way of dealing with sense organs is to classify them according to the type of stimulus to which they normally or chiefly react. It has been pointed out above (p. 241) that an isolated nerve can be stimulated in a number of ways, and the same applies to sense organs, the essential parts of which are in all higher animals made of specialized nervous tissue. But in spite of this, sense organs are generally specialized so that they react particularly well to one type of stimulus, which is said to be adequate for them, and they may be so shielded that other sorts do not normally reach them. For instance, the nerve-endings of the ear are so situated in the interior of the skull that only influences of vibration in a material substance and of acceleration can be transmitted to them. Some fishes with electric organs even have receptors specialized for picking up electric currents.

In spite of all this it is difficult to get away from the subjective aspect of sensation, for it is found that the same stimulus, when received in man by different sense organs, produces different sensations. A striking example of this is given by a tuning-fork or piano wire of low frequency. The sensation it gives through the ear is that of a note appropriate to its rate of vibration, but if it be touched only a shaking feeling is obtained. The converse of this is also generally true, that however a sense organ is stimulated the same sensation is obtained, a generalization first made by Johannes Müller in 1824. This is easily demonstrated by the experiment described on p. 241 in which pressure on the eyeball causes the sensation of light. The simple explanation of this is that pressure on the retina is interpreted as a source of light projected to a point such that it would give an image at the place stimulated. In other words sensation is a central phenomenon, and all impulses received by a particular set of cells in the brain are interpreted in the same general way. Normally such cells receive impulses only from the fibres of their proper sense organs, but direct electrical stimulation, for example of the part of the human cortex concerned with vision, shows that it is the brain-cells, not the afferent fibres, which determine the sensation. There is, however, no theoretical reason why sensations should not be the result of the pattern of impulses received, and there is evidence that the senses of touch and temperature may be mediated in this way. In reality the independence of stimulus and sensation provides further justification for discarding the traditional list of senses in dealing with animals; we do not know what sensations an animal feels, but we can find out to what stimuli it reacts.

It is often obvious without much experiment that an animal reacts to a stimulus, which must therefore have been picked up by a sense organ; when a paramecium meets some strange chemical in water and gives the avoiding reaction (p. 310) or when a dog lifts its leg and scratches its side where it is violently rubbed, there is clearly response. On the other hand, in those cases where a stimulus causes no sensible reaction, it cannot be assumed that the animal is incapable of reacting to it or that there is no change in the nervous system. As long ago as 1749 attempts were made to use the method of the conditioned reflex (p. 326) to find out if fish can hear, but it was only after Pavlov had rationalized the study of this type of behaviour that the method was widely used. It is obvious that a normally neutral or ineffective stimulus could not take the place of an effective one in eliciting a response unless the neutral stimulus were first received by some sense organ. By this means it has been found that vertebrates can pick up many stimuli which are normally without apparent effect on them, but unfortunately the method has been little used with other animals. This procedure also enables one to test the power of an animal to discriminate between two similar stimuli. A dog, for instance, is trained to salivate to the sound of a tuning-fork or the sight of a circle, and is then tested with a fork of different frequency or with an ellipse.

More recently, precise information on the effect of stimuli on sense organs has been obtained by electrical recording, particularly with the cathode-ray oscillograph, and the action-currents in single nerve-fibres have been observed. There are no appreciable differences between the potentials produced in the same fibre by different types of stimulus, so that the central nature of sensation is confirmed.

Most sense organs respond over a fairly wide range of

stimuli and discriminate to some extent between different intensities. An increase in the strength of the stimulus has two effects: it increases the number of impulses that are transmitted along a fibre in unit time, and (if it is applied to the whole sense organ) it raises the number of fibres along which impulses pass. Both increase the rate of arrival of impulses at the central nervous system. It has been stated that the smallest perceptible increment of stimulus is, for a given sense organ, a constant fraction of the total intensity, a generalization which is known as Weber's Law. It would be safer to say merely that the larger the total stimulus, the greater must be any increase in it for it to be appreciated.

Many sense organs are continually exposed to stimulation and so send messages to the central nervous system quite apart from particular reflexes which they initiate; they are called stimulatory organs. Those which are most important in this respect are the proprioceptors, all statocysts (including the vertebrate labyrinth), the eyes of molluscs, arthropods, and vertebrates, and the halteres of Diptera. Destruction of any of these, or section of their nerves, causes loss of muscle tone, although there may be recovery after a time, probably because the stimulatory organs which are left intact become compensated for the loss of the others. Without some stimulatory organs, muscles appear to be unable to function properly.

5.51. Proprioceptors

In the muscles and tendons, and in the connective and skeletal tissues, are a number of sense organs which give rise to no well-defined sensation, but which, notwithstanding this, are of great importance. They are described histologically as muscle-spindles (p. 181), Pacinian corpuscles, and so on, and the exact distribution of function between them is obscure. Collectively they are called proprioceptors, since they are concerned with stimuli which originate within the animal's own body, and they co-operate in the co-ordination of the position of the limbs. The sense with which they are concerned is called kinaesthetic. In man they permit the voluntary placing of a hand or foot in any desired position. It is possible with the eyes shut to touch almost any part of the body with fair accuracy; the ability to do this has presumably been acquired partly by practice, with unconscious memory of the exact tensions and movements required to place the finger in the right spot, but it is also possible to make the two index fingers meet, or nearly so, at any point out of sight behind the head that can be reached, even though the experiment has never been done before, so that some complicated unconscious calculations in solid geometry must occur also. The proprioceptors are concerned with recording these tensions and displacements of the muscles. The same mechanism is used to a much higher degree in all cases of manipulative skill where the movement is one which has been learnt but which is now carried out unconsciously. Examples are found in piano-playing and skating. The statement, surprising or incredible to a beginner, that one should be able to drive a golf-ball blindfold, is correct because the movements of the body and limbs should be the same on every occasion, and with adequate training of proprioceptors this can be attained. From this point of view success at musical performance or games-playing or typewriting depends on a good proprioceptive mechanism. In learning all these things the eyes are used, but unless they can very early be put in a subordinate position progress is impossible.

In the appreciation of limb movement by the proprioceptors two things are important, the angular displacement and the angular velocity; the smaller the first, the greater must be the second for the movement to be felt.

If the joints of the arm be considered in order from the shoulder down to the finger-tips, it is found that the sensitivity gradually decreases. This is of adaptive value in that a small angular displacement of a proximal joint of a limb means a big spatial movement of the distal parts.

In addition to making it possible for acts which were once voluntary to be carried out unconsciously, the proprioceptors assist in many reflexes which have never been consciously learnt. The most important of these are those by which the erect posture is maintained. The human body is a very unstable structure, and it is only by continual adjustments of the muscles of the legs and trunk that man can stand upright. The eyes and ears help in this, but the proprioceptors are also important, particularly those which record the pressure on the soles of the feet. The ability to balance the body when one is skating or crossing a stream in the Lake District is acquired by modifying the normal reflexes through practice.

One particularly important action of the proprioceptors is in the maintenance of the stretch reflex. A muscle responds to passive stretching by an increase in its tone, which obviously counteracts the effect of the stretching. To a great extent this will account for the maintenance of posture. If the body begins to fall to the right, the muscles on the left will be stretched; their kinaesthetic end-organs will be stimulated so that contraction will occur and the body will be pulled back to its former position. The full explanation of the maintenance of posture, however, is much more complicated than this, other more intricate reflexes being involved. Proprioceptors similarly allow the co-ordination necessary for walking in toads and mammals, and presumably for locomotion in all vertebrates.

Proprioceptive sense organs have been studied little outside the vertebrates, but it seems likely that active muscular movement would be impossible without stretch-receptors of some sort. They have been found in the muscles of earthworms, of Crustacea, and of many orders of insects. There are tension receptors on the maxillary palp and legs of the cockroach and the halteres of Diptera contain proprioceptors without which flight is impossible.

There are other receptors which, by the derivation of the word, are proprioceptors, but which are not usually called by that name. In the brain of mammals are cells which respond to changes in the acidity or osmotic pressure of the blood that supplies them. Injection of hypertonic salt solution into the internal carotid, for example, inhibits diuresis because the posterior pituitary is stimulated to produce less anti-diuretic hormone by such cells. Comparable cells in the pedal ganglion of slugs increase their spontaneous activity with dilution of the medium bathing them, which agrees with the increased activity of the animals in damp conditions.

5.52. Tactile Organs

The term 'mechanoreceptor' is now commonly used to indicate a sense organ that responds preferentially to mechanical stimuli such as touch, tension, pressure, acceleration, and sound. The human senses concerned have neither unity nor similarity, and as the sense organs are of many different morphological and histological types, the word seems to be of little value.

Many different sensory end-organs have been described in skin, but it now appears that most of these are artefacts. Three types can be made out with certainty. An arborization of fine, naked, axoplasmic filaments, less than one micron in diameter and probably ending freely, is found in all types of skin, both in the dermis and the epidermis. In hairy skin there are also special naked axoplasmic filaments surrounding the follicles, and these appear in an outer and an inner series. In glabrous skin and mucous membranes there are special capsules of cells containing arborizations of naked nerve-endings. Since what are usually considered as the four primary skin-sensations of touch, heat, cold, and pain can be appreciated by glabrous skin such as that of the sexual parts as well as by the general hairy skin of the body, no allocation of these sensations to particular nerve-endings is possible. Shaving reduces, but does not abolish, sensitivity to touch, and it is likely that hairs act mechanically as levers in magnifying the deformation of the sense organ caused by a light touch.

The sensitivity of the skin may be investigated by exploring the surface with glass fibres of varying thickness. Each fibre bends at a particular pressure, which can be observed, and so can be made to press on the skin with its own constant pressure. By this means it has been shown that the sensitivity of the tongue and nose is twenty-four times that of the loins, and other parts of the body come between these extremes. Separate stimuli up to as many as 600 per sec can be perceived as discrete.

In insects also, hair-like projections are important in the tactile sense. All over the body are fine hollow outgrowths of chitin, with a nerve-ending at the base of each of them. There are several different types, and some are certainly connected with other senses.

Subjectively, man can distinguish pain from touch, though from the point of view of the stimulus, pain, as caused for instance by pressure from the point of a pin, is merely an increased touch. But pain can also be provoked by excessive stimulation of other sorts, high temperature for example, and, quite apart from the subjective side, it can be shown that different sense organs from those of touch are being used. Some regions of the body, such as the cornea, and internal organs like the intestine, are deficient in ordinary touch sense, but are very sensitive to deformation—the slightest depression of the cornea causes pain. In the condition of analgesia which occurs in certain diseases the sense of pain is abolished but not that of touch.

The impulses that cause pain seem to be carried in special fibres. First pain, such as that caused by a pin-prick, follows the passage of impulses at 15 to 20 m/sec, along large myelinated fibres, and second or lasting pain, such as occurs after burning, follows slow impulses, travelling at less than 2 m/sec in the smallest fibres of all. It has been claimed that the first effect of a pain-stimulus on the skin is to cause the formation of histamine, and that this then acts on the nerve-endings.

The physical difference between a pressure on an end-organ which causes pain and one which merely causes a feeling of touch is quite unknown, so that the distinction remains a subjective one which cannot be applied to animals other than man. Probably all animals are sensitive to touch, and there is some evidence that some of them react violently to certain forms of it; this probably corresponds to the human pain sensation, for pain has no conceivable biological value unless it be the source of protective reactions. Tree-living caterpillars are continually being touched by the leaves and shaken by the wind, and give no apparent reaction, but quite a light touch of an unusual sort will cause them to drop down on their silken threads. The ordinary movements of the earthworm are controlled by the main part of the nerve-cord, but the convulsive movements which it makes when dropped into alcohol, stepped on, or otherwise strongly stimulated, are organized by the giant fibres. It is therefore likely that the two types of movement are started by different sorts of stimulus received by different types of sense organ. If violent or protective reactions to touch are said to be started by pain receptors, one must be careful to avoid any dogmatic assumptions of pain as a conscious state, for there can be no certainty of the existence of this in any animal other than man.

5.53. Temperature Organs

Some physiologists now claim that some at least of the sense organs that occur in skin respond to all three of the stimuli of touch, cold, and heat. If this is true, it is an exception to the general rule that sensation is determined centrally (p. 265); it is conceivable that different types of stimulus might cause different temporal patterns of nervous impulses but there is no evidence that this occurs. Touch and temperature were perhaps early connected in the vertebrates, for the ampullae of Lorenzini, which are specializations of the lateral line system (p. 290) in the skin of elasmobranchs, alter their frequency on warming or cooling as well as on pressure. In goldfish, too, the lateral line system seems to be sensitive to changes in temperature. This response may, however, be an accidental one, for it seems inevitable that a receptor that works, as does the lateral line system, by maintaining a flow of impulses the rate of which is varied on stimulation, must respond to changes in temperature by altering its activity. It could only not do so if the chemical reactions on which its impulses were based had a temperature coefficient of one. That a connexion between touch and temperature is neither necessary nor universal is shown by the fact that the sea-anemone *Calliactis parasitica* is very sensitive to touch but gives no response at all to temperature.

The fact that, if the right hand be placed in hot water and the left in cold, and then both be put into the same tepid water, the latter feels cold to the right and hot to the left hand, suggests that it is change of temperature that is felt—warmth when the skin is warming up, cold when it is cooling. But after a hot or cold object has been placed against the skin and removed, its appropriate sensation remains so that now cold must be felt when the skin is warming up and vice versa, and it is more likely that the different sensations can be explained in terms of adaptation.

It is obvious that many animals are very sensitive to change of temperature and must therefore have sense organs associated with it. Those of insects are widely distributed, with a high concentration in the antennae. The sense is especially important in many parasites, which find their prey by means of it. The bed-bug *Cimex*, for instance, will orientate to a tube 1° C above the ambient temperature and 1 cm away. Rattlesnakes (Crotalinae) are also sensitive to warmth, and can find their mammalian prey in absolute darkness. The organ is a pit near the eye, and it is sensitive to medium and long infra-red rays from 1·5 to 15μ. It seems to be a true radiation detector, and although the claim that owls can similarly detect mice by their warmth has been disproved, the discovery of this organ in snakes suggests that similar receptors should be sought elsewhere.

5.54. Chemoreceptors

There is no particular reason why the same sense organ should react to all kinds of chemical stimulus, and the fact that different chemicals have different effects suggests that there is more than one sort of chemoreceptor, or organ sensitive to chemicals; in fact there are at least six in vertebrates. For animals living in water the only prerequisite for a substance to be able to stimulate in this way is that it must be soluble. For land animals also it must be soluble, but if it be merely that, it cannot be appreciated unless it has been dissolved in the saliva or in mucus on the skin. If, however, it be volatile as well, it may be appreciated from a distance. This leads to the existence in man of the two senses of smell and taste, of which the former may be very important since it is a projected sense by which the animal can react to distant parts of its environment.

5.541. Taste. The taste organs in man are the taste buds which are found in the stratified epithelium of the tongue and, to a lesser extent, in other parts of the buccal cavity. They are lemon-shaped bodies, made up of a few cells with nerve-endings between them. The sensory nerves are the lingual branch of the fifth cranial nerve, the chorda tympani branch of the seventh, and the ninth and tenth. Similar taste buds are found in the oral cavity of other vertebrates, and in fish some are found in other parts of the body as well. The catfish *Ameiurus* and a few others have them all over the body, and will turn and snap at meat or meat-juice placed in contact with the side of the animal.

Four primary taste sensations, sweet, sour or acid, bitter, and salt, can certainly be distinguished, and there are possibly two others, alkaline and metallic, as well. Other tastes are made up of mixtures of these, but a good deal of the apparent taste of foods is derived from their smell, as is clear when the effects of catarrh on one's enjoyment of a meal are considered. The simple experiment of holding the nose while eating shows the same thing. For these qualities derived partly from taste but chiefly from smell the name 'flavour' has been suggested. Different end-organs are concerned with the different primary tastes, for the sensitivity of different parts of the tongue varies from one to the other, and there are drugs which suppress one or two of them without affecting the rest.

In some way taste must be connected with chemical constitution: alcohols, sugars (which are polyhydric alcohols), and α-aminoacids are nearly all sweet, and so is the beryllium ion. Bitterness is produced by the ions of ammonium, magnesium, and calcium—it is noteworthy

that these metals belong to the same group as beryllium—
but chiefly by the alkaloids and some other organic substances. All compounds with three nitro-groups are bitter
and so usually are those with two, but one seems to have
no effect on taste. Saltness is characteristic of some anions,
especially those of low molecular weight: chloride is more
potent than bromide, which is more potent than iodide.
Sulphate and nitrate are also salty. Sourness seems to be
exclusively connected with hydrion but its intensity is not
proportional to this. The metallic and alkaline tastes, if
they exist, are correlated with cations of heavy metals and
with hydroxyl respectively. It has been pointed out that
the four tastes are so distinct that it is incorrect to speak
of a single sense of taste. Why any substance should have
a taste at all is unknown. There are a few compounds, such
as dulcamarin, found in bittersweet, which definitely
excite two tastes.

Most animals react by reflexes and taxes (section 6.2) to
chemical stimuli, and any animal which takes food but
rejects other solid particles—a discrimination possible even
to *Amoeba*—may be loosely said to have a sense of taste.
Sea-anemones have a different pattern of chemical sensitivity from man. They respond, both by movements of
the tentacles and discharge of the cnidae, especially to
proteins and their derivatives. Carbohydrates, except possibly glycogen, are ineffective, and so are fats, but some
lipoids that can be extracted from food by alcohol but not
by ether are adequate. The jellyfish *Aurelia* is somewhat
similar, but responds to fats. *Periplaneta* has taste organs
on the labial and maxillary palps, and Hymenoptera
have them on the antennae. Bees have the four tastes, but
the list of sweet things that they can taste is not the same
as that for man. Butterflies and muscids have taste organs
on the tarsi of the legs: the former respond by uncoiling
the proboscis when their legs are brought into contact with

apple-juice, and experiments showed that they could distinguish between sugar, acid, quinine (which is bitter), and salt. Under conditions of starvation one butterfly responded when its legs were stimulated by a solution of sugar only one-two-hundred-and-fiftieth of the strength of the weakest which can just be appreciated by man. Frogs and toads appear to be poor in taste, responding according to some authors only to salt, and to others to salt and acid, but to make up for this they can taste distilled water as, apparently, can some mammals.

5.542. Common Chemical Sense. Cells in the nervous system which respond to changes in osmotic pressure are mentioned on p. 270. It is also possible that nematocysts respond to a lowering of the environmental osmotic pressure. In man, the mucous surfaces which are more or less exposed to the exterior—those of the nasal cavity, mouth, and larynx, the anus, and genital apertures—are sensitive to many chemicals ranging from the spices which cause a hot sensation in the mouth to smokes which cause crying and mustard oil and gas which irritate the skin. No taste is perceived, but the sensation leads to such reflex actions as coughing and sneezing. The sense concerned is called the common chemical sense, and it is active only with relatively high concentrations of substances and leads usually to protective reflexes. The distribution of the sensitive endings is much the same in other land-living vertebrates as in man, but in Amphibia and fishes they are found all over the skin. The endings are derived from the spinal nerves and, in the head, from the facial, and are distinct from those which are sensitive to touch.

5.543. Smell. In mammals the organs concerned with appreciating smells are nerve-cells with their bodies in the epithelium of the upper part of the nasal cavity, and the nerve connected with them is the first cranial. As has been pointed out above, land animals can only smell volatile substances, but mere traces of a compound are enough— mercaptan can be smelt at a concentration of 4×10^{-11} gm/litre. Even so, it is well known that the sense of smell in man is very poor compared with that in dogs and many other animals. The number of molecules which must enter the nose is, however, very large—about 2×10^{11} in the example just given. Most substances (other than gases) of strong odour have large molecules, so that their rate of diffusion is comparatively slow, but, as with taste, no explanation can be given for the possession of a smell by certain compounds and not others. Nothing useful is known about the analysis of smells, although several tentative schemes have been proposed. Electrical analysis of the discharge from the olfactory bulb in the rabbit has shown that the different parts of the nose have different sensitivities to different substances. The receptors in the anterior part respond mainly to water-soluble substances and those at the back to those that are fat-soluble.

The primates and seals have a poorly developed olfactory organ and are termed microsmatic. Most mammals are macrosmatic, and many of them are known to be very sensitive to smells. A few mammals, such as the toothed whales, have no olfactory organ and are termed anosmatic. Many wild-fowlers believe that some birds have a good sense of smell, but all the experimental evidence shows that most have little or none. The kiwi is an exception, and can follow trails like a dog. Reptiles and Amphibia have some sense of smell. Since smell is essentially the detection of air-borne particles, it is misleading to apply the term to aquatic Amphibia and fishes, but many of these use the nasal epithelium for detecting substances in the water.

The sense of smell is very important in insects; male moths find the females by characteristic scents which the latter emit. The sense organs are usually situated in the antennae, but in Orthoptera and butterflies they are present on the palps also, and in some flies on the labella. Bees are able to some extent to distinguish between odours, again by the antennae, and their discrimination is somewhat similar to that of man. *Trichogramma evanescens* is a chalcid parasite (Hymenoptera) which oviposits in the eggs of moths, and it distinguishes by smell between hosts which have been already parasitized and those which have not. It has been shown that there are at least two odours which it recognizes, one left by the feet of the previous chalcid and one arising from inside the parasitized egg. If parasitized eggs are washed, *Trichogramma* will pierce them with its ovipositor but will not lay eggs, so that it must be unable to recognize that the eggs are parasitized until it has pierced the shell. On the other hand, it will not oviposit on eggs which have been merely walked upon unless they have first been washed.

A special chemical sense possessed by many insects, such as Diptera, bees, and beetles, enables them to detect water vapour or apparently gradients of water vapour, in the air, so that they can find water from long distances. The organs used by blowflies are on the antennae, and this is perhaps general. In wireworms the response is more to saturation deficit than to relative humidity, so that the organs are perhaps evaporimeters.

Nothing is known about the way in which the sense of smell is excited. It is perhaps significant that many odoriferous substances have a well-marked Raman spectrum, that is they scatter monochromatic light to give a range of wave-lengths, and that the membranes sensitive to smell often, and perhaps always, contain a yellow pigment.

5.55. Organs of Balance

Many animals possess organs, which may be called generally statocysts, which enable their possessors to maintain a constant or given position with respect to the centre of the earth. The principle involved in all these is simple: a closed or nearly closed space has sensory endings on its inner surface, and contains particles of a higher specific gravity than the medium which surrounds them. Unless these particles are resting in one particular place they stimulate nerve-endings and so start reflexes which cause the animal to turn until the particles fall into their equilibrium position and the sense cells are no longer stimulated. The animal is thus able to orientate itself to the direction of the force of gravity. It is obvious that other forces might be able to move the particles; experimentally, centrifugal force can be substituted for gravity, and any sudden acceleration of the animal's body is sufficient to cause a reaction. In active animals accelerations are important in life and cause various postural and locomotory responses.

In vertebrates, the organ of balance is the pars superior of the labyrinth (or of the 'ear'), consisting of the semicircular canals and the utriculus (Fig. 35). For all these parts there is a bony cavity enclosing a membranous one; the latter contains endolymph, and between the membrane and the walls of the bony labyrinth is perilymph. On the inner surface of the ampulla of each canal is a sensory ending called a crista ampullaris, and the utriculus bears a similar structure called a macula. All these sense organs are supplied by the eighth cranial nerve. The details of their arrangement differ somewhat in the different classes of vertebrates, but their general arrangement, and probably their physiology, are similar.

They enable the animal to react to gravity in such a way as to right itself, or, if this is physically impossible, at least to counteract to some extent the way in which it is held or the inclination of the ground on which it is standing. A frog, for instance, placed facing downwards on a slope, stretches out its forelegs in front of it and raises its head,

thus bringing itself as nearly as possible into the ordinary
position. The traditional case of an animal reacting to

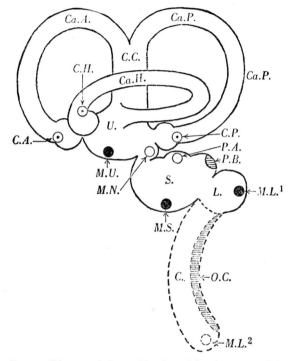

Fig. 35. Diagrammatic combination of the characters of the
membranous labyrinth in all vertebrate classes.

C., cochlea; *C.A.*, crista anterior; *C.H.*, crista horizontalis; *C.P.*, crista
posterior; *C.C.*, crus commune; *Ca. A.*, canalis anterior; *Ca. H.*, canalis
horizontalis; *Ca. P.*, canalis posterior; *L.*, lagena; *M.L.*[1], macula lagenae
in fishes and Amphibia; *M.L.*[2], macula lagenae in reptiles and birds;
M.N., macula neglecta or papilla neglecta; *M.S.*, macula sacculi; *M.U.*,
macula utriculi; *O.C.*, organ of Corti; *P.A.*, papilla amphibiorum; *P.B.*,
papilla basilaris; *S.*, sacculus; *U.*, utriculus. The ductus endolymphaticus
is omitted for the sake of clarity. After Löwenstein.

gravity is the cat, which falls on its feet no matter in what
position it is dropped. Stimulation of its labyrinth, caused
by its being in any but the vertical position in the air,
produces muscular movements which rotate it until its feet

are below and it is in equilibrium. The physical principles on which this is based are simple: first, Newton's Third Law of Motion, that action and reaction are equal and opposite, and secondly that the moment of inertia of a body depends on its radius as well as its mass. Suppose that the cat is held supine and dropped, and that its head inclines slightly to its right. It stretches out its hind legs, draws up its front legs, and twists the front part of its body to the right; by Newton's third law the hind part of the body must also rotate in the opposite direction, but it will not go so far to the left as the front part does to the right, because the hind legs are stretched out and the moment of inertia is therefore high. The cat then draws in its hind legs, stretches out its front ones, and twists to the left; this time, for the same reasons as before, the front part moves less than the hind part, and also moves less than it did at the first turn; the final result of the two twists is that the cat's ventral side has been turned towards the ground.

The function of the canals in appreciating angular acceleration is important in controlling eye-movements, as is shown by an experiment of Ewald. He removed both labyrinths from a dog, and found that it was then unable to catch a bit of meat which was thrown to it, and had some trouble in finding the meat after it landed. Before the operation it would readily catch meat in its mouth.

Consider a man turning his head and his gaze from the straight ahead position to a direction due right. If the movements of the head and eyes are examined carefully it is seen that first the head alone moves, there being a smooth compensatory movement of the eyes to the left which maintains their direction in space unchanged. While the head continues to move, the eyes now perform a jerk to the right to catch up with the head position for an instant, and are then maintained in this new direction of fixation while the head goes on. Thus while the head moves continuously, the eyes perform a movement in space which is a series of jerks to the right with stops, while relative to the head they move slowly to the left and in jerks to the right.

The cupula, which bears the crista, is gelatinous and very slightly springy, and extends across the canal, interrupting the continuity of the fluid. Before the movement of the head, the endolymph in the horizontal canal will be stationary, then when the head movement starts, the angular acceleration of the canal wall will cause the endolymph to lag behind. Since the inertia of the endolymph is small, after a fraction of a second it will assume the same angular movement as the canal wall. During this fraction of a second, while there was a relative movement, the endolymph displaces the cupula, bending it to the left, and stimulating the hairs of the crista. After the relative movement the cupula remains displaced since there is no relative movement of endolymph and canal, so the hairs stay bent. By a mechanism which is not fully understood, this maintained bent position of the hairs of the crista brings about the alternating movement, already described, of the eyes relative to the head, namely rapid jerk to the right and slow drift to the left. This double movement, which is referred to as nystagmus to the right (direction of nystagmus equals direction of rapid movement) can be evoked in fish held stationary, by causing a small displacement of the endolymph in the horizontal canal.

When the head movement ceases, the endolymph continues to move for a very short time, and covers a distance which is just sufficient to restore the cupula to its equilibrium position, and the eyes are no longer stimulated. The springiness of the cupula is so weak that it plays no part in the process just described.

The effect of this nystagmus mechanism, during normal head movements, is to keep the image on the retina stationary for most of the time, and to cause rapid movements of the image during the jerks. There is some evidence that a person is blind or partially blind during these jerky movements. If the reader looks at one of his eyes in a mirror, and then changes over to look at the other, he will not be able to see the eye movement, though he can see it easily if he watches someone else perform the experiment. Further, a steady movement of the image across the retina causes distress, as may be experienced by watching a film taken by an amateur who deliberately waves the camera about. Thus the nystagmus mechanism is useful in eliminating any sensation of motion of the image across the retina.

If a steady rotation of the body and head is maintained for 10–15 sec, then just as before, there is a transient movement of endolymph relative to the canal causing a displacement of the cupula, after which endolymph and canal move together. Now, however, the very slight springiness of the cupula causes it to return to its initial position over a period of the order of 15 sec. At the end of this time the crista is no longer stimulated. If a steady rotation is induced on a turntable, it can be seen that the movements of nystagmus cease, and if the eyes are closed no sensation of rotation remains. If now the rotation ceases, the endolymph by its inertia will maintain its rotation for a fraction of a second, and the cupula will be displaced. Nystagmus will be induced, and there will be a sensation of giddiness. Let us suppose the steady rotation was to the left (anti-clockwise as viewed from above), then when the motion ceases the cupula is displaced to the left; this is the direction in which it would be displaced in a normal rotation of the head to the right. This, as shown above, induces nystagmus to the right, and it is understandable then that this is in fact the nystagmus observed when rotation to the left ceases. The labyrinth is responsible for some other special reflexes, such as the one by which a duck ceases to breathe when it dives. Pointing the bill downwards stimulates the labyrinth so that respiratory movements cease.

Corresponding reactions to both angular and linear accelerations have been shown to occur in all vertebrate classes except reptiles. The resulting muscular movements largely consist in rotations of the eyes, but there are also movements of the head and limbs, the latter, when stimulated by a downward acceleration, sometimes moving in such a way as to prepare for landing.

The distribution of these functions amongst the various parts of the labyrinth is obscure, and not necessarily the same in all the vertebrate classes, but in general the ordinary static reactions to tilting and those to rapid linear acceleration are controlled by the macula utriculi, while the semicircular canals are concerned with angular accelerations. The canals have a much smaller reaction time than the utriculus. In elasmobranchs the sacculus and lagena also respond to tilting. Practically nothing is known as to the way in which the stimulus is actually received, but it is probably due to movement of the endolymph. All these organs are continually sending impulses to the central nervous system, and their rate of discharge is increased or decreased on stimulation. In man in a steady state the eyes seem to be the most important balancing organ, for an aircraft in cloud may be flown tilted, right or left or nose up, without the pilot being aware of it. The disinclination to fly in mist which is shown by many birds suggests that the eyes may be important for them also.

Some of the Protozoa, such as *Paramecium*, react to gravity, and so presumably possess some form of acceleration receptor. Statocysts are common in the coelenterates. In the Arthropoda they are invaginations from the external

surface lined with chitin, and in the Crustacea the particles they contain are grains of sand acquired from outside
at ecdysis. If a moulting prawn is provided only with iron
powder instead of sand it must of necessity use this to fill
its statocyst, and after this has happened it can be forced
to swim on its back by holding a magnet above it. In
determining the movements that result in the characteristic posture, the statocyst organs act in collaboration with
the proprioceptors. The halteres of Diptera, which signal
yawing (that is, rotation round a dorsoventral axis), work
on the principle of the gyroscope, and contain their own
proprioceptors. The beetle *Sisyphus*, which flies with its
hind wings only, uses its middle legs in the same way.

5.56. Sound Receptors

The pars inferior of the labyrinth of vertebrates (Fig.
35), consisting of the sacculus and the lagena and cochlea
derived from it, is concerned with the reception of sound.
In most of the mammals there is a more or less trumpet-
shaped pinna which collects sound waves and concentrates
them to the opening of the external auditory meatus.
Moreover, it can be moved by muscles and so used to
locate approximately the direction from which sound is
coming. In man it is probably functionless. At the inner
end of the external auditory meatus is the tympanum, a
stretched membrane which is set into vibration by the
waves which strike it. Its movements are imparted to a
chain of three ossicles, the malleus, incus, and stapes, which
stretch across the middle ear. The base of the stapes is
sealed by a membrane into an opening, the fenestra ovalis,
in the cochlea. The ossicles are so hinged on one another
that the movements of the tympanum are accurately
transmitted to this membrane, but they are reduced in size
because of the lever-system of the ossicles. Variations in
pressure in the air are therefore transmitted to the cochlea.

The ossicles, under appropriate experimental conditions, can be seen to move, and in rabbits and dogs it has been shown that their movements are to some extent reflexly reduced on receipt of a loud sound, by muscles attached to the malleus and incus. There is thus a certain amount of

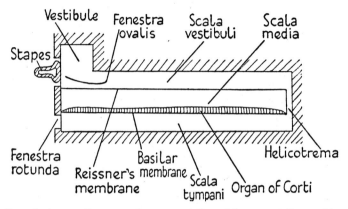

Fig. 36. A very diagrammatic representation of the mammalian cochlea, unwound. Diagonal shading indicates bone. The stapes is in the middle ear. and the fenestra rotunda also looks into this space.

automatic volume-control. The Eustachian canal, which leads from the cavity of the middle ear to the pharynx, prevents excessive differences of pressure on the two sides of the tympanum.

The cochlea (Fig. 36) consists of a tube wound helically round an axis of bone called the modiolus. In this runs the eighth (auditory) nerve, from which branches are given off to the sense cells. The tube of the cochlea is divided longitudinally into three, by two membranes running along its length; apically Reissner's, and basally the basilar. The uppermost subdivision of the tube thus formed is called the scala vestibuli, and the lowest the scala tympani. These two contain perilymph and are in communication at the inner end by a small opening, the helicotrema.

At the other end the scala vestibuli opens into the vestibule, in which the fenestra ovalis is an opening. The scala tympani has an opening, the fenestra rotunda, which is separated only by membrane from the cavity of the middle ear. The third division of the cochlea, between the two membranes, is filled with endolymph and is called the scala media. On the side of the basilar membrane which is bounded by endolymph is a series of hair-like sense cells, derived from the eighth nerve, which collectively make the organ of Corti, the essential organ of hearing. When the base of the stapes is pushed inwards, the resulting increase of pressure moves Reissner's and the basilar membrane downwards, and the membrane of the fenestra rotunda bulges outwards to compensate for this. Vibrations of the ear-drum are thus transmitted to the organ of Corti.

The best-supported explanation of the way in which sounds of different pitch can be distinguished is the resonance theory. It is now almost certain that the organ of Corti, although it appears as a continuous structure, is, in effect, a series of resonators, comparable to the strings of a piano. The resonators are arranged in order, with those for high notes at the basal end. This explains why it is possible for a man to become deaf for a limited region of the sound spectrum. By using a very fine drill to damage the organ of Corti in a guinea-pig it is possible to produce partial deafness for one or two tones only, and so to map out the parts of the cochlea which are concerned with different notes. However, the cells are not very sharply tuned, and a loud note of any one frequency will cause a length of membrane corresponding to about two octaves to vibrate. Electrical recording from a single cell has confirmed that it responds to this range of frequencies.

The ability of the ear to appreciate small sounds depends on their frequency; the human ear is most sensitive to notes of about 2,000 cycles/sec (roughly the third C above middle C—usually the highest but one on a piano). Frequencies from about 40 to 40,000 cycles/sec can be detected, and over the middle part of this range, from 500 to 4,000, people who have not been specially trained can detect differences of three parts per thousand, or about one-twentieth of a semitone. With two notes so close together as this, however, only a person with a musically trained ear can decide which is the higher.

The direction from which a continuous sound comes is determined by the phase difference between the images obtained by the right and left ears, which depends on the different distances which the sound has to travel to reach the two ear-drums. For sounds of high pitch (more than 800 cycles/sec) and therefore of short wave-length, the same phase difference will be given with more than one angle of the incident sound (for a phase difference of $1 + \alpha$ is the same as one of α) so that multiple images will be formed. Hence it is difficult to detect the direction from which a high-pitched note comes, and a very high note, such as the chirp of a cricket, seems to come from every side at once.

In all mammals the general mechanism of hearing is the same. Dogs are most sensitive to rather higher tones than man, and can certainly detect differences of a semitone, and possibly of less, and have a memory for absolute pitch better than that of most men. Aquatic mammals possess various devices suitable to their special environment. Bats are specially sensitive to very high-pitched sounds, such as those that they make themselves. Such sounds, because of their short wave-length, travel very nearly in straight lines, so that their reflection gives an accurate sound-picture of the solid world surrounding the animal. By this echo-sounding bats flying in the dark can avoid even quite small obstacles.

In other vertebrates the ear is more simple: there is no pinna; the external auditory meatus is short in Sauropsida and absent from Ichthyopsida; the middle ear of Amphibia, reptiles, and birds contains only one bone, the columella auris, which corresponds morphologically to the stapes, and in fish there is no middle ear.

Birds have a definite cochlea, not so well developed as that of mammals. It is obvious that their sense of hearing is very good, and this is borne out by experiment. Some cave-living species find their way, like bats, by the echoes from high-pitched notes.

Reptiles have a small cochlea, and lizards seem fairly sensitive to sound. Chelonians are apparently unresponsive, but sounds up to about 300 cycles/sec cause impulses to pass along the auditory nerve; the sensitivity of the ear of the alligator is very similar, and in both, the threshold for stimulation is lowest at about 100 cycles/sec. Snakes have no tympanum and have the columella attached to the quadrate; they cannot hear air-borne sounds, but they can hear those which reach the skull directly from the ground. In Amphibia the cochlea is represented only by the lagena, a small projection on the sacculus. Frogs can be shown to respond to tones of from 50 to 10,000 cycles/sec, and there is some evidence that they can appreciate differences of frequency up to 500 cycles/sec.

Fishes have no cochlea, but the macula of the sacculus is an auditory organ. The hearing of fish has been investigated by the method of the conditioned reflex. Most marine fishes can be taught to respond only to low-frequency tones and many are quite deaf, but some fresh-water fishes are sensitive to frequencies of a few thousands, and can distinguish an interval of less than an octave. This increased sensitivity may be correlated with the presence of Weber's ossicles, extending from the sacculus to the air-bladder. From an evolutionary point of view the lateral-line organs of fishes are undoubtedly connected with the labyrinth. They consist of canals containing fluid into which project hair-like sense cells, and the organ is stimulated by anything which moves the fluid and so bends the cells. There is a constant background of stimulation, and touch and pressure, slow currents of water, and low-frequency vibrations are specially effective in altering the rate at which impulses pass along the nerve. This sensitivity probably enables the fish to avoid rocks and to perceive the movements of other fish. In addition, the fluid is moved when the animal's own muscles are moved, so that the organ can act as a proprioceptor. *Necturus* reacts to low frequencies and streams of water by its lateral line organs, and presumably other aquatic Amphibia would do so also.

Outside the vertebrates, well-developed auditory organs are found only in the insects. Some grasshoppers and crickets (Orthoptera) possess a quite complicated organ in the tibia of each front leg; it consists essentially of a membrane which covers a series of sense cells. Grasshoppers respond to chirps made by other grasshoppers, and they will also respond to similar artificially produced notes of a range of frequency from 430 to more than 90,000 cycles/sec; in general they are more sensitive in the higher ranges. A female cricket finds a male by flying in the direction from which the latter's chirp comes, and no other sense than hearing is necessary so that she will answer a telephone call from him. If one of the female's ears is destroyed her sense of direction is impaired, but she can still find the male. Each organ is directional, and must respond not to pressure, but to either velocity or displacement, both of which are vector quantities. Different sounds are distinguished by variations in the wave-length of a low frequency modulation carried by the high frequency primary sound.

Somewhat similar organs are found in the abdomen of cicadas (Hemiptera), and on the abdomen or thorax of many moths (Lepidoptera), and both of these have been shown to respond to sounds, moths being sensitive up to

80,000 cycles/sec. It is possible that this sensitivity in the supersonic region may warn them of the approach of bats. Some caterpillars of the Lepidoptera respond to sounds, the receptors being the hairs on the anterior part of the body. Structures called chordotonal organs, similar to parts of the ears of grasshoppers but without the tympanum, are found on the halteres of Diptera, on the legs of ants (Hymenoptera), and on the antennae of most insects, but they may be proprioceptors. Bees and gnats can hear, and the ability may be general in the class.

5.57. Light Receptors

The infra-red detectors of snakes have been mentioned in section 5.54 but in general the only part of the electromagnetic spectrum to which animals respond in any special way is a narrow band of about one octave. The wave-length range is from $0.8\,\mu$ in the red to $0.4\,\mu$ in the violet, and since objects which are appreciably smaller than the wave-length of light cannot be seen, these wavelengths to which the eye is sensitive set a limit to the useful magnification of the microscope. A few animals, planarians and *Daphnia* for instance, react to the near ultra-violet, and some bees are insensitive to the red rays of longer wavelength, but broadly speaking all eyes respond to the same spectral region. This narrow single-octave band is that of the peak of the solar radiation curve, showing that eyes are adapted to seeing the wave-lengths which are most intense. It is interesting that X-rays falling on the retina excite it and give man the sensation of light.

Light-sensitive regions of the body are very widespread; even the Protozoa react to light, and in *Euglena* and some other forms there is a definite eye-spot, which is a carotin-containing part of the cell which is specially sensitive. Eye-spots also occur in Metazoa, though here they are simple cellular structures. In *Lumbricus terrestris*, for instance, there are at the base of the epidermis certain light cells, each consisting of a transparent lens-like structure which concentrates light on to a nerve-ending. The sea-urchin *Diadema antillarum* moves its spines when shaded, and shows greatest sensitivity in the blue. Eye-spots and eyes must operate in fundamentally different ways. In an eye-spot no image is formed, so there can be an impression only of more or less light, and the animal cannot perceive form. For perception of form, either a lens, or some alternative device such as the ommatidia of insects, is required to form an image. A physiologist was once invited on to the stage of a music-hall to play noughts and crosses on a blackboard with a man who was apparently thoroughly blindfolded. He behaved as though he could see, and the game was a draw. The scientific view to take of this phenomenon is to admit ignorance of how it was done, but to assume that somewhere a device which formed an image was involved. Thus a hypothesis that the skin of the nose had become sensitized to light would be rejected. A true eye capable of forming images is found only in the arthropods, molluscs, and vertebrates.

A reasonable explanation of stimulation by light is that the absorbed light initiates in the receptor a photochemical reaction which in turn by some means initiates a discharge in the nerve-fibre. In the vertebrate eye, it is claimed that as little as five light quanta may initiate a discharge, and we do not know what chemical reaction it is which can be triggered off by such a small quantity of energy, and yet which gives out the much greater amount of energy necessary to generate an action potential.

In many eye-spots the light-sensitive pigment is carotene, and it is interesting that this is chemically similar to visual purple (p. 302).

5.571. The Vertebrate Eye. The sensitive part of the

vertebrate eye, the retina, is surrounded and nourished by a surprisingly dense layer of blood-vessels, the choroid, outside which is the 'white' or sclera. The transparent cornea protrudes in front, which the reader may feel in his own eye by moving the eye while holding the finger over the closed lid. Behind this is the iris. This contains radial muscle-fibres supplied by sympathetic nerves and

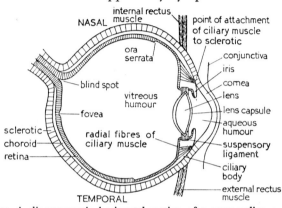

FIG. 37. A diagrammatic horizontal section of a mammalian eye. The thickness of the choroid and retina, and especially of the anterior continuation of the latter over the posterior surface of the ciliary body and iris, is exaggerated.

circular muscle-fibres supplied by the parasympathetic system. Behind the iris, lying in the aqueous humour and supported by the suspensory ligament, is the lens. About two-thirds of the refraction of the light rays is due to the cornea and about one-third to the lens.

Accommodation, i.e. focusing for near objects, is brought about by making the lens thicker and its surfaces more curved (Fig. 37). The ciliary muscle, shown only in section, is a ring running round the circumference of the iris and behind it. Its fibres have their origin on the sclera and their insertion in the ciliary body, and they run radially and towards the back of the eye. When they contract the ciliary body is pulled forwards and towards the centre of the pupil, so that the tension in the suspensory ligament which supports the lens is reduced. The lens now assumes its natural thick shape with highly curved surfaces, the change being probably brought about by the elasticity of the thin capsule that encloses it. Were the lens free, it would have its maximum curvature, and would therefore be suited for the vision of near objects, but in the eye the suspensory ligament is pulling on it all round, so that in the condition of rest it is stretched and is focused for distant objects. In accommodation the lens also moves forward slightly, but this is not important. Fishes and amphibians accommodate by moving the lens; in elasmobranchs the accommodation is for near vision, and the lens is moved away from the retina, while in teleosts it is for distant vision and the lens is moved back; in amphibians accommodation is very slight. Birds and reptiles (except snakes) squeeze the lens by the ciliary muscles, which are striped, and so thicken it. Some birds such as hawks also change the shape of the cornea. In snakes a special movement of the iris puts pressure on the vitreous which pushes the lens forward.

Fig. 38 shows a diagram of the structure of the retina. Little is known of the function of this very complex structure. Light rays forming the optical image pass through the transparent nerve-cells of the ganglion cell layer and the bipolar layer, and only about 10 per cent. are usefully absorbed by the sensitive elements, the rods and cones. The rest go on and are mostly absorbed by the layer of pigmented epithelium. Between them the rods and cones in man number about 10^8 cells. Many converge on to a single bipolar cell, so there are fewer of these, and many of these in turn converge on to a single ganglion cell, of which there are only about 10^6. Each of these sends a fibre to the brain. It will be seen that this convergence of the retinal elements would appear to reduce the visual acuity, for if all the cells converged on to one cell no form could be perceived at all. It is important also to notice certain cells in the bipolar layer which make connexions

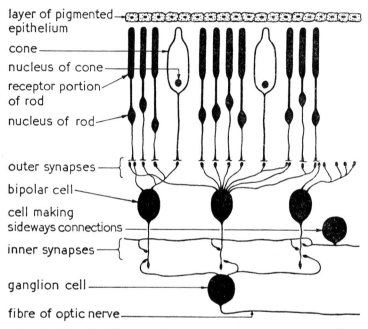

layer of pigmented epithelium

cone

nucleus of cone

receptor portion of rod

nucleus of rod

outer synapses

bipolar cell

cell making sideways connections

inner synapses

ganglion cell

fibre of optic nerve

FIG. 38. A simplified diagram of the nervous connexions in the mammalian retina.

laterally, for if these cells with their branches served to conduct impulses starting in the rods and cones they would only muddle the whole picture. It is tempting to think that they enable one part of the retina to control adjacent parts and have something to do with simultaneous contrast (p. 299).

The distribution of the rods and cones over the retina is not uniform. In man, the central part, the fovea centralis, where images are normally focused, contains only cones, and as the distance from this increases, the proportion of rods increases, until, at the periphery, there are scarcely any cones. The periphery of the retina is nearly colour-blind, so that it appears that cones are necessary for colour vision. Further, the periphery is much better at appreciating very faint light than is the fovea; a very faint star can often be seen only when one is looking not directly at it but slightly to one side. This suggests that the rods are concerned in appreciating low light intensities, that is, in twilight vision. It is not, however, possible to sustain this rigid distinction between the functions of the two types of cell. Although some nocturnal animals, such as the mouse, have no cones, this is not true of others, and squirrels, although colour-blind, have no rods. In some mammals there are sensitive cells intermediate in form between rods and cones. In birds also it is impossible to distinguish diurnal from nocturnal eyes by the distribution of rods and cones. The threshold intensity of flashes of light subtending a narrow angle has been claimed to be the same in man for the fovea as for the periphery, so that the apparent greater sensitivity of the latter might be partly due not to any difference in the receptor cells as such, but to the greater number of them that are connected to a single fibre of the optic nerve. This could not, however, explain their greater sensitivity to the star, which is the best point source we have. Conversely, the greater discrimination of the fovea is probably due to the fact that here each cell has its own fibre. Some mammals have no fovea, but in many birds there are two, and the density of cones over much of the retina is as high as in man's fovea. This, combined with the better shape of their eyeballs, giving them freedom from the effects of curvature of the image in depth, must make their appreciation of detail excellent over the whole eye.

Where the optic nerve enters the eye there are no sensory cells, so this gives rise to a small blind area, which, owing to the inversion by the lens, lies in the temporal half of the field. If the reader uses his left eye only, while reading *this* line, he will observe that the black dot on the left disappears at a certain point, only to reappear as the eye moves farther on. He may experiment with black, white, or coloured dots on a background of any colour, and always the blind area appears to be filled in with the appropriate colour. This apparent miracle may be clearly explained in terms of the relation between the retina and the brain. Consider a person looking at say a uniform green surface, and that while he does so a hypothetical operation is performed, whereby a slit is made in the retina by a single cut, and that the sides of the cut are pushed outward to leave an artificial blind gap. We will suppose no cells to be destroyed. All the cells of the retina continue to receive green light, the message conveyed by the optic nerve will be therefore unaffected, and consequently the impression received by the brain will also be unaffected, so that no blind spot will be noticed. We may suppose that the natural blind spot is not perceived for a similar reason, and this is equivalent to saying that there is no centre in the brain which represents the blind spot. If this explanation is correct it is not true to say that the brain 'fills in' the blind spot, but rather that it 'sews it up'.

Professor Hering cut a hole in a white door connecting his room with the next, the walls of which were painted white and had moderate illumination. If the room in which he sat was dark, then looking through the hole he saw the white wall of the adjoining room, so that the hole appeared as a white disc. When his room was brightly lit, the aperture changed dramatically to black, so that it appeared as if the lights in the next room had been extinguished. In the same way, when lights are switched on in the evening, the sky seen through an open window appears to blacken. Hering also showed that the black print of a page reflects about 10 per cent. of the incident light and that the ratio of a bright to a moderate reading light was at least 100 to 1, so that it followed that black print in a bright light is actually ten times as bright as white paper in a moderate light. That the black print, just like the hole in the door, appears black, is the phenomenon of simultaneous contrast. We can barely conceive how the world would appear in the absence of this phenomenon.

There has been much discussion as to whether simultaneous contrast is determined by events in the eye or in the brain, but it now seems probable that it is mediated by the eye, and possibly by the brain as well.

Hering deduced the occurrence of another phenomenon, simultaneous adaptation, by a brilliant argument as follows: In the experiment of the hole in the door, consider the case where both rooms are equally illuminated. Just as before the bright white door must reduce the brightness of the hole, but now when this is done the hole matches the surrounding white door, and is indistinguishable from it. What is true of the hole must be true of the door, since they are all part of a uniform surface. Therefore each part of the door must have its brightness reduced by the neighbouring parts, and brightness thus becomes self-regulating.

Powerful car headlamps, scarcely noticeable on a sunny day, may be unbearable at night. The difference indicates the extent of dark adaptation which represents an increase of 10,000 times in the sensitivity of the retina. In the dark-adapted condition, not only does sensitivity increase, but at the same time visual acuity decreases. It has always been known that one cannot read in a dim light, but only recently are we learning why. It used to be thought that, pupil size apart, the whole of dark adaptation was due to the accumulation of visual purple in the rods, as it was noticed that this pigment became bleached on exposure to bright light and was formed again in the dark. Recent measurements show, however, that a change of a mere 2 per cent. in the amount of visual purple will accompany a fifty-fold increase in sensitivity (with a constant-size artificial pupil). It is possible that much of dark-adaptation is due to an increase in the number of rods converging upon a single ganglion cell, and this theory explains the observed decrease in visual acuity. We have no idea how this change in convergence may come about.

Thus dark adaptation is probably due to four events:

1. Change in pupil size (from 2 to 8 mm diameter).
2. Simultaneous adaptation.
3. Increased convergence of the retinal elements.
4. Increase in amount of visual purple.

Full colour vision is relatively rare. It is found in many diurnal fishes, in urodeles, in tortoises, in diurnal lizards, and in birds. The spectrum of sensitivity is generally similar to that for man, but some fishes and birds have a closed colour-circle, and fail to distinguish red from purple. Frogs have poor and toads no colour discrimination. The only mammals with a fully developed colour vision are the Primates.

Light may be mixed by superimposing coloured patches from separate lanterns. Some results, which are very different from those of mixing paints, are as follows:

$$Red+green=yellow;$$
$$Yellow+blue=white;$$
$$Red+green+blue=white;$$
$$Blue+green=blue\ green;$$
$$Blue+red=purple.$$

Purple is the only extra-spectral colour, that is, it is the only colour not given by a single wave-length. All the many thousands of different shades of colours can (except for the purples) be matched by some single wave-length and the appropriate amount of white light. Brown is peculiar in that one cannot produce an isolated patch of brown light on a screen in a dark room. If one attempts to do this by projecting light through brown glass, the patch formed is yellow or orange. By projecting white or other coloured light near it, it may be made to appear brown. Thus brown is a contrast colour. Black and grey are also contrast colours (see p. 299).

Young's theory (1802), often, for no good reason, called the Young-Helmholtz theory, supposes that there are three kinds of receptors, which, because they contain different pigments, absorb, and so respond to, red, green, and blue light respectively, and evoke the corresponding sensations. The theory does not claim to explain the phenomena of colour mixture, it merely states that when various combinations of the three receptors are stimulated, various other colours such as yellow or white are perceived. Its chief merit is that it is in line with Müller's Law (p. 256), although it was put forward before this was enunciated.

If the eye is removed from a freshly killed frog and the cornea and lens are cut away, it will survive for several hours provided that it is kept moist. If a fine electrode leading to an amplifier is carefully lowered on to the retina, when all is well, action potentials can be picked up from cells of the ganglion cell layer. On Young's theory we should expect no response in darkness, a steady response in white light, and a steady response in either red, green, or blue light according to whether the electrode had chanced to alight on a red, a green, or a blue receptor. What we get is astonishingly different.

First of all, from some cells, there is a steady discharge in the dark, and this ceases when the light is switched on.

Nobody knows what the significance of this dark discharge is, but it is likely to be important, since the corresponding phenomenon is found in the labyrinth, the ear, and in other sense organs.

As one tries cell after cell by moving the electrode to different positions, different results are obtained. Sometimes a cell is found which responds rapidly when the light is switched on, and then the discharge falls to a lower rate which is maintained while the light remains on, and ceases as the light goes off. Fibres from such cells are called 'on' fibres. There are other cells which respond by discharging for a fraction of a second, only at the onset and at the cessation of the light. While the light is maintained there is no discharge. The fibres from these are called 'on-off'. Other cells give a short burst of discharge only when the light is switched off, and are called 'off' fibres.

Retinal action potentials in the human retina cannot be examined, but if, as we may guess, on and off effects occur there too, then it is odd that we do not observe special effects at onset and cessation of illumination. However, if we look at any pattern, then on moving the eye, the light falling on one cone will change as the pattern moves over it, and in this way 'on' and 'off' effects may be induced. It is noticeable that vision deteriorates considerably if the eye is held quite still (the reader may try this), and it may be that good acuity is possible only when 'on' and 'off' effects are induced by eye movements.

Light on one part of the retina may affect the discharge of neighbouring parts, both in vertebrate and invertebrate eyes, and this may be the physiological basis of simultaneous contrast.

There can be no doubt that rhodopsin (visual purple) plays some part in vision, but what this may be is uncertain. It is bleached by light and broken down to a protein (scotopsin) and retinene (vitamin A aldehyde,

p. 67), while in the dark retinene is changed to an active form from which rhodopsin is reformed. The wave-length for maximum absorption of quanta by visual purple is the same as that for maximum sensitivity of the retina. This, combined with the effect of deficiency of vitamin A in producing night-blindness, suggests that it is necessary for seeing in a dim light (scotopic vision). Animals that have vitamin A_2 instead of A_1 have a related eye-pigment, porphyropsin, the absorption maximum of which similarly corresponds to the spectral sensitivity of their eyes. How the breakdown of rhodopsin produces effects on the rods or cones is still a matter for speculation, as is its possible part in colour vision. It has been claimed that there are several other light-sensitive pigments in the retina, and that each of these, alone or in conjunction with rhodopsin, is responsible for a particular colour.

5.572. Invertebrate Eyes. The eyes of molluscs vary considerably in structure; those of the cephalopods are noteworthy for being very similar to vertebrate eyes. They have good form-discrimination, but there is no good evidence of colour vision. The snail *Littorina littoralis* is said to be able to respond to the plane of polarization of the light.

The eyes of arthropods are of two sorts; ocelli, and compound or faceted eyes. The former are found in both the larvae and adults of insects, and most of them are probably no more than light-sensitive structures; some of the more complicated of them may form crude images.

The faceted eyes are characteristic of adults. Each is made up of a large number of elements called ommatidia, each of which has a refractive body called a cone (it has no relation to the vertebrate cones), and below this a nervous retinula. The ommatidia are separated from one another by pigment, so that only rays which are nearly parallel to the axis of the cone will pass right to its bottom. There is more than one sort of ommatidium, and in the types known as eucone and exocone the refractive index of the cone gradually decreases from the centre to the periphery. With this structure it is possible for a cone to form at its base a real erect image of an external object. Since the pigment and the great length of the cones relative to their radius prevents all but nearly parallel rays from reaching the retinulae, the effect of this optical system is to give a real erect image of an object placed outside the eye, each ommatidium focusing a small part of it. That this is how the eye works in the glow-worm *Lampyris* can be shown under the microscope. This type of image is called an apposition image. When, as in dim light, the pigment is withdrawn, there is, presumably, overlap, and a superposition image occurs. In the type of eye called pseudocone, a similar apposition image is formed, but the parts formed from separate ommatidia are not erect, so that the total image is made up of dots of light like a half-tone plate. The method of working of the last type of insect eye, known as acone, is obscure. Some of the simpler types of compound eye, with few ommatidia, seem to have no function but that of appreciating light for phototaxis.

Colour vision is found in several insects. For instance, honey bees may be trained to feed always at a card of a certain colour, say red, placed amongst cards of other colours and grey cards of different darknesses. Early workers did not include the grey cards, and without them a colour-blind animal might distinguish between the chosen coloured card and the others not by their colours but by their brightnesses. Gnats, drone-flies, butterflies, a few beetles, and the bug *Notonecta* can also distinguish colours. No arthropods other than insects are known to have colour vision, but some differential sensitivity to different wave-lengths has been claimed for a few crustacea and spiders. Some arthropods can perceive the plane of polariza-

tion of the incident light. Bees use this power to determine
the direction of their food-supplies, and the ability is also
possessed by ants, sand hoppers, Cladocera, *Eupagurus*,
and *Limulus*, so that it appears to be a general property
of the compound eye. But caterpillars of the pine sawfly
are said to orientate by the plane of polarization, and they
have only simple eyes, and flies react to it as readily by
their ocelli as by their compound eyes. Nothing is known
of the mechanism.

Physiologically, arthropod eyes are of two sorts. In the
majority, called 'slow', stimulation of the ommatidium
causes only a single monophasic electrical response in the
optic nerve-fibre, corresponding to the 'on' effect in
vertebrate eyes. In 'fast' eyes, which are found in rapidly
flying insects such as Diptera and Hymenoptera, there is
a positive 'on' wave, and a negative 'off' wave. Many
arthropods, when placed in a rotating cylinder painted
with black and white stripes, fixate on one of these and
rotate at the same speed. Those with slow eyes cease to do
so when the stripes are passing at the rate of five to ten a
second, showing that at that frequency discrimination
ceases to be possible, but those with fast eyes go on rotating
until the frequency is about 200 a second. Slow eyes can
be converted to fast by removal of part of the optic lobes
of the brain, suggesting that the distinction lies not in the
eyes themselves but in the central nervous system. The
slow eyes of the nymph of the dragonfly *Aeschna* become
fast eyes in the imago, apparently by the movement of the
optic lobes closer to them.

6

BEHAVIOUR

THE subject of animal behaviour may be approached by several different routes, but the only one with which a textbook of physiology is concerned is that which starts from observed changes in the whole or a part of the organism. For the purposes of this chapter, behaviour means the reactions of effectors to stimuli, and a simple piece of behaviour is the muscle twitch which has already been considered. When the animal is taken as a whole its reaction to a single external stimulus is usually complex, several muscles, glands, and other effectors acting together to give a co-ordinated response. It is these responses, and their relations to the appropriate sense organs and co-ordinating system, with which the physiologist may legitimately deal, his aim, as in other branches of his subject, being to state his results in the simplest possible terms of physics and chemistry. A second and subjective approach, which may have its place in biology, regards the animal as a lesser man capable of thinking, of starting reactions independently of external stimuli, and of being conscious of its own activity. It is rightly called animal psychology, and uses, as far as possible, the methods of human psychology. A third type, called ethology, is now popular, and is referred to briefly below, but since this book is about physiology, the stress in what follows is on the mechanistic aspect of animal behaviour.

One of the difficulties in the study of behaviour is that an animal does not always react in the same way to the same stimulus. This is most true of the higher animals, but even an amoeba may at first engulf a particle of sand or carmine on contact, and after a number of contacts may cease to do so. The reaction may be said to depend in part on the physiological state of the animal, or in psychological language the animal may be said to learn and to have memory. In the extreme case of man, what we generally think of as mental states or events—love, anger, dreams, and so on—may have profound effects on reactions, and the same is perhaps true of some mammals and birds. The thorough-going mechanist will say that the mental events are themselves mere manifestations of glandular and nervous changes, which are brought into being by happenings in the external world—the sight of the loved one producing love, a lump in the pillow the dream, and so on. Whatever may be the cause of mental events, the physiologist must be aware of their influence and of that of experience, and must plan and interpret his experiments accordingly.

6.1. Behaviour in the Protozoa

The Protozoa are best treated apart from the rest of the animal kingdom, because they are made up of protoplasm which is not divided into cells. As a consequence there can be no cellular co-ordinating system, and although it is sometimes possible to recognize organelles which are specialized as effectors (e.g. cilia) or receptors (e.g. eyespots), they cannot be so easily studied as separate entities as can the muscles and sense organs of higher animals. Although the types of response may be the same as those of the Metazoa, the mechanism by which they are brought about must be different.

It is traditional to start with *Amoeba*, and even if this animal is the degenerate which most protozoologists now consider it, its behaviour is, in the words of Dobell, pleasingly simple. In contact with a surface it moves, by means of its pseudopodia, in an approximately straight line, though it has been stated that its actual path is a sine curve. Its method of locomotion is described in detail on p. 171. If the front end of the animal comes in contact with a solid object, the direction of flow of the protoplasm is altered to make an angle with that which it had before. If only a small part of the anterior end has been stimulated, the angle is small, and the effect is that the amoeba moves round the obstacle. If the obstruction is large, so that contact is made over the whole of the ends of the advancing pseudopodia, the direction of flow turns through a right angle or more and the line of movement changes accordingly. In both cases the final result is that the obstacle is avoided. Such a reaction, in which the animal is forced to move away from the stimulus, is called a negative taxis. In this case it occurs because pseudopodium formation is inhibited in the stimulated region. *Amoeba* gives a similar response to other stimuli besides contact; for instance, it moves away from unduly hot water or any solution of unusual composition, and will travel down a beam of light away from the source, because pseudopodia form more freely on the side which is worse illuminated. If a pseudopodium comes into a spot of very intense light focused up through the culture, it is withdrawn: others are put out, come into the light, and are again withdrawn, and this goes on until there is sudden reversal of the direction of streaming, and the animal moves away from the spot. The larger the area of pseudopodium which comes into the light, the fewer the number of contacts before reversal occurs. The light acts by changing plasmasol to plasmagel, and the same effect is produced when a large area is stimulated once as when a small part is stimulated several times. If the same amoeba be watched coming into spots of light on successive occasions, it can be seen to learn by experience, for the number of contacts necessary for reversal progressively decreases.

Besides these negative reactions *Amoeba* has some positive ones. Sometimes when a pseudopodium comes in contact with a surface, instead of withdrawing it sticks to it, and the whole animal moves up to it. This happens particularly when the amoeba is freely suspended in water and not otherwise in contact with a solid object. The feeding reaction, in which two pseudopodia are put out to surround a particle, is another positive reaction. While an amoeba is feeding it does not give the response to a beam of light described above. This fact, and the two types of reaction to contact, show that the behaviour depends not only on the external stimuli, but also on the internal state of the animal. It reacts automatically, but it does so to the whole situation, and not to an isolated element in it.

Paramecium is an example of a protozoan which is much more active than *Amoeba*. It swims by means of its cilia, and its locomotion may be analysed into three parts. It moves forwards, because the cilia beat backward; it rotates to the left on its long axis, because they beat not directly backwards but slightly to the right; and it pivots round its posterior end towards the dorsal surface because the cilia on the ventral side (by the oral groove) beat more strongly than the dorsal ones. The last two partially counteract one another, because on account of the axial rotation the direction of pivoting is being continually changed. The total result is that the animal moves along a solenoidal course, rotating on its axis as it goes. The three factors, forward speed, rate of rotation, and diameter of the solenoid, vary more or less independently as the beat of the cilia changes. The cilia in the oral groove, which are visibly different from the others, are not necessary for this peculiar type of locomotion, for it is given by fragments of paramecia which possess no oral groove. Such fragments also give the reaction described below. It follows that the ordinary movement and the variants produced in it by external stimuli are brought about by different types of beat of the uniform cilia which cover the body.

All unfavourable stimuli are met by the same response, an avoiding reaction or phobotaxis. The forward stroke of the cilia is reversed, and those on the left side strike towards the oral groove instead of away from it. All three factors in the locomotion are thereby affected—the animal moves backwards, its rotation is slowed, and the rolling round its posterior end towards the aboral side is increased: in extreme cases the rotation stops altogether and the animal swings round in a circle in a plane perpendicular to its previous direction of motion with its body as radius and its posterior end as centre. The phobotaxis is given when the anterior end receives a stimulus of touch, high or low temperature, strong light, or unusual chemical conditions. It lasts for a brief interval, less than a second, during which the paramecium has gone back about two lengths, and then normal movement is resumed. On account of the wide angle through which the body has been rolling it is unlikely that the line of motion will be the same as before, and the obstacle, spot of light, or whatever else it was that gave the stimulus, may be avoided. If it is not, another avoiding reaction is given, and a succession of them may lead to a complete reversal of the direction of movement. No special sensitive organelle is known in *Paramecium*, but the avoiding reaction is not given when the posterior end is touched.

The avoiding reaction is almost the only method by which *Paramecium* can deal with strange situations. When it is given, as described above, because the anterior end receives a stimulus, it is generally protective in the sense that it enables the animal to avoid the source of the stimulus. But it is also given in general adverse conditions, and then has no value whatever. If the temperature of a culture of *Paramecium* be gradually raised, the rate of movement increases and at about 30° C avoiding reactions begin, and are repeated very rapidly. The result is that there is little forward motion, but the animals dance backwards and forwards over short distances rather like particles in Brownian movement. After a time they may become acclimatized to the new temperature or they may die; in either case the phobotaxis ceases. It is possible that on the basis of this adaptation the reaction may be assimilated to the klinokinesis discussed below (p. 315).

The avoiding reaction is also responsible for the chief positive behaviour of *Paramecium*. If a drop of very dilute acid be placed in the middle of a large drop of a culture of *Paramecium* on a slide and left for a little while, it will be found that all the animals have collected in the acid. More strictly, the acid diffuses out, so that there is a concentration gradient from the centre of the drop of culture to its edge; the paramecia collect in the middle part of the drop, so that they are above a certain concentration of hydrion. It appears as if they had been attracted to the acid, but this is not the case. Their swimming may be considered as random, and so sooner or later all of them enter the central parts of the drop of acid. It happens that they can do this without giving an avoiding reaction, but that when they are swimming down a hydrion gradient they do give it at a certain concentration. The acid diffuses out as a spherical shell, so that once a paramecium has entered the acid it cannot get out. The avoiding reaction will alter the course of the paramecium, but its new direction will still bring it up against the shell somewhere else. It is as if all fell-walkers had to turn back at meeting the 3,000-ft contour when they met it going downhill, but not when going up: sooner or later (if they lived in England) they would all be trapped on Scafell, Helvellyn, or Skiddaw.

Paramecium has two definite positive reactions: sometimes on contact with a surface it does not give the avoiding reaction, but puts out trichocysts by which it anchors itself to the surface. This happens especially when it receives a contact stimulus on two sides, so that it tends to collect in this way in corners such as those between the glass walls of its container and the surface film of water. When two paramecia hit each other, one at least of them usually gives the avoiding reaction, but if they meet by their ventral surfaces, and if the animals are in an appropriate condition, they may stick together and undergo conjugation.

In all the free-swimming 'infusorians'—ciliates and flagellates—which have been investigated the chief reaction is a phobotaxis similar in general principles to that of *Paramecium*. The details vary with the type of locomotion, but in all there is reversal or stoppage of movement and a turning to one side. In a few cases the avoiding reaction is adapted to orientate the animal with respect to the direction of the stimulus. This is illustrated by *Euglena*. If one part of a culture of this animal is illuminated and another not, all the individuals collect by the avoiding reaction either in the light or in the dark, according to the external conditions; they are behaving just like *Paramecium* collecting in an acid. But in addition to this they also orientate so that they swim either towards the source of light (usually when it is weak) or away from it (when it is strong). The probable mechanism of this is as follows. The convexity of the eye-spot is opaque, and the concavity is sensitive to light, so that as the animal rotates, unless it is facing directly towards or away from the source of light, it is alternately exposed and shaded. This alternation of stimuli causes the avoiding reaction to be given until the eye-spot is uniformly illuminated. The stimuli then cease, and the animal continues on its course without further deviation. In the language of the next section, this is klinotaxis.

6.2. Simple Behaviour in the Metazoa

In the Metazoa effector and receptor are nearly always separated spatially, connexion between them being maintained by the nervous system or by this system aided by hormones. From an elementary point of view the study of behaviour is the study of reflexes, for behaviour may be considered as made up of many individual reactions of organs such as muscles and glands, and these may all be stimulated through the nervous system. An animal may move towards the light, and with sufficient anatomical knowledge similar movement could be induced by electrical stimulation of the appropriate nerve-fibres. The particular reaction to each electric shock could be stated in the same terms as the frog jerks discussed in section 4.31. Studies which have been carried out on the development of behaviour in ontogeny suggest that behaviour patterns develop as wholes, and that their resolution into separate reflexes is artificial, but this does not mean that no useful results can be obtained from such an analysis. In any case the total behaviour is much more complicated than any single reflex, and it is consequently useful to study it as a whole as well as in its parts.

The response of an animal to a stimulus in such a way that the resulting movement has reference to the direction from which the stimulus comes used to be called a tropism. In strict usage this term is now restricted to the bending response of a fixed organism, and as most animals are motile it has little application in zoology. The term now used for a reaction of this sort in which the whole animal moves is taxis (plural taxes). The particular type of taxis is shown by a prefix indicating the sort of stimulus concerned. Thus photo-, geo-, rheo-, chemo-, aero-, and thigmotaxis are reaction to light, gravity, a current, chemicals, air, and contact respectively. A taxis is positive when

the animal moves towards the stimulus, negative when it
moves away from it. Reactions in which the rate of a
response depends on the intensity of a stimulus, although
there is no orientation of the body in relation to the
stimulus, are called kineses. It is possible for these to lead
to apparently positive or negative reactions.

6.21. Kineses

If the rate of movement of an organism depends on the
intensity of some external factor, there will always be a
higher density of the organisms where the intensity of the
factor is such as to reduce the rate of movement, a phenomenon familiar to anyone who has taken a long journey
by car: wherever the speed of the vehicles is reduced, as in
towns, the cars come more closely together, and so their
density is increased. This type of response is called orthokinesis, and is found in woodlice as well as in automobiles.
The common species *Porcellio scaber* is often inactive, and
its average speed, including these stationary periods, is
lower the greater the humidity of the air. The result is that
it congregates in damp air, often under stones and logs,
and only occasionally wanders through the drier regions
between them. Orthokinesis can only occur when the ecological pattern provides the opportunity; most birds are
active in the light and inactive in the dark, but they are
not orthokinetic because in the daytime no dark places
are available to them.

In other animals, while the rate of movement may vary
little, the rate of turning may depend on the intensity of
a stimulus. The planarian *Dendrocoelum lacteum*, for example,
is continually changing its direction, and does so more
often in a high light intensity than in a low one. Moreover,
it adapts to the light, so that in any given intensity the
rate of turning falls. The result of this is that on the whole
the animal is more likely to turn when it is going up a

gradient than when it is going down, and so, by movements
which are basically random, it gradually approaches
regions of low intensity. A movement of this sort is called
a klinokinesis.

6.22. Taxes

The study of taxes is made difficult by the fact that the
directions of two stimuli received by an animal may be
such that their effects are opposite, and also by the fact
that the effect of a stimulus is not a fixed one. It depends
on the other stimuli which are being received and on
the internal condition (and hence the past history) of the
animal. Thus *Planaria alpina*, a turbellarian living in mountain streams, becomes positively rheotactic and swims upstream only when its reproductive organs are developing.
When it has laid its eggs it becomes negatively rheotactic
and moves down again. The eggs of the moth *Porthesia* are
laid at the bottom of trees. The larvae are at first positively
phototactic, and move up to the top of the tree, where they
start feeding on the leaves. Food changes the sign of their
reaction to light and they move slowly down, eating the
leaves as they go. In experiments on taxes it is therefore
essential that the conditions should be exactly controlled,
and the one stimulus carefully isolated.

Taxes may be held to describe a number of the ordinary
pieces of behaviour in animals, particularly in invertebrates. The desire of the moth for the flame is proverbial,
and the swarming of bees and many other insects is probably a phototaxis. Many fishes orientate themselves to
face upstream and maintain their position relative to the
bank. This is apparently rheotaxis, but it is in reality a
special sort of phototaxis, for they are reacting to moving
images of objects on the bank going past them. The blowfly *Lucilia sericata* lays its eggs as a result of chemical stimuli
which it normally receives from putrefying material, but

the natural conditions can be in part replaced by ammonium carbonate or other substances. Oviposition is here a kind of chemotaxis.

A taxis is essentially a forced movement, and in some cases taxes can be shown to be due to an altered muscle-tone on one side of the animal. It has been shown, for

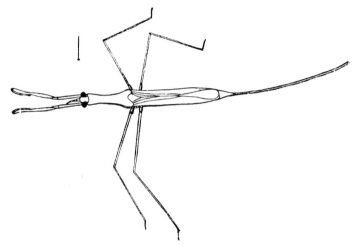

FIG. 39. Position of the water-scorpion *Ranatra* when the right eye is towards the light. After Holmes.

instance, in many insects that a reduced light intensity on one eye of the animal causes a decreased muscle-tone of the legs of the same side. For example, if the bug *Ranatra* be illuminated from one side, the legs of the bright side are bent, indicating a high tonus of the flexor muscles, while those of the darker side are extended (Fig. 39). The same result is obtained if one eye is covered with an opaque black varnish; the legs are flexed on the side of the normal eye, stretched on the side of the blackened eye. A normal insect under lateral illumination necessarily takes longer steps with the legs on the dark side than with the others, and so moves in a curve towards the source of light. When it has come to face the light it will be in equilibrium, the muscle-tone will be the same on both sides, and it will move straight forwards. In the same way when an insect with one blackened eye is illuminated from in front and starts to walk, as it normally would do, towards the light, it takes longer steps with the legs on the side where the eye is blackened than with those of the other side, and hence walks in circles.

When an animal which behaves in this way is placed under the influence of two sources of light, its behaviour can be predicted by simple physical methods. Each source of light has its own effect on the muscle-tone, depending on the intensity of illumination it gives at the sense organs. This in turn depends on its own luminosity, the distance from it to the receptor, and the direction of incidence of the light. These are straightforward physical things which can be measured, and it is easy to calculate from them the intensity and direction of a single lamp which would have the same effect as the two, that is, of their resultant. It would be expected that the animal would move towards the resultant, and this is found to be the case.

Such a forced movement, in which the direction-finding is due to an altered muscle-tonus, is called a tropotaxis. It is the type of behaviour originally described by Loeb under the name of tropism. It depends on the existence of stimulatory organs (see p. 267) which are easily influenced by outside stimuli. The tests for a tropotaxis, other than direct observation of muscle-tone, are that under the influence of two stimuli the animal moves approximately along the resultant, and that where there are bilateral sense organs extirpation of one of them causes circus movements. Animals react to other kinds of stimulus besides light in this way. Most of the cases where an animal orientates to gravity by means of a statocyst are of this sort, for unilateral extirpation of the sense organ causes rolling movements. Occasionally chemotaxis, movement towards a source of a diffusing chemical substance, is similar, as in *Planaria*, *Nereis*, and insects. In the case of the last the sense organs are in the antennae. When two stimuli of different sorts are acting on an animal, and its response to both is a tropotaxis, the two are compounded and the animal moves along the resultant just as it would if they were of the same sort. Thus the slug *Agriolimax* is both negatively phototactic and negatively geotactic. If it be placed on an inclined plane and illuminated from the side, it moves upwards at an acute angle away from the light. The path with two stimuli is not always strictly along the mathematical resultant, as there may be a systematic deviation either towards the weaker or towards the stronger source. If the sources are unequal, the animal usually turns in towards the stronger as it approaches, as would happen if the resultant were being exactly followed.

As is normal with sensory stimuli there is some adaptation of these taxes, so that in the last experiment, for instance, the path of the slug becomes more and more nearly vertical, as it becomes adapted to the light.

There is another type of taxis, called a telotaxis, in which definite turning reflexes are given unless a sense organ receives the stimulus from a particular direction. This differs from a tropotaxis in two ways. When one lateral sense organ is extirpated there are no circus movements; the definite reflexes are still given until the animal is in equilibrium. With two stimuli the animal does not move along the resultant, but reacts to one only of them. In phototelotaxis, for instance, as shown by *Eupagurus*, the crab goes towards one of the two sources of light, and may suddenly change its direction and go towards the other. The recognition of tropotaxis and telotaxis as two distinct types of behaviour solves the problem of Buridan's ass, which could find no reason for going to one rather than the other of two similar bundles of hay at equal distances from it. If it had reacted to hay by a tropotaxis, it would have walked midway between them and starved, but if by a telotaxis, it would have visited and eaten each in turn.

The crustacean *Leander* reacts to gravity by a telotaxis, and according to some authors it is the normal way by which insects orient in light.

In a third type of reaction the attainment of orientation is indirect. The animal swings the anterior end from side to side, so that there is alternate stimulation of the two sides. This enables it, in a purely physiological sense, to compare intensities of stimulation which are successive in time. If it varies the size of the lateral swing until they are equal, it must be moving either directly away from or directly towards the direction from which the stimulus comes. This type of reaction, called a klinotaxis, is shown very clearly by blowfly larvae, which swing away from the source of light and so are negatively phototactic. If there are two sources of stimulation, response, as in tropotaxis, is to the resultant.

It is customary to separate, under the heading of transverse orientations, those responses to stimulation which set the long axis of the animal at an angle to the direction of incidence of the stimulus. In the light-compass reaction (or menotaxis) the animal maintains a temporarily constant angle to the direction of incident light, so that, so long as the latter is constant, it travels in a straight line. By this mechanism, amongst others, ants find their way back to the nest, using the direction of the sun as a guide. The compound eye of arthropods is very suitable for this sort of reaction, for all that the animal has to do is to keep the image of the source of light on one ommatidium. The reaction is found also in caterpillars and some molluscs, which have simple eyes. When compound eyes are used it seems to be physiologically the same as telotaxis, and with simple eyes the same as tropotaxis, for it is affected in the same ways by two sources of light, but the term taxis is, in the view of some workers, best restricted to movements directly towards or away from a source.

Many animals, notably some Crustacea, place their bodies transversely to the direction of gravity, and a few, such as *Apus*, do so to light. Again these reactions are physiologically similar to tropotaxis, but there is no locomotion directed by the stimulus. In general the response to gravity is to keep the ventral side downwards, so that it is called a ventral earth reaction, and the response to light is to keep the dorsal surface towards the light, so that it is called a dorsal light reaction. Obviously if these two are present together, they will in most circumstances reinforce each other.

6.3. Instincts

There are many cases where the reaction of an animal appears to be to a complex situation rather than to an elementary stimulus. Such responses are not called taxes or tropisms, but there seems no reason to regard them as being essentially different. For example, shrikes (butcherbirds) of the genus *Lanius* which have been reared in cages treat a piece of food which is given them in a peculiar way: they drag it after them until it becomes caught in a nail or some other projection, a piece of behaviour which agrees with the natural habit of the birds of impaling insects on thorns. Here the stimulus is 'food in the mouth', which cannot be reduced to light, temperature, or any other single factor, but the response is, nevertheless, as definite as is any taxis. The famous case of the pine processionary caterpillar studied by Fabre is another example of this sort of thing. A caterpillar in the ordinary way will walk where its legs carry it, but as it goes it leaves a trail of silk behind it, and if a second caterpillar comes on to this it is bound to follow the first. The result of this is that the caterpillars move about in close single file, each one following its leader, and the processions are only broken by accidents which push an individual out of its path. Fabre was fortunate enough to induce a company of the caterpillars to make a closed circuit round the top rim of a large flower-pot. The march went on for seven days, interrupted only by pauses for sleep at night, and was finally broken by chance.

To such reactions as these the word instinct is generally applied, but many of the instincts of animals are much more complicated. They start with a piece of behaviour like those which have just been described, and then go on to several more acts in sequence, in such a way that the performance of one seems to act as the stimulus for the next. This is very well illustrated by the solitary wasps, which bury other insects and lay eggs in them. *Ammophila holosericea*, for instance, digs a hole in the earth, catches a caterpillar and stings it, then carries it into the hole, lays an egg in it, and finally closes the hole. This sequence is invariable, each act being the stimulus for the next. When a wasp was just about finishing closing the hole another stung and paralysed caterpillar was placed near by, and the wasp saw it. The sight of the caterpillar, the last part of the act of bringing a caterpillar to the hole, gave the impulse to bury, so the wasp reopened the tunnel. When she reached the bottom the sight of the egg and caterpillar already in position acted as stimulus for closing, so she carried on with this for the second time. But again she saw the caterpillar on the surface and again she reopened the hole, and then closed it for the third and last time. Sometimes, however, the behaviour of the wasp is more complicated than this. Two nests may be dealt with at the same time, and further caterpillars may be added as the larvae grow, the two nests being visited in turn.

A similar rhythm operates in the building of spiders' webs. *Araneus nauticus* is a species which makes a regular web similar to that of the common garden spider, *Epeira diademata*. The web is constructed in five stages (Fig. 40)

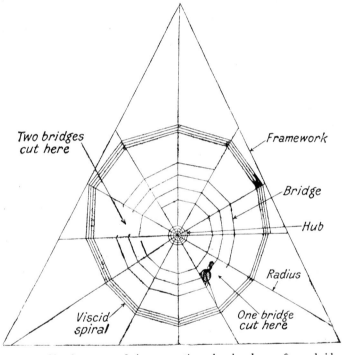

FIG. 40. Circular snare of *Araneus nauticus*, showing how, after a bridge is cut, the spider cannot remake it, but crosses over by another bridge. After Hingston.

and the completion of each of the first four stages serves as a stimulus for the performance of the next. First, a framework is attached to surrounding plants, then a series of radii are taken from this into a centre; next comes a very close-wound spiral forming a hub round the centre, and fourthly the radii are joined by a series of bridges formed by a spiral of fairly high pitch. All these parts are made of non-sticky silk, and are used as a framework not only to support the last stage but for the spider to walk on. The fifth stage is the viscid spiral, which is spun close together from without inwards; in order to make this the spider uses the bridges to cross from one radius to another. When a bridge is cut the spider does the best she can without it; she uses the next one, and so has farther to travel. Even if all the bridges in a sector are cut, so that the spider has to go right into the hub and out again, she is quite incapable of making a new bridge to save herself the journey. Even if all the bridges of all the sectors are cut no more are made. The spider goes on laying the viscid spiral, although now the framework is so weak that different radii come in contact and the result is a complete mess. Only the performance of one act, that of making the radii, can act as a stimulus for the making of the bridges.

This is analogous to a phenomenon common in learning repetition. We may know a poem perfectly by heart if we start at the beginning, but if we are asked to start at the third verse we may be helpless. Here saying one line acts as a stimulus for saying the next, and we can only find an individual line by going right through from the beginning. The two phenomena are, however, distinct, for the spider's behaviour is innate, whereas the other is learnt.

There has recently developed, under the name of ethology, a new vocabulary in the study of behaviour. The complex stimulus that starts a chain of reactions is called a releaser (or sometimes an innate releasing mechanism, a phrase which is also used for the hypothetical system within the animal which sets the instinct in motion). The preliminary part of the chain of reactions is called appetitive behaviour, and the final act is said to be consummatory. This is too rigid a nomenclature for general use, since many of the so-called innate mechanisms have been shown to be modified by experience, and in many instinctive acts there is no consummation, but a continuous cycle of responses. In feeding, for example, taking in food to satiation, digesting it, defaecation, taking in more food, and so on, go on from birth to death in a series of cycles or waves. Many of the elements into which this cycle can be broken down are dependent on relatively simple reflexes or hormonal actions which have been described in Chapter 1, and others, though more complicated, have been shown to depend on particular regions of the brain; cessation of feeding in rats and mice, for example, depends on the stimulation and activity of the ventromedial hypo-thalamic nuclei. Even the consummation of sexual activity in copulation is not, for the female mammal at least, an end, for it leads on to the processes of pregnancy, the reflex acts of birth, and the instinctive behaviour of care for the young. In both sexes of most birds copulation is a brief and psychologically small incident in a complex instinctive reproductive season.

In ethology the term 'action specific energy' is used for a mysterious something which accumulates in the animal until it is discharged in the performance of the instinctive act, but the physiologist, like the physicist, restricts the term 'energy' to something that can be measured in the dimensions one in mass, two in length, and minus two in time. Action specific energy is in fact comparable to pressure or to electrical potential rather than to energy, but so long as it can be neither measured nor related to any structures in the organism, the concept must be regarded with suspicion.

Instincts as defined in this chapter, that is complicated chain-reflexes which are not learnt, are characteristic of the behaviour of insects. The notable thing about them is that they are subject to very little variation. Birds also are largely instinctive, but their behaviour is considerably modified by experience, and many things, such as a knowledge of suitable food, which in insects are possessed by an inherited instinct, in birds have to be learnt either by experience or from the parents. An insect feeds on the correct food plant, and can only with difficulty be induced to feed on anything else: a chick will peck at anything which is moving or is otherwise conspicuous, and it is only after a time that it learns to restrict itself to food which is suitable.

It is often difficult to determine what, in the higher animals, is instinctive behaviour and what is learnt. As the animal develops physically, so new forms of behaviour come into existence, and it may be impossible to determine how far these are inevitable (they are not innate, since they are not present when the animal is born) and how far they are the product of experience. Nest-building in rats appears to be instinctive, in that it occurs in primiparous females that have been reared in isolation, but it does not occur if they have been fed only on soft food so that they have had no practice in carrying things. There is probably little in the behaviour of mammals and birds which is fully instinctive in the sense of being unaffected by experience.

While taxes and kineses can be explained, at least theoretically, in terms of relatively simple reflexes, instinctive behaviour is much more complicated. One may, however, reasonably suppose that the immense number of cells and synapses in the central nervous system are enough to provide all the pathways required for the most complicated behaviour. It is through these, and through the phenomena of inhibition and facilitation, rather than through the hypothetical concepts of ethology, that we may hope to progress towards an understanding of instinct. The endocrine glands are also important, especially in determining the dominance of a particular instinct at a particular time.

It is salutary to compare instinctive behaviour with the relatively simple reactions of an anemone such as *Metridium senile*. In a uniform and neutral environment there is a slow rhythmic expansion and contraction, which is purposive in the sense that it must increase the chance of an encounter with food. If mucus from a mussel, at a dilution of one part in a million, comes in contact with the disk, the body may lengthen greatly and bend from side to side with the mouth open. This also is purposive in that in nature molluscan mucus is generally followed by a mollusc, which the anemone can catch by means of its nematocysts. Ingestion, digestion, and, after several days, defaecation will follow before the old rhythm is resumed. There is thus a chain of reactions which must be carried out by nothing more complicated than the nerve net, for that is all the anemone possesses. Instinctive behaviour may be qualitatively different, but in view of the complication of the nervous systems of Metazoa, there is no reason to assume so.

6.4. The Conditioned Reflex

The formation of a conditioned reflex is the simplest type of learning, and accounts for much animal behaviour. An ordinary reflex, in which a muscle or gland reacts in a particular way to a stimulus, is inherited, but it is possible for new reflexes to be acquired by association during the life of the animal. The classical work on this was done by Pavlov on the salivary reflex of the dog, and a description of this will suitably explain the subject. A dog without previous training salivates when meat is present in its mouth. The strength of the reflex is conveniently taken as proportional to the amount of saliva produced. This is easily measured: a minor operation to bring the opening of one of the salivary glands on to the side of the neck is first performed, and a tube of standard bore is then attached to the opening. The rate at which drops of saliva fall off the end is an accurate measure of the rate of secretion. Almost simultaneously with the receipt of the meat by the dog the experimenter applies some other neutral stimulus, such as the sound of a tuning-fork, of which the animal normally takes no notice. The combination, food plus fork, is repeated a number of times, and then the fork is sounded alone: the dog salivates. A new, conditioned reflex has become established. For the formation of a conditioned reflex it is usually necessary that the neutral stimulus which is to become conditioned should be applied very shortly before the effective one. In some cases, however, conditioning has been possible to a stimulus which precedes the unconditioned one by a considerable time, and in a few cases to one which succeeds the unconditioned one.

Conditioning of strong or unusual stimuli is often difficult, and so is the transformation of an unconditioned stimulus for one reflex into a conditioned stimulus for another, but these have occasionally been accomplished. Electrical stimulation of the foot, or pricking deeply enough to draw blood, which both normally lead to withdrawal of the affected part (and, by human standards, pain) have been conditioned as stimuli for the salivary reflex.

If there be applied, at the same time as the conditioned stimulus, a third strong stimulus, such as a flash of light, the response is not given; the new stimulus has upset whatever mechanism exists, and there is said to be external inhibition. The reflex can also be made to disappear in another way, by giving the conditioned stimulus many times without the unconditioned one. It becomes ineffective, and there is now said to be internal inhibition.

In this case the mechanism of the conditioned reflex is still intact, for if the conditioned, but now ineffective, stimulus be given, and with it a flash of light, there is disinhibition—the conditioned response is given. The strong third stimulus has inhibited the internal inhibition. Inhibition can spread from one reflex to another. When one is internally inhibited, and the stimulus is continually applied, any other conditioned responses which the animal has formed are progressively lost, and the dog finally goes to sleep. Sleep is therefore regarded as a state of general inhibition.

The neural basis of the conditioned reflex is presumably facilitation in the central nervous system (p. 251). The two stimuli come together so frequently that the nervous impulse from the originally neutral one finally takes the path of the other, and so causes its response. In mammals, conditioned reflexes are often formed in the cerebral cortex, but this is not necessary, and the fact that they occur in quite simple invertebrates shows that no very high degree of nervous organization is necessary.

The formation of conditioned reflexes can be used to test the ability of an animal to distinguish stimuli. When a dog has been taught to salivate to a C fork, it will at first do so also to any note anywhere near this. But if C is sounded and food given, and alternately a G fork is sounded and no food is given, it will learn to distinguish between them—it salivates to C but not to G. This must mean that the two notes can be distinguished by the ears. It is only a matter of experiment to find how far this discrimination will go.

Conditioned reflexes have been formed experimentally very widely in vertebrates, and in turbellarians, annelids, arthropods, and molluscs. The best-known experiments on invertebrates are those on bees. Incidentally these show that the stimulus may be complex. The bees were trained to fly to a card bearing a pattern which had been associated with honey. It was found that solid black marks, whether triangles, circles, or squares, could not be distinguished apart. On the other hand, two concentric circles, triangles, or squares formed another group which could not be distinguished from one another, but which could be distinguished from the first group. The bees therefore react to a pattern, not to the shape of the figure.

It is probable that conditioned reflexes play a large part in the ordinary learning and behaviour of most Metazoa. The animal begins life with a limited number of inborn reflexes, but as it grows it forms new ones through the constant association of factors in the external environment. Newly emerged moths of the species *Plusia gamma* seek flowers by scent only, but after a few experiences they learn the appearance of suitable flowers and find them by sight as well. It has been said above that dogs salivate when meat is put into their mouths, and this is almost the only condition under which new-born puppies salivate at all. But, in general, dogs, and men too, learn very soon to salivate at the mere sight or smell of food, and it is a matter of common experience that this is so. Without any special physiological experiments conditioned reflexes are formed because the taste stimulus of food is regularly preceded by stimuli of smell and sight. The way in which it was long ago shown that chicks learn to peck only at suitable food was by the formation of a conditioned reflex. At first they peck at anything moving or bright, but they very soon learn to avoid wasps and other objectionable things. When these are taken into the mouth their taste acts as an unconditioned stimulus for them to be ejected and avoided. In time the mere sight of them acts in the same way. The school of human psychology known as behaviourism seeks to explain all human behaviour as being built up by conditioning from a few simple reflexes.

6.5. Trial-and-Error Learning

The last type of behaviour which will be considered here is learning by trial and error. The simplest case of this is that in which an animal has the choice of two exits from an enclosed space. One leads to a mild electric shock or some such nocuous stimulus, and the other to a reward of food and the comparative freedom of the normal living-quarters. There may be at first nothing to determine the animal to use one exit rather than another, and it takes the two indiscriminately, but in time it learns always to go to the one which leads to the reward. For clarity the two paths are generally distinguished in some definite way, as by a difference in illumination, but some animals can learn to go merely to their right or left. The design of the apparatus is varied to suit the animal—a glass Y-tube for worms, a tank of water for rats, and so on. Learning of this sort has been shown to occur in earthworms, in Crustacea, and in vertebrates. Whereas the worms need several hundred trials, crayfish need only fifty, and the higher mammals require only one or two. In the earthworm the nerve cord is involved, but not any special part of it. A worm that has learnt to find its way out can still do so when the cerebral lobes have been removed. In mammals it is chiefly the cerebral cortex that is used, but, again, not any special part of it. If the posterior third of the cortex of a rat which has learnt its way out of a trap be destroyed, the animal no longer remembers how to escape, but it can learn to do so again.

This sort of thing has obvious similarities to the conditioned reflex, but it differs from it in that the learnt response has reference to a reward which comes after the response. There seems, however, to be no need to regard the two as being very different. If the animal goes on down the wrong path it receives a nocuous stimulus which would cause a retreat—this is an unconditioned reflex. In time the other things associated with this—bright light or turning to the left or whatever it may be—form a conditioned reflex, and the animal goes the other way. In the same fashion, the other exit, where it leads to a reward of food, takes the animal to a stimulus which would, by an unconditioned reflex, cause a positive reaction. Here also a conditioned reflex can be formed, and the particular conditions associated with the right exit act as a conditioned stimulus. A very small turning towards one or other of the exits may serve as a conditioned stimulus for the reaction normally produced by the reward or shock, as the case may be. Trial-and-error learning may then be said to consist in the formation of double conditioned reflexes, one positive and the other negative. It is true that the more complicated cases of trial-and-error learning, such as maze-running in rats, do not admit of such a simple explanation, but with them we leave physiology and enter psychology.

Trial-and-error learning is the basis of most of the behaviour of animals which is too complicated for explanation by inherited reflexes or simple conditioned ones. It is particularly concerned with cases where an animal is set a problem to solve, that is a situation which it has not met before.

7

REPRODUCTION

WHATEVER may be the dictionary definition of reproduction, the word means in biology the production of an animal or plant which is in some way a different individual from the parent or parents which gave rise to it. An exact definition is difficult, but the general meaning of the word is simple. It is convenient and fairly logical to divide the methods of reproduction used by animals into sexual and asexual, but it must be noticed that the meaning of the second of these words does not correspond exactly with the use a botanist would make of the term; most of the asexual means of reproduction found in animals correspond more to the vegetative methods of propagation of plants than to the asexual method by means of spores.

7.1. Asexual Reproduction

Since there is less to be said about asexual reproduction than about sexual, it is convenient to take the former first, but it cannot be defined in any positive way. It is reproduction in which there is neither any sexual process, nor anything which can be interpreted as a reduced sexual process. It can take place in a number of ways, and the placing of these together under one head is probably more convenient than logical.

7.11. Fission

In its more restricted meaning fission implies the division

of a cell, and consequently it can only be a method of reproduction in the Protozoa. In them it is the normal and characteristic method by which increase in number is brought about. It consists in a division of the cytoplasm of the animal, preceded by an orderly division of the nucleus. In a few cases, such as in *Actinophrys* and *Amoeba*, it has been possible to make out that there is a mitosis similar to that of metazoan cells, and differing from this only in that the nuclear membrane remains intact. In other species either the individual chromosomes are too small for it to be certain that longitudinal division takes place, or the constancy of their number has not been established, but since there is general resemblance to mitosis the process is regarded as a reduced form of this and is called cryptomitosis. True amitosis is only universally admitted for the meganucleus of the Ciliophora, and even this it is possible to regard as the last stage of degeneration.

When fission results in the existence of two daughter individuals each about half the size of the parent it is said to be simple and binary. Sometimes there is more than one division before the products separate and start to lead independent existences, so that several small individuals result. This end may be brought about in two ways. In repeated fission there is more than one ordinary binary division in quick succession: an example is *Vorticella*, which produces eight small motile forms by three divisions. In multiple fission there are several divisions of the nucleus so that a syncytial condition is temporarily produced, and then the cytoplasm falls apart round the nuclei. Multiple fission is associated with a peculiar condition of the nucleus known as polyenergid in which several sets of chromosomes appear to be present: when the nucleus divides, these sets separate. Multiple fission always occurs in the formation of spores, and is then called sporulation. Spores, in the strict sense, are the products of reproduction of a zygote (p. 337), so that this type of reproduction is closely comparable to the asexual reproduction of plants. It occurs in many Protozoa, but is best seen in some of the parasitic forms such as *Monocystis* and *Plasmodium*.

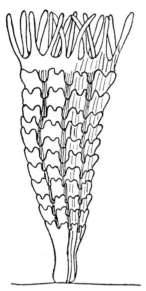

FIG. 41. Scyphistoma of *Aurelia aurita*, dividing transversely to form medusae. The process of division is called strobilization, and the successive medusae which split off from the top and swim away are ephyrae.

Budding is the name given to fission in which one of the products of the division is much smaller than the other. It has no relation to budding in the Metazoa. It occurs, for example, in *Arcella*.

7.12. Fragmentation

Fission is sometimes taken to include not only the division of the Protozoa, but also all cases where a Metazoon divides into two or more parts without there being any very special structures concerned in the process. For this it is better to use the word 'fragmentation'. *Hydra* is said occasionally to divide into two, and division of this sort is normal in many other coelenterates. The scyphistoma of jellyfish such as *Aurelia* produces a number of medusae by successive transverse divisions (Fig. 41). Actinozoa such as *Metridium* divide in two longitudinally, and the majority of the corals do the same. In the last case, however, the polyps remain attached, so that a colony is produced. The process nevertheless belongs here, as it is quite distinct from budding.

Fragmentation has been observed in a species of *Convoluta* and is a normal method of reproduction in some oligochaetes, particularly the freshwater families Aeolosomatidae and Naididae, and in some genera of the latter sexual individuals have never been found. Division takes place at a definite point called a fission zone, which is

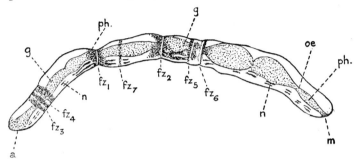

Fig. 42. *Chaetogaster* undergoing asexual multiplication; the general appearance is shown.

Seven fission zones are present; *a.*, anus; *fz.₁–fz.₇*, the fission zones in order of their appearance; *g.*, gut; *m.*, mouth; *n.*, nerve-cord; *oe.*, oesophagus; *ph.*, pharynx. After Wetzel.

usually formed at a fairly characteristic level (*n* segments from the front, where *n* is approximately constant). This is a region where several new segments are interpolated, and where reconstruction of tissues takes place, the activity being primarily epidermal. Usually the breaking of the animal into two parts does not take place till some reconstruction has occurred, but in some species it precedes even the formation of new segments. In many cases new fission zones appear before fragmentation occurs, so that a chain of as many as eight parts is formed. The whole is co-ordinated and swims as one animal until just before separation (Fig. 42). In some polychaetes there is regular and spontaneous fragmentation into short lengths, usually of two, three, or four segments, although in one species single segments which regenerate fore and aft are separated.

The pattern of breaking is constant for each genus. In the syllids there is also another type of fragmentation, in which new heads are formed before fission, and this produces special reproductive individuals which have no function but to swim to the surface of the sea and liberate gametes, so that it alternates with sexual reproduction. An example is the Palolo worm mentioned below in connexion with seasonal spawning (p. 340). In some genera, such as *Nereis*, the reproductive individual is rather different in appearance from the normal, and has been given its own generic name.

The type of protozoan fission called plasmotomy is probably best considered here. It is a division of a multinuclear organism independently of its nuclei, and may be subdivided according to the number and type of the products. It occurs in *Opalina*, where it is binary, and in the Mycetozoa, where it is multiple. The reverse process, plasmogamy, in which two or more cells flow together without fusion of their nuclei is also known, and in a few sponges comparable compound larvae are formed.

7.13. Gemmation or Budding

Gemmation or budding perhaps corresponds to what botanists call vegetative reproduction, and, as with that process in plants, it may lead primarily either to an increase in the number of individuals or to the production of a colony. It is difficult to separate it formally from fragmentation, but in practice there is seldom likely to be confusion. A bud is much smaller than the parent, is lateral, and is formed as a whole from a small group of embryonic cells. Budding is characteristic of the coelenterates and the ascidians. Lateral buds grow on *Hydra* when the food-supply is good, particularly (in the laboratory) in April and May. Secondary and even tertiary buds may be formed before separation begins. This last process is carried out by the bud seizing on to some solid object with its tentacles, and pulling itself apart from its parent. Except that it may grow one or two more tentacles, and will at the proper season form gonads, the bud at the time of detachment is a perfectly formed *Hydra*. In most of the other coelenterates, whether Hydrozoa or Actinozoa, the buds do not become detached, so that a colony is formed. Budding only occurs occasionally in the Scyphomedusae, where the scyphistoma sometimes multiplies in this way.

There are several species of compound ascidians, which bud in different ways. In the larger number of genera, of which *Clavellina* is an example, a hollow median stolon grows out from the ventral side of the abdomen, and on this buds grow. Blood-vessels and other structures grow into these and are common to the whole colony. In a few genera, such as *Botryllus*, the buds are formed from paired outgrowths of the atrium, and in *Doliolum* the buds are formed at one point, become detached, and then migrate to another place where they become attached again. It is maintained by some workers that in the budding no regard is paid to the germ layers from which the new tissues normally come, but by others this is strenuously denied.

7.2. Sexual Reproduction

The essence of sexual reproduction is that two cells come together and fuse. The fusing cells are called gametes, the resulting structure is a zygote, and the orderly process by which the cytoplasm of the two mixes and the nuclei become combined to form one is called syngamy. It is also referred to as conjugation, but since this word is used in protozoology in a rather different sense its use in this way is to be avoided. Fertilization is the same thing as syngamy, but the two words are used with slightly different values. Syngamy is generally chosen when the emphasis is on the phenomenon of fusion as a whole, fertilization when the process of fusing is being considered. In fact the slight difference in meaning between fusion and fusing corresponds to that between syngamy and fertilization. Since in some cases one of the gametes may be induced to develop without the other, fertilization is sometimes used with the meaning 'the process whereby one gamete causes another to develop'. The fact that sometimes the nucleus of one of the fusing cells divides before nuclear fusion takes place but after the two cytoplasms have mixed, makes a formal definition of gametes and of fertilization practically impossible, for in these cases the cytoplasm which fuses is that of a different pair of cells from those to which the fusing nuclei belong.

It is obvious that syngamy by itself leads to a reduction of the number of individuals. By itself, then, it does not lead to a perpetuation of the race unless the gametes exceed in number the parents which produce them. This is normally the case.

It follows from the definition of syngamy as the fusion of two cells that the Protozoa are the only animals in which it can take place between adults. In this phylum there are a few species where ordinary full-grown individuals may fuse, as in *Polytoma*, and the partner which bears all the cytoplasm in the syngamy of ciliates may perhaps be regarded as full-grown: it is certainly full size. Such gametes are called hologametes, and the small specially prepared ones merogametes. Outside protozoology the terms are never used since they are unnecessary.

The Protozoa also differ from the Metazoa in that the two fusing gametes may be both alike so far as the microscope can distinguish. They are then called isogametes. More often in the Protozoa, and everywhere outside this phylum, the gametes differ in size or form or both, and are called anisogametes. The smaller may be called simply a microgamete and the larger a megagamete, but more often the one which is small is also more active, and is called a male gamete or a spermatozoon, and the other, large and sluggish, is called a female gamete or an ovum. The first term is often shortened to sperm, and the second translated as egg. At this point, where dimorphism of gametes begins to be developed, sex, as distinct from sexual reproduction, begins. The differentiation of the sexes is another thing still—the existence of two types of adult to produce the two types of gamete. Although primarily the difference need concern only the reproductive organs (such is the case in the coelenterates) it may affect accessory structures, as in the frog, the whole external appearance, as in many birds, or the general mental outlook, as in man. An animal which produces both male and female gametes is a hermaphrodite. Much has been written about the possible reasons for the existence of sex and sexual reproduction, but all the alleged explanations are teleological rather than physiological.

In the Metazoa the preparation of the gametes involves a meiosis, that is a process of cell division in which the chromosomes are reduced to the haploid number. In the Protozoa this is difficult to make out, but it has been observed in widely separated species—in *Actinophrys, Paramecium,* and some amoebas—so that it is probably the normal thing. In most Sporozoa and in the Volvocina meiosis occurs immediately after syngamy, and the animal lives nearly all its life in the haploid state. (This is of course also the case in the gametophyte generation of plants.)

The term conjugation is used to mean the coming together of two Protozoa so that syngamy follows, a process which is most familiar in *Paramecium.* Here two adult individuals unite by their ventral surfaces, and nuclear changes then take place. Finally, one daughter nucleus from the first individual goes across and fuses with a nucleus which has remained in the second individual; meanwhile another nucleus similarly travels from the second to the first. The two motile nuclei may be regarded as male gametes, and the non-motile ones, with their associated cytoplasm, as females. In most Protozoa other than the Ciliophora conjugation consists merely in the ordinary fusion of two gametes, and is therefore synonymous with syngamy, but the name is also applied to plastogamy, a process which occurs in the Mycetozoa and in *Amoeba diploidea*, where two masses of cytoplasm fuse without union of the nuclei.

By far the majority of Metazoa have the sexes separate, and even in those species which are hermaphrodite cross-fertilization is the usual thing. Before fertilization can occur the gametes must be brought together. In many marine animals all that happens is that prodigious numbers of eggs and sperms are shed into the sea, so that, small though the chance of any two individuals meeting may be, in total there are very many unions. That gametes of both sexes are liberated at the same time is ensured by the seasonal rhythm of the animal. The exact cause of this rhythm is unknown, but in a general way it may be related to changes in the environment. In very few animals are the gonads continuously active. In *Planaria alpina* their development is brought on by temperatures of less than 10° C., in the oyster high temperatures are necessary, and in the vertebrates, which are discussed more fully below, the seasonal change in light is the most important factor.

Not only must the males and females be ripe at the same time, but their gametes must be liberated more or less together, and this also must be determined by some environmental change. In the oyster a sudden rise in temperature is effective. The most precise examples of rhythm are found in the polychaetes called Palolo worms, *Leodice fucata* in the Atlantic and *L. viridis* in the Pacific. They swarm at a very limited period—the last quarter of the October–November moon in *viridis*, and the last quarter of the June–July moon in *fucata*. The worms live in tubes, from which the heads normally protrude. The night before the swarming the animals change their position so that the tails protrude, and as soon as the sunlight touches the water on the morrow the tails break off and swim by themselves to the surface. They emit eggs or sperms from the anterior wound where they broke off from the main body of the worm, and then die. There is also a lunar periodicity in other worms, and in some sea-urchins and molluscs. The reason for this, and even its value, is problematical, since some animals reproduce well enough without it, and a species which has a lunar rhythm in one place may be without it in another. Even Palolo worms from some areas do not swarm, but if those from the swarming areas are kept in the dark in the laboratory, they swarm at the same time as their relatives which have been exposed to the moonlight.

This may be due to persistence of a previously imposed rhythm, or to some pervasive factor which fluctuates with the moon's changes. Fluctuations in the height and other properties of the ionosphere have a lunar periodicity, but how these could affect animals is unknown; it is noteworthy that lunar swarming is often associated also with sunset or sunrise, when again there are changes in the ionosphere.

In addition to a periodicity affecting both sexes there may be some device to ensure that eggs and sperms are liberated in close proximity to each other. *Odontosyllis enopla*, the Bermudan fire-worm, swarms on the second, third, and fourth days after full moon throughout the year, at 55 minutes after sunset whatever the state of the sky. When the females swim to the surface they begin to glow, and then, as each one starts to release her eggs, she swims in circles of two or three inches in diameter and becomes highly phosphorescent. A male, which has been waiting ten or fifteen feet below, swims straight for the centre of the circle, flashing as he does so, and the two swim together in slightly wider circles emitting eggs and sperms. If the female ceases to be phosphorescent he does also, and he is incapable of finding her. The worms are not luminous at other times.

In some species the shedding of gametes is determined by some substance released by the opposite sex. Under normal circumstances in *Nereis limbata* (an American Atlantic form) several males swim round a female and shed sperms, and she then liberates eggs. If the sexes are confined in the laboratory, the gametes are retained, but the addition of water which has contained females causes the release of sperms, and sperms cause liberation of eggs. A similar type of mechanism operates in the oyster, and it is probable that something of the kind is widespread.

Hydra has a variant on this indiscriminate shedding of gametes: the ovum is retained in the body of the parent, but protrudes so that the sperms shed generally into the pond may reach it.

It is only in water where there are no strong currents that this wide release of the two sorts of gametes is likely to be successful. In the tidal zone and in running waters there is usually some more exact conjunction of the two sexes. In the salmon the female scrapes a hole on the river bottom, and lays her eggs in this; the male sheds a cloud of sperms ('milt') over them, and the stream helps to mix the two. Fertilization in the frog is carried out during a sexual embrace called amplexus. The male recognizes the female by the warty skin which she develops in the breeding season, and holds on to her because she is stout. The eggs are laid, and their contact with the symphysis pubis region of the male acts as a stimulus for the emission of his sperm. When all the eggs have been laid the female is much thinner, the stimulus which causes the male to hold her is removed, and she is released.

Sperms are motile by a tail which is in effect a flagellum, and so they cannot live on dry land. Terrestrial animals must therefore have some means of bringing sperms and eggs into contact, and they normally do it by placing the sperms inside the body of the female: the act of doing this is called copulation or coition. Such conjunction of the sexes is also found in some aquatic animals, such as the cartilaginous fishes and the turbellarians, and many gastropods, cephalopods and crustaceans. In some groups, such as most reptiles and birds, there is no special organ for carrying the sperms, the genital apertures of the two sexes merely being apposed, but in others a special intromittent organ, the penis, is present. In the snail this is highly muscular. In mammals it contains erectile tissue which consists of yellow fibres and strands of smooth muscle enclosing spaces in communication with both arteries and veins. The smooth muscle of the organ, and the muscular walls of the arteries, are normally contracted, but in sexual excitement they relax, so that the organ becomes filled with blood and turgid. In this state it is inserted into the vagina of the female, and the semen containing the sperms is ejaculated by contractions of the muscles of the vas deferens and urethra.

In some animals an ordinary part of the body is used to transfer the sperm. In *Octopus*, for instance, a specially modified tentacle, the hectocotylus, places it in the mantle cavity of the female. The male spider sheds a drop of semen on to a leaf, or sometimes on to a small web which he spins specially for the purpose. To this he applies the end of his palp, which has the terminal joint modified to contain a tubular seminal vesicle. The palp containing the sperms is then inserted into the genital opening of the female. This might almost be called artificial insemination. Male and female scorpions perform a dance, a 'promenade à deux' in which the male holds the chelicerae of the female. He extrudes a packet of sperms, or spermatophore, and guides his partner over this. She presses down until its valves are within her genital aperture, and stands immobile until the semen is absorbed. She then leaves it and the pair separate.

7.21. Fertilization

However the gametes are brought near one another, the final act of fertilization can only take place when egg and sperm have come into contact. This depends chiefly on the activity of the sperm. It is characteristic of the male gamete that it is motile, and in nearly all classes of animals it consists of a head containing the nucleus, a short middle piece, and a tail which is simply a flagellum. In general, sperms are inactive in the testis, and only start to swim when they come into the fertilization medium, whether that be the sea as in starfishes or the secretion of the prostate as in mammals. This implies either that the medium contains something which positively activates the sperm, or that it removes an inhibitor, and substances of the first class are common although they have not been certainly identified. The activity of sperms of starfishes, sea-urchins, and many worms is greatly increased by egg-water, that is, water in which unripe eggs have been washed, and at the same time their respiration-rate is raised and their life-span increased. The effects are to some extent interspecific, but individual species show great differences in their reaction. *Echinus esculentus* sperm has its activity increased four times by egg-water, while that of *E. miliaris* is scarcely affected. Strychnine, thyroxine (see p. 226), and some other substances have similar effects to egg-water, and it is notable that thyroxine also raises the basal metabolism of the organism, for in increasing the activity of the sperms it is doing fundamentally the same thing. The semen of the salmon contains a substance which inhibits the movement of sperms, but it loses its action on dilution, so that the sperms become active when they are liberated into the river.

The metabolism of mammalian sperms is broadly similar to that of other tissues, but the cells contain very small reserves and most of their energy is obtained from external fructose which is present in the secretion of the seminal vesicles. Experimentally they can use glucose and mannose as well when these are added to the medium surrounding them. Glycolysis appears to be of the normal type, the citric acid cycle operates, and cytochromes are present. Fructose is also present in the semen of the rough-hound and the locust. Sea-urchin sperms use mainly phospholipids, and these are used also in mammals, particularly when the sperms are still in the epididymis.

In nature, sperms probably seldom live for more than 24 hours after leaving the testis, and fertilizing power is lost sooner than this, but in a few species, such as bats and some snakes, they are stored in the female for months, or even, as in the honey-bee, for years.

Sperms have been described as swimming towards crystals of thyroxine, but there seems to be no evidence of any natural chemotaxis towards the egg in animals comparable with the way in which fern spermatozooids are attracted to the archegonium by malic acid. The mere prodigality in the number of sperms probably ensures that many of them are brought close to an egg, although in the mammals that have been examined (rat, rabbit, ferret, ewe) it seems that of the hundred or thousand million sperms in one ejaculate, only a few hundreds or thousands reach the Fallopian tube, where fertilization occurs. In man the distance which the sperms have to travel to meet

the egg in the tube is about 25 cm; their speed of movement is 2–3 mm/min, so that their journey would take
them about 2 hours, which is well within their life span of
up to 40 hours.

It has been shown that in a number of mammals, ranging from the rat, where the sperms are ejaculated into the
uterus, to the cow, where they are placed in the vagina,
the time from copulation to their appearance at the site
of fertilization is only about 15 minutes so that they must
be sucked up by the female tract.

In the rabbit, and perhaps more generally, the sperms
do not acquire the capacity to enter the egg until they
have been in the female's body for some hours. Then, if
one touches the jelly which surrounds the egg it nearly
always burrows in normally to the surface. The penetra-
tion is assisted by the enzyme hyaluronidase and others,
and by absorption by the egg. In the hamster and the
guinea-pig capacitation appears to involve, or to be, removal of the acrosome, a structure formed from the Golgi
bodies during the differentiation of the sperms from the
spermatids.

In elasmobranchs, urodeles, reptiles, birds, some molluscs, and many insects several sperms enter the cytoplasm, but when one of the male pronuclei has begun to
fuse with that of the egg, the others degenerate; some
evidence suggests that this is caused by a substance diffusing from the successful pronucleus. In other species, the first
contact of egg and sperm causes a change in the cortex
of the egg which passes over the surface in less than two
seconds, and reduces the chance of entry of another sperm
to one-twentieth of normal. Further changes, taking about
one minute, render the egg quite impermeable, by the
formation of a fertilization membrane. This, in some
animals appears to be merely the pre-existing vitelline
membrane which has been lifted up and made visible, and

in all cases the membrane is only a sign of much more fundamental changes. There is, however, no regularity in the changes in oxygen consumption, respiratory quotient, and so on, since these depend also on the stage of development of the egg at which fertilization takes place.

7.22. Reproductive Rhythm in Mammals

It has been pointed out above that in animals which liberate their gametes freely into the sea synchronization of the escape of eggs and sperms may be assured by a seasonal rhythm affecting both sexes. It is equally important that, in animals with definite conjunction of the sexes, both male and female should be fit for intercourse at the same time. This also is often brought about by a reproductive rhythm which has some connexion with the seasons. The nesting season of birds, the rutting season of many mammals, and the menstrual periods of women are obvious examples which have been known from the earliest times. In a discussion of the factors which determine this rhythm it is convenient to start with mammals, since more is known of them than of the other classes.

The rhythm is most marked in the female. The essential part of the ovary is the Graafian follicle. When this is ripe (Fig. 43) it consists of a vesicle with an outer wall or theca and an inner one called the membrana granulosa. Attached to the latter at one side is a mass of cells, the discus proligerus, which contains the ovum. The cavity of the vesicle contains a fluid, the liquor folliculi. The theca is formed from the general stroma of the ovary, while the membrana granulosa, discus proligerus, and the ovum itself are developed from the original cubical epithelium on the surface of the foetal ovary. It is improbable that this epithelium sinks in to form any new follicles after birth and in almost all the mammals which have been examined oogenesis is confined to the period shortly before and shortly after birth. Exceptions in which it has been observed in the adult are the cat, the nine-banded armadillo, and a few lower primates. Ovulation consists in the rupture of the follicle and the liberation of the ovum into the body cavity. Only a few follicles burst together; in the rabbit the normal number is five or six on each side, and

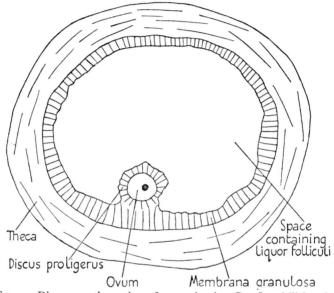

Theca

Discus proligerus

Ovum

Space containing Liquor folliculi

Membrana granulosa

FIG. 43. Diagrammatic section of a nearly ripe Graafian follicle of a rabbit, × 125.

in the human being but one, the ovaries apparently working randomly.

After ovulation the cells of the membrana granulosa and of the theca increase in size so that in the place of the follicle there is formed a dense mass of cells known as the corpus luteum.

The process of growth and degeneration of the follicle, with its accompanying changes in other parts of the body, is called the oestrous cycle.

The simplest sexual rhythm in mammals is annual, for most wild mammals breed at one season only of the year. Traditionally this is the spring, and with very few exceptions the Insectivora, Carnivora, Rodentia, and non-ruminating ungulates breed about April in the Northern hemisphere, and September in the Southern. In most Artiodactyla, however, the rutting season is the fall, which, since they have a long period of gestation, leads to the birth of young in the spring. Some mammals with a short true gestation period also copulate in autumn, but the development of the embryo is delayed. Either, as in the weasels and other small carnivores, there is delayed implantation, the blastocyst remaining quiescent in the uterus, or, as in bats, the sperms are stored until spring. When an animal is moved from one hemisphere to another its breeding season may change so that the animal is still sexually active at a time of increasing or decreasing light intensity, as the case may be. Red deer which have been imported into New Zealand continue to rut in the fall, but this is six months different from their time in Europe. Sheep taken from Britain to South Africa have changed similarly, sometimes during their first year in the new home.

The oestrous cycle fits into this annual breeding cycle, but it is not necessarily synchronous with it, for although some animals, such as the fox, are monoestrous, that is have one ovarian cycle in a breeding season, others are polyoestrous, and have several cycles fitting into the year. There is no essential difference between the two cases, but polyoestrus is best regarded as a secondary rhythm imposed on the main one. There are four phases of the cycle.

1. Dioestrus, a quiescent period when there is no sexual activity. The long period of quiescence between breeding seasons is called the anoestrus.

2. Pro-oestrus, a preparatory phase during which the follicle is developing.

3. Oestrus, the period of heat. At this time there are usually changes of hypertrophy in the external genitalia, and it is only at this time that the female shows any sexual desire: at other times males are repelled. There are also changes in the walls of the vagina, which become cornified. In many animals ovulation occurs in this period, but the rabbit, ferret, cat, and some others ovulate only after copulation. (This peculiarity of these animals makes them very suitable for research where the exact time relations of subsequent events are required.)

4. After oestrus there is a degenerative metoestrus (or postoestrus), but this is generally merged into the state of pregnancy (when fertile union has occurred) or pseudo-pregnancy (when it has not).

Ovulation takes place in the rabbit 10 hours after copulation. The half-dozen ova are packed, with some other cells from the follicle, in albumen which clots round them when the liquor folliculi escapes. The mass is carried to the ostium abdominale by the cilia of the body cavity, and it then enters the Fallopian tube, forming a plug at the top of this. By this time the thickest density of the up-swimming sperms has nearly reached the top of the tube, and the chance of fertilization is high. The sperms liberate a protease which dissolves the albumen, so that when the eggs are fertilized they can be carried down the uterus by the cilia of the tube. Fertilization has occurred within 16 hours from copulation. Division of the egg starts in the Fallopian tube and continues in the uterus. The beginning of the attachment of the foetus to the latter starts on the eighth day.

It is likely that the course of events in other mammals is similar, but the time relations will naturally be different. It would seem that where ovulation takes place without reference to mating the chance of fertilization would be greatly lessened.

Changes in the endometrium (the lining of the uterus) have begun even before the embryo has arrived, but they become more marked after this. The superficial epithelium degenerates, and the embryo sinks in against the connective tissue. By a growing together of tissues from both embryo and mother the placenta is formed, and to make the maternal part of this the uterus grows out into villi, and its blood-vessels, particularly the veins, increase greatly in size. As pregnancy continues the uterus increases in size, and its cavity becomes greatly enlarged to hold the developing embryos. The vagina also increases in size. Other changes occur in pregnancy, particularly the development of the mammary glands so that milk can be supplied to the young at, or (in man) a day or two after, birth. In the later stages of pregnancy the animal often behaves differently from the normal by retiring from the herd, making a nest, and so forth. Seals migrate long distances to land for parturition to take place.

Pseudopregnancy is a state which occurs at the end of the oestrous cycle in many mammals when fertilization has not taken place. It consists in the same phenomena as pregnancy, but they are developed to a lesser degree. The changes in the uterus begin, but cannot go to the stage of the formation of the placenta, and there is some enlargement of the mammary glands. The bitch collects material for a bed, and the doe rabbit plucks her fur as she does to shelter her young in the ordinary way. In most mammals, but not in the rat or mouse, dioestrus is simply a short and not very marked pseudopregnancy.

The growth of the Graafian follicles is not itself the factor which determines the other changes, since oestrus occurs when all the follicles have been destroyed by X-radiation. It does not occur, however, if both ovaries are removed in their entirety. It is therefore likely that an oestrus-producing hormone is manufactured by some part of the ovary other than the follicles. Such a hormone was first discovered in extracts of ovaries in 1912, and has since been found in the placenta and in urine of both males and females, but particularly in that of females at about the time of ovulation and when pregnant. Extracts of all these induce oestrus within 2 days after being injected into spayed mice, but neither the urine nor any organ normally has oestrogenic properties unless either an ovary or a placenta be present. Several substances with oestrogenic properties have now been isolated, such as oestrone, oestriol, oestradiol, equiline, and equilenin: collectively they are known as oestrins or oestrogens, and form a group of closely related sterols. The primary product liberated by the ovary is almost certainly oestradiol, which is the most active, and it is probable that the others are derived from this. Its formula is

The oestrogens are not specific. A number of related synthetic substances have been shown to produce oestrus.

Oestrus is usually followed by pregnancy or pseudopregnancy, and the change-over to this phase is marked by the development of the corpus luteum. In those animals, such as mice, in which there is scarcely any pseudopregnancy, the corpora lutea develop very little and soon degenerate unless copulation occurs. If a female mouse is mated with a sterile male, fertilization cannot occur, but the corpora lutea persist much longer than usual, and there is a marked pseudopregnancy which postpones the onset of the next sexual cycle for 7 days. (Normally the whole cycle only takes 5 days.) Pregnancy or pseudo-pregnancy is associated with the production by the corpus luteum of a hormone called progesterone (or progestin, or luteo-sterone) which has the structure

This, in addition to sensitizing the uterus for the attach-ment of the embryo and producing the characteristic changes in the reproductive organs and mammary glands, also inhibits oestrus and ovulation. Oestrus can therefore occur again only when the effects of the corpus luteum have worn off. The corpora lutea are normally necessary for the maintenance of pregnancy, for in most animals abortion occurs if they are removed. In some, however, such as man, horse, cat, and rat, their persistence is not essential, and their function is probably taken over by the placenta itself.

The discovery of oestrogen and progesterone gives an immediate cause for oestrus and pregnancy, but it does not fully explain either the rhythm or the first onset of oestrus at puberty and in each annual season. It is now certain that the anterior part of the pituitary gland is at work here. It produces several different hormones (see pp. 230–4), some of which act on the reproductive system. Injection of suspensions of the anterior pituitary into adult females causes ovulation, followed, as would be expected, by luteinization (formation of corpora lutea). Similar treatment of immature females leads to a precocious oestrus and ovulation. These effects agree in import with the entire cessation of sexual activity caused by removal of the pituitary. It is now known that two hormones are produced, one inducing the ripening of the follicle and the other the transformation of the follicle into the corpus luteum. They are known respectively as the follicle-stimulating hormone (FSH) and the luteinizing hormone (LH). The two together are necessary for ovulation.

The interaction of the anterior pituitary and the ovary seems to be mutual, for in castrates the gonadotropic activity of the pituitary increases. Moreover, it can be lowered again by the administration of oestrogen.

The cycle may then be pictured as follows (Schema 7): first, the pituitary produces follicle-stimulating hormone, which induces the ovary to form oestrogen. The latter brings on the characteristic phenomena of oestrus, and also reduces the activity of the pituitary. Oestrus is followed by ovulation and luteinization as a result of the presence of luteinizing hormone. (It is obvious that corpora lutea cannot be formed until ovulation has occurred.) Meanwhile the inhibition of the pituitary by oestrogen has removed the stimulus for any further ovulation or production of oestrogen, and then with the depressant factor removed the pituitary becomes active again. The ovary is again stimulated to produce oestrogen, and a second cycle has begun. Where the FSH/LH ratio is high, as in the mare, oestrus is long and ovulation occurs before it is over. Where the ratio is low, as in the cow, oestrus is short and ovulation does not take place until it is finished. Cold and other factors may upset the balance, so that oestrus and ovulation do not go together, with sterility as the inevitable result. The maintenance of the corpora lutea is brought about by a third anterior pituitary

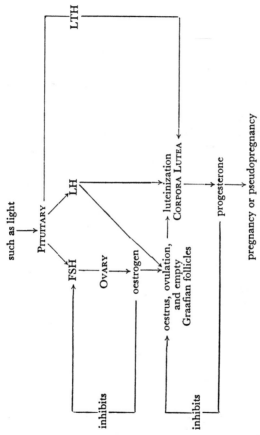

SCHEMA 7. The oestrous cycle in mammals

hormone, prolactin or the luteotropic hormone (LTH), which also stimulates milk secretion.

To make the story reasonably complete we must know the immediate cause of the secretion of gonadotropic hormones by the anterior pituitary, and here the oestrous cycle can be linked up with the longer seasonal cycle. If doe ferrets are exposed to electric light in winter, they come to full heat in 38–64 days, although they are not normally in season until April. It is the visible and particularly the ultra-violet rays which are effective, and similar results are obtained for a spread or a concentrated dose of the same total magnitude. Hypophysectomized animals (i.e. those in which the anterior pituitary has been extirpated) do not respond. Raccoons also have been induced to breed 6 weeks before their normal time by exposing them to an increased light intensity.

In sheep, the effective influence is the change from an increasing to a decreasing light ration, and this produces oestrus just as easily when it occurs at an experimental day-length of $13\frac{1}{2}$ hours as when it occurs, under natural conditions, with one which is much longer. Clearly, if this were not so the system could only work at a restricted latitude. While all the mammals that have been investigated are dependent in some way on light, the exact form of the stimulus differs from one species to another so as to be ecologically suitable. There is even some slight evidence that the sexual success of nocturnal Malayan forest rats is increased by the full moon. Since in an experiment a blind ferret did not respond to light, it is probable that the stimulus is received by the eyes, and there is some evidence that a substance secreted by the hypothalamus passes through the hypophyseal portal system to the anterior pituitary and stimulates it to secrete. In the ferret, which does not ovulate spontaneously, the activity of the hypothalamus is initiated by copulation.

In these experiments the effect of temperature was eliminated, but it has been shown that in some rodents a variation of temperature is also necessary to maintain the cycle. Temperature may possibly be an important accessory factor in nature, and food may also have an influence. The oestrous cycle of mice is shortened by the proximity of a male, and may be suppressed, in the absence of a male, by the presence of other females. In domestic animals, such as the cow, that may breed at any time of the year, it seems likely that excess of food or some other factor has eliminated the necessity for light or any other external stimulus to start the cycle in operation.

In the Old World monkeys and in man the oestrous cycle appears to be replaced by the menstrual cycle, which is marked by a flow of blood and mucus from the uterus. By investigations on monkeys, together with some evidence from man, it has been shown that the two cycles are closely interlocked. First, there is the interval dominated by oestrogen, when the follicle is maturing, leading up to ovulation. During this time the endometrium is unspecialized and thin. After ovulation, a corpus luteum is formed, and progesterone becomes the dominating hormone; under its influence the endometrium thickens and becomes vascular and glandular, the premenstrual period. This represents a preparation for the ovum, and is obviously a condition of pseudopregnancy. When fertilization does not take place the corpus luteum degenerates, and so both hormones are reduced in quantity. As a result of this the endometrium breaks down and the blood and cells resulting are discharged in menstruation. There is a brief post-menstrual period before the next follicle begins to mature. Thus the periods of pro-oestrus and oestrus are represented by the interval, pseudopregnancy by the premenstrual period, and the dioestrus by the menstrual and post-menstrual periods. In the human menstrual cycle ovulation probably occurs between the thirteenth and seventeenth days, counting from the beginning of the menstrual flow (Schema 8), with modifications when the cycle is of unusual length. It must be added that the agreement between the two cycles is not exact, as in monkeys menstruation quite often takes place without ovulation; the proximate cause of menstrual bleeding seems to be a sudden lowering of the amount of oestrogen in the blood, but it can also be produced by progesterone.

Cyclical changes in the reproductive organs are not so obvious in the male as in the female, but they are nevertheless there. The interstitial cells of the testis produce a hormone called testosterone which is closely allied to the ovarian hormones; its formula is

(Androsterone is less active and is found only in urine.) Injected into castrated rats testosterone prevents degeneration of the accessory sexual organs—vasa deferentia, prostate gland, &c.—which they would otherwise suffer. Rats castrated before puberty show no sexual behaviour, but if they are injected with a derivative of testosterone their accessory organs develop and they copulate when presented with females. Testosterone is not formed if the anterior pituitary is removed, but hypophysectomized animals do make it if they receive injections of luteinizing hormone. Buck ferrets which receive artificial light in winter become sexually interested and their accessory

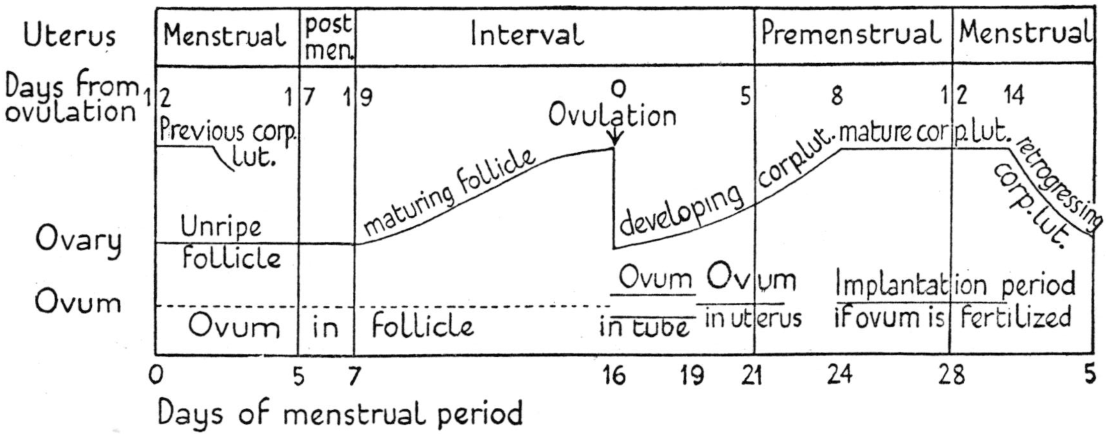

SCHEMA 8. The relationship of the human menstrual cycle to the normal mammalian cycle. Slightly modified from Corner

organs develop, but the unions are sterile, because spermatogenesis is incomplete. Cotton-tail rabbits (*Sylvilagus transitionalis*) treated in the same way produce sperms. These observations suggest that the male is influenced similarly to the female, but the details of the process are even less well known. There is no evidence that males undergo rhythmical changes similar to the oestrous cycle of females, and there is no reason why they should. In most mammals (the rabbit is an exception) the female is only willing to receive the male while she is on heat—that is just about the time of ovulation—and provided that the male is then able to discharge active sperms fertilization is reasonably certain. The case of those animals, such as the rabbit, where ovulation occurs only after coition, may be regarded as a refinement which makes assurance doubly sure. The mechanism by which ovulation is brought about is obscure, for it takes place even if coition occurs when the vagina and vulva are anaesthetized, the ovaries transplanted, and the sympathetics cut. It can be induced experimentally by the hormone of the anterior pituitary or by strong electrical stimulation of the central nervous system.

Normal copulation only occurs when the brain is intact and when there is a proper complement of sexual hormones. The males of lower mammals mount the female successfully at the first attempt, but some others, such as the chimpanzee, need considerable practice, and in all the degree of sexual excitability is modified by experience. Smell, vision, and tactile stimulation of the skin of the snout and lips are all important in producing the sexual behaviour of male rats, and elimination of one or two of them leads to reduced excitability. Elimination of all three makes copulation impossible.

This account of the control of reproduction is simplified, since there seem to be many species differences, and a given hormone often has different effects when it is injected into different animals. The sex hormones have been shown to influence many enzyme systems.

7.23. Reproductive Rhythms in Other Vertebrates

The oestrous cycle occurs in mammals only, but other vertebrates are influenced seasonally in a very similar way to mammals. The normal breeding season of birds is the spring, and this is the time when days are lengthening. That birds are very sensitive to light is shown by the phenomenon of the dawn chorus—the outburst of song from all species which occurs just before sunrise. The testes of birds are subject to great seasonal variation in size, becoming much larger in the breeding season than at other times. Excess of artificial light in winter may bring on a premature swelling of the testes of a number of species; in the starling (*Sturnus vulgaris*) only a very restricted spectral band in the yellow and red is effective. In *Junco hyemalis*, a Canadian finch, it has been shown that it is not the light itself but the resulting activity which is responsible for the change. Birds are active if they are awake, and they keep awake so long as it is light. Finches were confined in a cage in which a rod on an endless belt moved along the perch at regular short intervals. The birds became quite used to skipping over the bar, but by so doing they were prevented from sleeping. Although they were kept in dim light which was shown by control experiments not to be effective in itself, their testes hypertrophied to the spring size. Similar experiments on starlings caused production of sperms when the length of day reached a certain threshold; this varied, but was about $12\frac{1}{2}$ hours. It is likely that here too activity is important, but in other species the effect of light seems to be direct.

In general, light is clearly the important factor in initiating the breeding season in birds, and the important thing is the absolute length of day, not, as in many mammals, the changing day-lengths. There are some difficulties in applying this explanation universally, for many birds in the tropics have breeding seasons, even though the maximum change in day-length is very small, and the seasonal increase in the gonads of birds that migrate from the southern to the northern hemisphere begins before they start their journey. There is some ecological evidence that breeding seasons may be connected with food supply or rainfall, and in a careful experiment breeding was induced in the tropical red-billed weaver-finch, *Quelea quelea*, by feeding it with green grass. Rain plus dry grass had no effect, nor did rain added to green grass increase the induction of breeding. It has also been suggested that changes in the composition of the light, including the ultraviolet, may be important in the tropics (where many plants also are seasonal). Temperature is undoubtedly often an accessory factor, for sexual activity may cease altogether in cold weather, as may often be seen in an English spring, when May frosts cause the cessation of pairing and the abandonment of the nests of many birds.

The exteroceptive factors act by stimulating the anterior pituitary to produce hormones, just as they do in mammals. In the house sparrow (*Passer domesticus*) adrenaline causes regression to a juvenile state both in birds at the height of the breeding season and in those which have been experimentally brought into breeding condition by light or pituitary extracts, so that it appears to be antagonistic to the pituitary. Possibly the effect of activity in the Junco is to lower the blood adrenaline and so enable the pituitary to act at a lower threshold.

The final coming together of the sexes is a result of sexual display, in which both cock and hen take part in a series of behaviour patterns in the two sexes, ending in coition. (Courtship is a bad word, since the behaviour to which the name is given usually takes place after partners have been selected.) Presumably the display acts by stimulating the anterior pituitary; in other words it is an aphrodisiac leading to synchronization of orgasm. The degree to which birds are dependent on this sort of stimulation varies with the species. The barndoor fowl lays eggs throughout the year whether cocks are present or not, but pigeons will normally only lay eggs after pairing. Here it is presumably merely the sight of another individual which is the stimulus, for if two hen pigeons are confined together they may both lay eggs. The period over which sexual activity is maintained depends on the subsequent behaviour of the bird. Generally one nest is built, and a characteristic number of eggs are laid; if the nest is destroyed, another will be built, and if the eggs are removed as they are laid far more than the normal number will be produced. The house-sparrow, for instance, normally lays a clutch of four or five, but it has been induced to lay as many as fifty.

Little work has been done on reptiles, but in many species reproduction is seasonal. The testes of some snakes have an annual cycle of size and spermatogenesis similar to that of birds, and, as the increase begins in early spring, light in some form is probably the stimulating factor. Hypophysectomy or ovariectomy in pregnant viviparous snakes causes resorption or abortion of the embryos.

Most of the work on Amphibia has been done on *Xenopus laevis*, the clawed toad of South Africa. It is a tailless species in general similar to the common frog, but the mating embrace is lumbar instead of axillary, that is to say the male clasps the female round her waist, in the region of the urostyle. In the laboratory these animals show no sexual behaviour even if they are brought in during the mating season. Amplexus can, however, be induced at any time by injections of anterior pituitary extract. Ovulation follows, and the larvae from the unions have been reared through to a late tadpole stage. In the female, anterior pituitary extract can be replaced by progesterone, and sometimes this will induce mating and ovulation even in hypophysectomized or immature individuals. Several other frogs and toads are broadly similar, and it is therefore probable that the pituitary is as important in the sexual life of Amphibia as in that of mammals and birds. Since artificial sunlight in December makes frogs try to spawn it is probable that light is again the important climatic factor.

Many fish have a breeding season. Little experimental work has been done, but in the stickleback and minnow temperature seems to be the most important exterceptive stimulus. This might have been expected, since fish are largely shielded from the effects of light.

The pituitary hormone is not specific, for implantation of the anterior pituitary of the frog into immature female mice activates the reproductive organs and although mouse anterior pituitary has no effect on *Rana pipiens* it induces ovulation in the newt *Triturus viridescens*. Mammalian pituitary and sex hormones also produce signs of sexual maturity in immature lampreys. Progesterone has been extracted from the ovaries and blood of viviparous snakes.

7.24. Hermaphroditism

An animal which produces both male and female gametes is called a hermaphrodite. In many of the Protozoa, such as *Paramecium*, hermaphroditism may perhaps be primitive, but in the majority of animals in which it occurs it seems to have some connexion with the environment, for it is common in parasites and in the freshwater and terrestrial forms of some groups, but is rare in the sea. It is obvious that in parasites and in animals living in small isolated ponds hermaphroditism accompanied by self-fertilization would greatly increase the chance of the production of offspring, and might therefore have been evolved by natural selection, but in fact self-fertilization is rare, and ova and sperms are not usually produced at the same time. An animal which forms first sperms and then ova is protandrous, and if the order is reversed it is protogynous. In many animals, such as the snail and the earthworm, this alternation of sex is seasonal, but in some others there is no retrogression to the original sex once the change has taken place. The term hermaphrodite is not very appropriate for these, as there is just one very real, though perhaps slow, change of sex during the life-history. The best-known example is the mollusc *Crepidula fornicata*, the slipper limpet. The larvae of this are male when newly hatched, but if they settle down on the floor of the sea they become females. Others settle on top of them, produce sperms, and fertilize the females below. After a time these males begin to change their sex, and other males settle on their backs. This goes on till a pile of half a dozen or more molluscs is formed, those at the bottom being females, those in the middle hermaphrodite, and those on top males, of which the later ones are waiting for the animal below to change its sex. Each individual is at first functionally male, then hermaphrodite, and finally female, with the exception of the first in a chain, which is female only, and the last, which is male only.

This type of sex reversal is probably similar to that which sometimes occurs in vertebrates. An occasional hen has become a potent cock, and development of the secondary sexual characters of a cock is frequent in old hens. Whatever the exact mechanism of the determination of sex in vertebrates, the line between male and female is a thin one, and intersexes, with some of the attributes of both sexes, are not uncommon. They occur occasionally in man, and regularly in the toad, where Bidder's organ, at the anterior end of the testis, is probably a rudimentary ovary.

7.25. Parthenogenesis

Parthenogenesis is the reproduction which occurs when a cell which appears by its origin and structure to be a gamete develops without fertilization. By our previous formal definitions it is therefore a type of asexual reproduction, but the morphological evidence that it derived from ordinary sexual reproduction is too strong to be ignored. It follows from what has been said above about the limited life of sperms that it is very improbable that a male gamete could develop parthenogenetically, and in fact it is only in a few Protozoa, such as *Actinophrys*, where the distinction between the gametes is slight, that one ever does.

In a very few animals, such as some rotifers and some species of wasps and sawflies (*Hymenoptera*), parthenogenesis is the only known form of reproduction, and no males are known. More usually it alternates with typical sexual reproduction, but the degree to which it replaces this and the regularity of the alternation vary considerably. Probably in the majority of cases the alternation is quite irregular. In *Paramecium* and some other ciliates the good effects of conjugation on a culture can be replaced by those of endomixis, a special sort of parthenogenesis in which in a single individual the meganucleus and much of the micronuclear material are destroyed just as they are at conjugation. The details of the nuclear division and reconstruction vary, but one scheme is shown in Fig. 44.[1] The

[1] If, as is now claimed by some workers, a pair of micronuclei always fuse before the reconstruction, endomixis is a process not of parthenogenesis but of autogamy.

frequency with which endomixis and conjugation occur depends in part on the genetic nature of the stock, in part on external factors such as temperature, and in part on

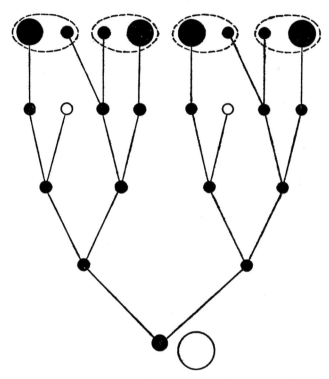

FIG. 44. Diagram of the behaviour of the nuclei at endomixis in *Paramecium caudatum*. White circles indicate nuclei which disappear.

the time measured in asexual generations from the previous endomixis or conjugation. In bugs of the family Aphidae the wingless females which hatch in spring from the eggs which have survived the winter reproduce parthenogenetically, and several similar wingless parthenogenetic generations, all females, follow. Finally in autumn winged females and males are produced, and together they give rise to fertilized eggs which survive the winter and begin the cycle again. There is no constancy in the number of parthenogenetic generations, and the production of males and winged females appears to be connected with falling temperature or shortage of food or both. The Cladocera such as *Daphnia* and many rotifers are similar.

In some insects (Cynipidae or gall-wasps) there is a regular alternation. For example, the individuals of *Neuropterus lenticularis* which appear in March are all females. They lay parthenogenetic eggs in buds of the oak, and in the galls so formed the larvae of the next generation develop. The imagines which emerge from the galls in June are very different from their parents, and were formerly designated by a different generic name. Some are male, some female, and between them they produce fertilized eggs which are laid in oak leaves. The pupae remain in galls on the dead leaves until the following spring, when they come out as the next parthenogenetic generation.

Lastly, in the bees parthenogenesis is facultative, that is, it appears to be under the control of the female laying the eggs. The queen (the female) copulates only once in her lifetime, and stores sperms in a receptaculum seminis for months or sometimes years. Only if the eggs are to be fertilized are sperms allowed to escape on to them as they are laid.

It is obvious that in the absence of any special arrangement parthenogenesis would mean a halving of the chromosome number in each generation. The details of the methods by which this is avoided are matters for a textbook of cytology, but it may be said here that almost all the ways conceivable by man are used by some animal or other. In Crustacea and Aphidae only one polar body is given off at maturation, and there is no reduction division; in bees the eggs are formed normally, but those which develop without fertilization all form males and there is no reduction in spermatogenesis.

Paedogenesis is the name applied to parthenogenesis when it occurs in a larval form. It is found in Cecidomyidae (Diptera) such as *Miastor*. It should strictly be distinguished from neoteny, which is ordinary sexual reproduction by a larva.

8

THE ANIMAL IN RELATION TO ITS ENVIRONMENT: REGULATION

MANY factors of the inorganic world affect the life of animals, some of the chief being: concentration of chemical substances, particularly oxygen, water, the hydrogen ion, and metallic cations; osmotic pressure; temperature; light intensity. A full account of the relationship between these and animals belongs not to physiology but to ecology, but the changes which alterations in the environment produce in the animal itself rather than in its behaviour may properly be considered in this book. Particular examples of such changes have been mentioned in the sections on effectors and behaviour, and the present chapter deals only with the means by which an animal makes itself to some extent independent of its environment, that is, by which it regulates. The story of organic evolution is to a great extent one of increasing independence; whereas Protozoa are greatly affected by nearly all the factors listed above, mammals can stand considerable variations in all except oxygen.

8.1. Hydrogen-ion Concentration

The more primitive animals are very sensitive to changes in acidity, but all animals which possess a body fluid, that is, all the coelomates, maintain an internal environment of approximately constant hydrogen-ion concentration, and they do this by exactly the same method as is used by the biochemist in the laboratory. Any acid will act as a buffer;

that is, if its degree of dissociation (y) is plotted against the pH of the corresponding solution (x) a curve of the type shown in Fig. 45 is given. Along the straight part of the curve a big change in degree of dissociation corresponds to a small change in pH. If hydrogen ions (in the form of another acid) are added to the solution, they will, by

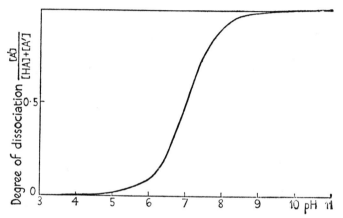

Fig. 45. Graph relating the dissociation of an acid of dissociation constant 10^{-7} to the pH of the resulting solution. Such an acid will act as a buffer between pH 6·5 and 7·5. Other acids will give similar curves shifted either to the right or to the left according to the value of the dissociation constant.

the law of mass action, drive back the dissociation of the acid originally present, and along the straight part of the curve they must do this to a considerable extent before the final pH is very much altered. The solution thus resists change of pH, and is said to be buffered. The position of the straight part of the curve depends on the particular acid used, the hydrogen-ion concentration corresponding to its mid-point being numerically equal to the dissociation constant. Thus acetic acid, with a dissociation constant of 10^{-7}, buffers best at a hydrogen-ion concentration of 10^{-7}, i.e. at pH 7, and is effective from about pH 6·5 to pH 7·5. The degree of dissociation corresponding to the middle of the straight part of the curve may be obtained by adding a salt of the acid, which depresses the ionization in the usual way. It is customary, but incorrect, to name the buffer by the salt. Strong acids are not considered as buffers, because their dissociation constant is very high, and so they only work in very high concentration of hydrogen ion where buffering is seldom important.

Since the product of the concentrations of hydrion and hydroxyl is constant, a similar argument to the above can be applied to bases.

All animals buffer their blood and other fluids by proteins, bicarbonate, and phosphate. The normal pH varies from one animal to another but is usually between 7 and 8.

8.2. Water

Water is an essential food, and it is obvious that animals cannot become independent of an external supply, but the embryo has in certain cases managed to do so. This is best shown by the vertebrates, which become better at storing water as the evolutionary scale is ascended. In the development of Amphibia and fish a considerable amount of water is absorbed by the embryo from the environment, in addition to that which is obtained from the yolk and by combustion; for example, in the trout (*Salmo fario*) the yolk supplies 59 mg of water for the embryo up to the time when it can absorb water through the gut, and 71 mg have been taken in from outside. In the reptiles less than one-third of the total water inside the shell at hatching has been absorbed from outside, for the egg has a coating of albumen, and much is got from this. The sole function of the white is in fact to store water. The birds have gone farther: their egg is shut off from the outside by a wall through which water travels slowly; the egg is termed cleidoic. The embryo derives all the water needed for development from the materials already in the egg—from the yolk, from combustion, but chiefly from the albumen. In fact, the eggs actually lose some water during development, and fail to develop unless they do. The mammals derive the water required during development from the mother.

Most invertebrate eggs absorb water from outside during development, as the fish and Amphibia do, but some of the insects may be independent.

It has been suggested that the development of the cleidoic egg has had far-reaching effects on the nitrogen metabolism. It has been pointed out in Chapter 2 that the nitrogen in most invertebrates and aquatic vertebrates is excreted in the form of ammonia, but that in terrestrial vertebrates it is in the form of either urea or uric acid, and that these animals can be divided into the Amphibia, Chelonia, and mammals, which are ureotelic, and the birds and Squamata, which are uricotelic. This distinction corresponds to the one just described between those animals whose embryos take in water from outside, and those which carry it with them in white of egg. The cleidoic egg, which is laid on land, has no means of getting rid of soluble waste products, and if all the nitrogen which would be excreted during embryonic life were to accumulate inside the shell as urea, the concentration reached would almost certainly be toxic. It was a condition of the evolution of the cleidoic and terrestrial egg that uric acid, which is insoluble, should be formed instead. For this to be the case it was necessary that uricase, the enzyme which in most ureotelic organisms destroys uric acid, should be lost. The uricotelic vertebrates have also lost arginase and the power to carry out the ornithine cycle.

Parallel with the change in the chief form of excretory nitrogen has gone a change in the material oxidized to provide energy for the embryo. In fish and Amphibia it is chiefly—up to 90 per cent.—protein. In the chick over 90 per cent. is fat. The advantages of this in the cleidoic egg are that more water is provided per gramme of material burnt, and that less waste nitrogen is formed.

Mammals are ureotelic; they have solved the problem of terrestrial life by viviparity; they presumably arose from reptiles which still laid their eggs in damp places and had not developed uricotely.

It must be added that not all physiologists regard this explanation of the origin of uricotely as the true one. It is pointed out that urea is not really very toxic, and that the cleidoic egg of the elasmobranchs, which excrete urea in both embryo and adult, remains unexplained. The alternative explanation for the uricotely of birds and reptiles (and insects) is that it saves water, and so is an adaptation to arid terrestrial life. Uric acid forms supersaturated solutions, from which it separates as an almost insoluble solid; the way in which water is saved by this in birds and insects is described in section 2.55. The shell of the cleidoic egg is merely an additional method of saving water. The elasmobranchs have taken to keeping urea in the blood in order to raise its osmotic pressure (see below). The cleidoic egg is in their case an adaptation to this— the egg is closed so that the urea can be retained, and the egg develops under conditions similar to those in the adult.

Land-living animals, whether they use lungs or tracheae, necessarily lose water from their respiratory surfaces, which must be kept damp if they are to work efficiently, and the more successful groups counteract this loss by having a thick and impermeable cuticle (no doubt serving other purposes as well) so that evaporation from the surface of the body is reduced. In the insects the effective barrier is a superficial layer of wax only $0.25\,\mu$ thick. The keratinized skin of amniotes serves the same purpose. Here there seems to be some reflex control, for the loss through the skin increases when the animal is anaesthetized. Rather more than half the total water loss of normal rats takes place through the skin, although they have few if any sweat glands, and the proportion rises to three-quarters when they are anaesthetized.

The evaporative loss from desert-living rodents is much less than that from the laboratory species of rats and mice, and the loss from camels and merino sheep is less than from other ruminants. All these animals of hot climates produce a very concentrated urine.

8.3. Osmotic Pressure and Ionic Concentration

The biological effects of substances in solution are produced in two ways: through the osmotic pressure, which is independent of the chemical properties of the solute, and through the direct action of particular ions. There is some regulation to both of these.

8.31. Osmotic Regulation

All living membranes seem to be semipermeable, or, to be more accurate, they have differential permeability for water and solutes. Consequently, no tissue can be in equilibrium with its surroundings unless the osmotic pressures inside and outside are the same. This is the case in most marine invertebrates. The depression of the freezing-point (Δ) of sea-water is $2 \cdot 0°$ C, and that of the blood and body fluids of invertebrates which live in the sea is about the same: they are said to be isosmotic with sea-water. As the salinity of sea-water varies (it is lower, for instance, in estuaries and other places where much fresh water comes in), so does the osmotic pressure of their blood. They cannot regulate, and are said to be poikilosmotic. Unless their tissues can withstand a varying osmotic pressure, they are confined to a narrow range of salinities, and are then said to be stenohaline. Most marine animals do not penetrate far into estuaries, and many, but not all, do not survive for long if they are transferred to dilute sea-water in the laboratory. Although they cannot regulate, they may be able to become acclimatized to low salinities, and in general the more gradual their exposure to dilution, the longer they live.

The blood of the Chondrostei is isosmotic, but whereas in invertebrates the internal osmotic pressure is maintained largely by the very ions present in sea-water, in these fish it is largely produced by urea and trimethylamine oxide. Excretory products have here been put to a good use, and, as has just been pointed out above, they are found even in the egg, and possibly the cleidoic egg has been evolved to make this possible.

In the animals which have been considered so far, regulation is not necessary because their body fluids are in osmotic equilibrium with the surrounding medium, and they are subject to little variation of the latter. There are other groups of animals, called homoiosmotic, which maintain a constant internal osmotic pressure whatever the outside conditions. In the marine teleosts the depression of the freezing-point of the blood is about 0·8° C, less than half that of sea-water. Either their membranes must be impermeable, which is not likely, or they must be continually doing work to prevent or counteract the continual loss of water and resulting concentration of the blood. The second of these alternatives has been shown to be true. To make up for the water which escapes they drink sea-water and absorb it, and get rid of the excess salts which are thus passed into the body by excreting them back into the sea through special cells on the gills. The kidneys secrete small quantities of urine which is isotonic with the blood, so that very little water is lost in that way. It is probable that the cartilaginous fishes can act similarly, although they will seldom need to do so. A few Crustacea, such as *Leander serratus* and *Palaemonetes varians*, have hypotonic body-fluids, and can regulate over a wide range (Fig. 46).

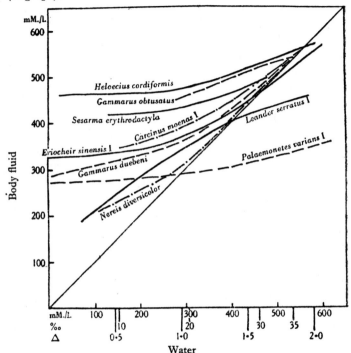

FIG. 46. Relation of the external to the internal medium in various brackish water animals: (*Heloeciu scordiformis, Sesarma erythrodactyla* (Edmonds, 1935); *Gammarus obtusatus, G. duebeni* (Beadle and Cragg, 1940); *Carcinus moenas* (Dural, 1925; Picken, 1936); *Eriocheir sinensis* (Scholles, 1933); *Leander serratus, Palaemonetes varians* (Panikkar, 1941); *Nereis diversicolor* (Beadle, 1937). The left-hand ends of the curves show, on the abscissa, the approximate low-salinity tolerance limits. I, urine isotonic with body fluid. After Beadle.

Some teleosts, notably the eel and the salmon, habitually go from the sea to freshwater, and back again, and are called euryhaline. This term is also appropriate for animals which live in estuaries, where the salinity of the water varies from hour to hour, and in rock pools, where rain may lower the salinity, or evaporation may raise it well above the normal.

Most estuarine animals can regulate to some extent (Fig. 46). If the shore-crab *Carcinus maenas* is placed in water which is hypertonic to sea-water (a position in which it may find itself in drying rock pools) the osmotic pressure of its blood follows that of the water, but if the external medium is hypotonic to the sea, the osmotic pressure of the blood is something between its normal value and that of the new medium. The crab is only poorly homoiosmotic, since there is considerable variation, but it is able to maintain its blood at a different pressure from the medium. It does this by secreting excess water through the gills and antennary gland. Other species which act in the same way are the flatworm *Gunda ulvae*, and the polychaete *Nereis diversicolor*. In both these the first obvious effect of their being placed in dilute sea-water is that they swell; this means that they have absorbed water, but they do not do this to as great an extent as they would if their walls were non-living membranes. It has been shown that as they swell their oxygen consumption goes up, so that presumably a 'respiratory pump' is at work supplying energy to keep the animal in equilibrium (Table 5). This is confirmed by the fact that in the presence of cyanide, which is a respiratory poison, *Nereis* swells passively and cannot regulate. The chief way in which this energy is used is apparently in driving a hypotonic fluid out through the nephridia. The animal is thus taking up pure water and losing water with some salts in solution, so that its body fluids become diluted. Their osmotic pressure, however, does not fall to that of the external medium. The concentration of the coelomic fluid of a worm which has been placed in 25 per cent. sea-water and allowed to come

TABLE 5

Oxygen Consumption and Water Absorption of Nereis diversicolor *in Dilute Sea-water. Two Specimens were used for each Length of Time. (From Beadle)*

Time in hours in 25 per cent. sea-water	Percentage increase in weight	Percentage increase in respiratory rate	Percentage of sea-water equivalent to body fluid
4·25	47	32	55
4·25	54	26	54
22·25	87	42	37
22·25	135	0	38
50·75	74	136	38
50·75	35	26	42

to equilibrium is the same as that of 55 per cent. sea-water, and comparable values are given for other strengths, but the more dilute the surrounding medium the greater the discrepancy. A full complement of the cations normally present in the sea is necessary for regulation to go on. In *Gunda* the water which is absorbed goes first into the parenchyma, and then into the gut cells, where it forms vacuoles in which it remains.

The body fluids of all animals living in fresh water have a higher osmotic pressure than the medium so that they must be homoiosmotic. The depression of the freezing-point of natural fresh waters varies, but is in general about 0·003° C. Characteristic values for the blood of the animals inhabiting it are:

	Δ °C
Anodonta . . .	0·09
Astacus fluviatilis . .	0·8
Salmo fario . . .	0·5

All these animals will tend to absorb water from their surroundings and, to prevent oedema, must have some means of excreting it. The Protozoa do this through the contractile vacuole. This organelle is absent from most marine forms, and in *Paramecium* and several other ciliates its rate of pulsation bears an inverse relation to the osmotic pressure of the external medium, while if its activity is inhibited by cyanide the animals swell. There is, therefore, little doubt that its chief job is to act as an osmotic regulator, and the excretory function commonly attributed to it is very small (see p. 103). In most other animals the regulation is largely done by the excretory organ. In the Turbellaria the nephridia are probably used; they are absent from the marine Acoela, and the rate of pulsation of the terminal vesicle in cercariae goes down as the external osmotic pressure increases. In *Astacus* the antennary gland excretes a urine which is hypotonic to the blood. It is interesting to compare the structure of the gland in this animal with that in the closely related marine lobster, *Homarus*. In the crayfish the coelomic part, which is probably concerned with filtering, and the absorbing tubule are large, whereas in the lobster the resorbing tubule is almost missing, but the labyrinth, which is probably secretory, is large. This distinction holds fairly generally for the marine and fresh-water arthropods, and a similar one applies to some other phyla.

In the vertebrates the excess water is excreted through the kidneys, and in freshwater teleosts and Amphibia the glomerulus is well developed, presumably for this purpose. Other mechanisms are at work too, particularly a reduced permeability of the skin. In a pithed frog the excretion of water goes up five times, suggesting that the permeability of the skin is decreased by the action of the nervous system. Excretion can also be raised by the action of pituitrin. In the eel *Anguilla* the gills, which in sea-water are freely permeable and excrete chlorides, &c., to maintain the osmotic pressure of the blood lower than that of the medium, in fresh water become impermeable to both chloride and water. This probably makes it easy for the fish to pass from the sea to fresh water. Cormorants, penguins, and other sea-birds eliminate much sodium chloride through the nasal glands, and turtles and probably other marine reptiles do so through orbital glands.

A homoiosmotic freshwater animal may be harmed by being put straight into the sea, just as a homoiothermic animal may be harmed if it is put in ice-cold water. It can, however, withstand slight changes of external osmotic pressure, and even fairly large ones if they are made gradually, but the limit is usually well below the salinity of sea-water (Fig. 46). The advantage of a constant internal environment is that the metabolic processes of the animal are not upset by sudden variations in the concentrations of ions present.

The ability to regulate may be a property which the animal carries with it from the egg up, or it may be acquired during ontogeny. The fish are examples of the first. There is no appreciable change in the depression of the freezing-point of tissues of *Salmo* from the eggs in the oviduct through all the embryonic stages up to the blood of an adult. The Amphibia (frog, toad, newt) are different. The egg in the oviduct has a depression of the freezing-point of $0.48°$ C, about that of the blood of the adult, but on fertilization the depression drops to $0.045°$ C. It rises during development, rapidly at first, and more slowly after gastrulation. The pronephros is active well before hatching, so that perhaps regulation develops as an organ for carrying it out is formed. Amphibian eggs will not develop in water isosmotic with the serum of the adult. Cladoceran eggs are similar to those of the frog, showing a fall of osmotic pressure on fertilization and a subsequent gradual rise. The ability of *Nereis diversicolor* to regulate improves as it grows older, young worms being less sensitive to changes of osmotic pressure than are larvae, and adults less sensitive than the young forms.

8.32. Ionic Regulation

Osmotic equilibrium is not the same as ionic equilibrium, and it seems that no animal, marine or otherwise, has body fluids which agree exactly in composition with the external medium. A small part of the difference is due to a Donnan effect introduced because there are present in the plasma proteins to which the membranes are impermeable, but if body-fluids are dialysed against sea-water, so that this effect is eliminated, differences are still found. Some representative values are shown in Table 6. Sulphate is almost univerally low, but the other ions are more variable; the differences are large only in the decapod Crustacea and in the cephalopods. A peculiar and perhaps important fact is that magnesium is very low in the active crustaceans and much higher in the sluggish forms.

Analysis of the urine of arthropods and molluscs shows that much of the difference is produced by differential excretion. Thus an ion such as magnesium, which in decapod plasma is hypotonic to sea-water, is hypertonic to plasma in the urine. There must in addition be uptake of some ions against a concentration gradient, probably by the gills. Isolated gills of the crab *Eriocheir sinensis* absorb sodium chloride from a solution only one-fortieth of the concentration of that of the animal's blood, and this absorption stops in the absence of oxygen or in the presence of cyanide, so that it is, as usual, an active metabolic process.

Marine teleosts excrete chloride, and probably sodium and potassium, mainly through the gills, other ions by the kidneys; there is no good evidence for endocrine control. Frogs actively absorb sodium and chloride, but not potassium or calcium, through the skin, and control is by hormones from the anterior pituitary.

TABLE 6

Ionic Regulation in Some Marine Invertebrates. (From Robertson)

	Concentrations in plasma or coelomic fluid as percentage of concentration in the same fluid dialysed against sea-water					
	Na$^+$	K$^+$	Ca^{++}	Mg^{++}	Cl$^-$	SO^{--}
Coelenterata						
Aurelia aurita	99	106	96	97	104	47
Echinodermata						
Marthasterias glacialis	100	111	101	98	101	100
Tunicata						
Salpa maxima	100	113	96	95	102	65
Annelida						
Arenicola marina	100	104	100	100	100	92
Sipunculoidea						
Phascolosoma vulgare	104	110	104	69	99	91
Arthropoda						
Maia squinado	100	125	122	81	102	66
Dromia vulgaris	97	120	84	99	103	53
Carcinus maenas	110	118	108	34	104	61
Pachygrapsus marmoratus	94	95	92	24	87	46
Nephrops norvegicus	113	77	124	17	99	69
Mollusca						
Pecten maximus	100	130	103	97	100	97
Neptunea antiqua	101	114	102	101	101	98
Sepia officinalis	93	205	91	98	105	22

8.4. Temperature

In the majority of animals the body temperature is not greatly different from that of their surroundings, and so the rate of respiration (apart from specially stimulated activity) depends on the latter. Figs. 47 and 48 show this. The temperature of the lizards is almost the same as that of their surroundings, and their carbon dioxide production corresponds. Such animals are called cold-blooded or poikilothermic. They are handicapped by both low and high temperatures. In the former their activity is greatly slowed down, and in the latter they have no means of preventing themselves from becoming overheated and so dying. It has been shown that American insects and reptiles which normally live in deserts where the surface temperature is above 50° C cannot survive this in the laboratory for more than a few minutes, and they rapidly die if they are tethered in the sun in their natural habitat. In ordinary circumstances they escape by burrowing, and are only occasionally exposed to the temperatures measured by the thermometer.

The actual temperature of cold-blooded animals depends on the balance between the receipt and loss of heat. The chief ways in which heat is received are by the metabolism of the body and by radiation from the sun, and the chief forms of loss are by conduction and convection and by evaporation. In water, radiation is of little importance, except perhaps for large animals near the surface, and evaporation of none. The animals rapidly lose heat to the water, which is a good conductor, and maintain a temperature a little above that of their surroundings, like any other body which is producing heat.

On land two types of situation are important. Animals which have a large damp surface, either internal or external, may lose so much heat by evaporation that they are cooler than their surroundings, and since the rate of evaporation depends not on the relative humidity but on the vapour pressure deficit, the difference will be larger the drier the air and the higher the ambient temperature. Earthworms, molluscs, insects, and Amphibia all show this effect, and some of them may have temperatures as much as 10° C below that of the atmosphere. This is the same phenomenon as that of the wet-bulb temperature in a hygrometer, but the final temperature reached in the animal is affected also by the metabolism, and may be slightly (in molluscs) or considerably (in Amphibia) above that of the wet-bulb.

The other case is that of relatively dry-surfaced animals in sunlight. They may absorb enough radiant heat to raise their temperatures well above that of the atmosphere. Insects and reptiles show this effect very well, but it is a purely physical effect, which applies also to inanimate objects and warm-blooded animals, and allows the possibility of sunbathing in Switzerland when the air temperature is well below freezing-point.

Both cooling by evaporation and heating by insolation may be of some slight importance in protecting the animal from extremes, but neither can be called regulation. Locomotory behaviour, such as the kineses discussed in Chapter 6, are probably of much greater value as protective devices for the invertebrates.

Birds and mammals are warm-blooded or homoiothermic. Their resting metabolism, that is their energy production irrespective of exercise, goes up as the temperature goes down, in such a way as to keep their body temperature constant. They are in fact living thermostats. The actual temperature maintained depends on the species, and is subject to slight variation with the individual and with activity. Fig. 47 shows how the body temperature of the cat remains approximately constant in varying environmental temperatures. The graphs in Fig. 48 show that the different behaviour of the cat and of the lizard is correlated with an increased carbon dioxide production at the lower temperatures in the former; at $35°$ C the regulating mechanism is beginning to break down. The chief seat of the increased respiration is the muscles, and in the extreme case this is obvious when shivering takes place. The mechanism is dependent on the nervous system, since animals paralysed with curare behave like lizards or any other cold-blooded animals. This type of regulation is called chemical, and can deal only with a lowered external temperature, but there is another type, rather badly called physical, which adapts its possessor to higher temperatures

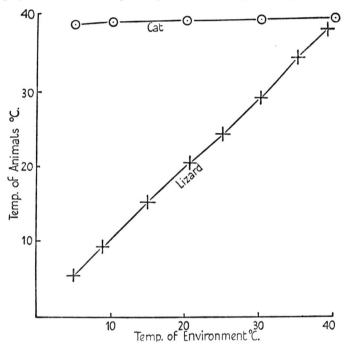

FIG. 47. Body temperatures of cat and lizard (*Cyclodus gigas*) in different environmental temperatures. Redrawn from Martin.

than normal by control of heat loss. This takes different forms. In man, of the total heat produced 5 per cent. goes in heating food, drink, and respired air, 15 per cent. in evaporating water from the lungs, and the rest in cooling and evaporation from the skin. When the external temperature is increased, or when as a result of exercise more heat is produced, the rate of heat loss is raised in two ways.

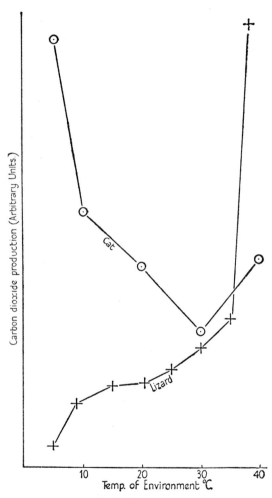

FIG. 48. Carbon dioxide production of cat and lizard at different environmental temperatures. Cf. Fig. 47. Redrawn from Martin.

The cutaneous blood-vessels are dilated so that heat is taken to the surface more rapidly, and the sweat glands are activated so that evaporation is increased. Both these are under the control of the central nervous system.

Sweating is found in various mammals, including horses, dogs, and sheep, but is possibly not present in all. Another device is an increased rate of breathing, which is found in rabbits, pigs, cattle, and sheep, and in the sparrow. Since there is little or no reduction in the tidal volume, there must presumably be some other device to prevent the increased intake of oxygen from raising the metabolic rate. Tachypnoea, or breathing in rapid short pants, gets over this difficulty, for it increases the loss of water from the mouth and trachea without increasing the oxygen which goes to the lungs. It is found in the dog and in the fowl.

The temperature to which the biological thermostat responds is generally that of the surface of the body; in man the face is especially important and in fowls the head. This type of control makes the system very responsive to changes in ambient temperature, but allows considerable variations of temperature within the body. An efficient circulatory system is necessary, especially in large animals, to prevent the development of too great a difference between the internal and surface temperatures.

The high temperatures of most birds and mammals are dependent on the possession of an insulating layer of hair or feathers or fat, and this, by changing in thickness seasonally or from moment to moment, may produce a crude form of temperature control. In birds the position of the feathers is especially important; heat is not lost steadily, but in bursts as the feathers are disturbed and the warm air which has been trapped between them is released. The fluffed-up appearance of birds in cold weather, so that they have a thicker insulating layer, is well known. The long wool of the merino sheep, which is adapted to hot climates, actually seems to prevent the animal from overheating, for when it is shaved off, at an air-temperature of 38° C the skin temperature rises by 3° C and the rate of panting is doubled. The man who wore an overcoat in summer because 'what keeps out the cold will keep out the heat' is thus vindicated.

The scrotum of mammals acts as a very efficient local thermostat, and this is perhaps its primary function. Sperms develop well over a rather narrow range of temperature, which is slightly below that of the body. The position of the testes outside the body-cavity provides this, and the contraction of the muscles of the scrotum, aided by some vascular reaction and sometimes by sweating, maintains the temperature constant within a very narrow range. The temperature of the testicles of a bull varied only between 95° and 98·5° F when the temperature of the air ranged from 59° to 100° F.

Homoiothermy is acquired at some definite point in ontogeny, and the chemical and physical mechanisms arise independently. Not many species have been investigated, but the variation shown at birth is illustrated by Table 7.

TABLE 7

Showing the Forms of Temperature Regulation present at Birth or Hatching. (From Needham)

	Chemical	Physical
Guinea-pig . . .	+	+
Rabbit . . .	+	−
Mouse	−	−
Cat	+	−
Man	+	−
Chick	+	+
Pigeon	−	−

The mammals which can regulate at birth are those which are born open-eyed and active, and similarly the birds which can regulate on hatching are those which are nidi-fugous, that is which leave the nest as soon as they have broken the shell. Mammals which are born naked and blind are cold-blooded until some days later, when they begin to be more active, and so, likewise, are nidicolous birds, which remain in the nest for some time after hatching. The homoiothermy is at first imperfect, and in the edentates, lemurs and camels it remains so throughout life, helping, in these last, to conserve water.

In many of the social Hymenoptera there is some communal regulation by such methods as opening or closing the nest entrances, and fanning with the wings. In the honey-bee in summer there is apparently some chemical regulation, similar to that of mammals, but it seems to be imperfect, and there is a report that the metabolic rate of a crab increases as the ambient temperature falls. Sphingid moths are unable to fly when their body temperature is below a certain value (20° to 30° C, according to the species) and achieve this in cold weather by fanning with their wings until they have warmed up enough. In this they resemble bats, whose temperature falls in the daytime and has to be raised by shivering until it is high enough for them to fly.

8.41. Hibernation

In winter practically all poikilotherms which are unable to migrate from the cold regions cease moving, feeding, and other activities, and live quietly with a very low metabolic rate. The temperature at which inactivity sets in varies; usually it is a little above zero, though the pond-snail *Planorbis* is active under the ice. This quiescence is probably brought about simply by the reduction in metabolism which is an inevitable result of the falling temperature, and calls for no special physiological comment. A similar state is induced in many insects and snails by desiccation.

In many mammals, particularly insectivores, bats and rodents, the onset of winter induces a deep sleep which is accompanied by temporary poikilothermy, and it is best to restrict the term hibernation to this. During hibernation the oxygen consumption falls very low—in the dormouse, *Muscardinus avellanarius*, from a resting value of 8,000 m.l. oxygen per kilogram per hour, to 300—and the pulse and breathing rates are reduced. This may result in the accumulation of carbon dioxide and the onset of Cheyne-Stokes breathing—that is, periods of breathing alternating with periods when no air is taken in. It is probably this retention of carbon dioxide which has led to some of the very low respiratory quotients which have been recorded for hibernants, the true value being probably always about 0·7, indicating that, as would be expected, fat is the chief fuel.

The simplest explanation of hibernation would be that the low temperature induced sleep and its accompaniments, but this cannot be a complete explanation. The marmots of North America hibernate in their burrows and their body temperature follows that of the surroundings, which is usually about 2° C. If it rises to 15° C they wake up, and their temperature rapidly goes up to its normal value of 32° C, but exactly the same thing happens if the external temperature drops to freezing-point. Further, aestivation, sleeping in summer, appears to be very similar to hibernation, and hibernating animals such as dormice and marmots sometimes aestivate. Specimens of the African insectivore *Centetes ecaudatus* at the London Zoological Gardens hibernated at the same time each year, quite irrespective of the environmental conditions. The golden-mantled ground-squirrel, *Citellus lateralis*, continued to hibernate at the proper time of year even when it was confined in the laboratory at a constant temperature of 35° F and under 12 hours daily illumination, with unlimited food, water, and bedding.

In bats, the accumulation of food reserves seems to be an important internal cause, just as it is in the diapause of insects (see below). The hormone balance of the animal is important, and during hibernation the anterior pituitary, thyroid, and adrenal cortex are reduced in size or activity or both, while the islets of Langerhans are increased.

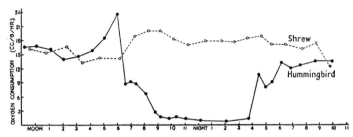

Fig. 49. The rate of metabolism of a male anna hummingbird and of a shrew (*Sorex cinereus*) over a 24-hour period. After Pearson.

Experimentally, injection of insulin induces a state resembling, though not identical with, hibernation, while adrenaline and thyroxine may wake hibernants. It seems that hibernation is fundamentally a way of avoiding the ill effects of low temperatures, but that other factors are concerned in producing it. It is in a sense the very opposite of regulation. The whole physiology of the animal is modified while it goes on, the nitrogen metabolism is altered, and new reflexes may even appear. Hibernating bats roll over if they are placed on their backs, although they do not normally behave in this way.

For a long time hibernation in birds, fervently believed in by eighteenth-century naturalists, was strongly denied by modern scientists. It is now known that many species of humming bird regularly become torpid and poikilothermic, and reduce their metabolism at night, and wake again before daybreak. This behaviour is perhaps connected with a very high resting metabolism during the day so that it acts as a system for saving food (Fig. 49). A few other species of bird, mainly American, are similar, and at least one, the poor-will, *Phalaenoptilus nuttalii*, of Colorado, is known to hibernate through the winter. This bird is known to the Indians by a name which means 'the sleeping one'. Swallows may become torpid in cold weather, but recovery is only possible if complete torpidity is not reached.

8.42. Diapause

It is convenient to put here the phenomenon of dia-pause, which, although it occurs in cold-blooded animals, has some physiological similarity to hibernation and serves basically the same purpose. It is an arrest of development much greater and more prolonged than any that could be explained as a simple physical effect of low temperature or other adverse conditions. It includes the state of in-activity of the cysts of Protozoa and the winter eggs of many pond animals, but has been closely studied only in arthropods, and especially in insects. It is a device to avoid conditions of low temperature and poor food supply, and to ensure that the active stages are produced when these are near their optimum. Since it often occurs in immature stages, it may appear as an arrest of development. In arthropods the stimulus for diapause is nearly always the length of day and night, but only rarely, as in the red locust, which diapauses if it emerges from the pupa in decreasing days, is the changing day-length important, as it is in birds. Temperature and food supply may have subsidiary effects in the onset of diapause, but the former is the important agent in its cessation. A period at a low temperature is necessary before development can be resumed, and there is an optimum temperature, on either side of which diapause is prolonged. During diapause the oxygen consumption falls, but can usually be detected.

The respiratory quotient is about 0·7, suggesting that fat is the substrate, and the occasional very low values which have been reported are probably due to the retention of carbon dioxide. Much of the respiration that is left is not sensitive to cyanide. The hormonal control of diapause is described in section 5.11.

8.43. Migration

One way of avoiding adverse conditions, especially low temperature and the reduction in food-supply to which it often gives rise, is by migration. This may be defined as a periodic to-and-fro movement of a population between two areas, and is known in many fish and birds, in some mammals, and in a few insects and other invertebrates, notably butterflies. Two aspects of it are of special interest to physiologists—the system which controls the onset of the migratory movement, and the sensory means by which the correct direction is determined.

All migration is probably connected with breeding, in that this takes place at one end only of the journey. The nesting of birds and the spawning of salmon and eels at the end of their migrations are well known, and breeding in a special area takes place similarly in seals, whales, and some herbivorous mammals, and in many marine fish such as herring and plaice. There is no doubt that the gonads begin to become active about the time when migration begins, and those of birds decrease in size at the end of the breeding season in time for the return migration. Non-breeding herrings, which may be 2, 3, or 4 years old, do not migrate. There can be little doubt that the physiology of migration is part of the general gonadal-pituitary cycle discussed in the last chapter, and that the initiation of migration depends partly on the phase reached in the cycle, which has been determined by the accumulated influence of the season in bringing the endocrine system into the appropriate state, and partly on the trigger-effect of particular conditions such as change in temperature and high barometric pressure. The first makes migration possible, while the second causes it to begin. Little experimental work has been done on the trigger-stimuli, but it has been shown that excess or deficiency of daylight will hasten or delay the migratory restlessness of caged robins and other birds, and it is known that migration of many birds occurs predominantly under anticyclones. Temperature is important, and the waves of advance of many species over Europe in the spring follow particular isotherms very closely. In salmon and other fish migration is accompanied by increased activity of the thyroid, and there is some slight evidence that the same is true of birds. It has been suggested that migration occurs in animals which have a hypophyseal-thyroid system which is easily disturbed, so that the animals are strongly affected by external factors. In this a parallel may be drawn with hibernation, where also the endocrine balance is greatly altered.

More attention has been paid in recent years to the navigational basis of migration. In salmon, the movement appears to be basically a rheotaxis, modified by the recognition of the chemical properties of particular rivers. In the sea the fish tend, at the appropriate time, to keep in water of low salinity, which will be found near the mouths of rivers, and especially in water of similar composition to that in which they were hatched. A sudden lowering of the salinity, caused by a freshet, makes them enter the river, and thenceforward the upstream migration is a visual or tactile rheotaxis. Descent is largely passive, and must happen to any river-living animal if rheotactic responses are lost.

In the writings on the navigation of birds there has been much confusion between homing and migration.

While migration may involve homing it does not necessarily do so; in some species, notably the cuckoos, the
young emigrate alone and after their parents, so that they
can neither have memory of where they are going nor
passively follow the others; the young cuckoos have never
even known their parents. While memory undoubtedly
plays a part in the final few miles of migration—where,
for instance, a swallow returns, as it often does, to the same
barn that it occupied in the year before—it is extremely
unlikely that the necessary cues for the rest of the journey
could be learnt. This may be, for the swallow, four thousand miles or more, and although the average speed of
northward travel may be only about 25 miles a day, many
lengths of this (and many other migratory journeys) are
carried out at high speeds. If, with the amount of stimulation that they can get in conditions like this, birds can
form conditioned reflexes, they are performing very much
better than any experimental animals known to us, and
there is no evidence, in the experiments on learning in the
laboratory, that this is so. Since most homing depends on
previous learning of the territory to be covered it is probably quite different in nature from migration. The few
cases of successful return of birds which have been displaced large distances over unfamiliar country are not
more than are to be expected by chance wandering, followed by visual homing when the bird comes into a region
that it knows. In a few experiments it has been shown that
the directions in which released birds (pigeons, Manx
shearwaters, gulls) disappear from sight are more closely
concentrated round the home direction than would be
expected by chance, but the numbers which are not successful are much higher than in migration, which is
characterized by the movement of almost all of the population in the same direction.

There is little doubt that for every migratory population

there is a standard direction at each season, for not only can this sometimes be seen, but experiments in the displacement of migrating birds have shown the usual direction to be generally maintained. Birds are often distracted from their standard direction by guiding lines such as coasts, river valleys, and mountains. How the bird determines the standard direction remains a mystery. Its persistence when the bird is displaced hundreds of miles (if the few experiments on storks, starlings, and crows may be generalized) shows that it cannot be determined by local clues, such as temperature gradients or winds, but that it must be dependent on something global or celestial in scale. Most of the hypotheses proposed, such as those dependent on terrestrial magnetism or on forces produced by the rotation of the earth, have been shown to be physically impossible or extremely improbable. There is a little experimental evidence that birds can orientate themselves when they can see the sun or the stars, but not when these are obscured, but these conclusions are based on very few observations and much repetition is necessary before they can be accepted. Navigation of this sort is theoretically possible, but demands that the bird shall be provided at least with a chronometer and an artificial horizon. It does not meet the difficulty that some migration continues when the sun is obscured by clouds and when the bird has crossed the equator. To account for the last point, either there should be a period of confusion, in which the bird has no bearings, or the bird must instantaneously reverse its reaction when it passes under a sun which is vertical at noon. The first does not seem to have been recorded, and the second seems unlikely.

REFERENCES

FOR vertebrate physiology any of the larger textbooks on human physiology may be consulted, such as:

STARLING's *Principles of Human Physiology*. Edited by C. Lovatt Evans. 12th ed. London, 1956.
SAMSON WRIGHT. *Applied Physiology*. 9th ed. Oxford, 1952.

Both of these give references.
As a readable account of the biochemical aspects of physiology (not confined to the mammals)

BALDWIN, E. *Dynamic Aspects of Biochemistry*, 3rd ed. Cambridge, 1957

is invaluable.
For insect physiology there is a full account, with a bibliography, in

WIGGLESWORTH, V. B. *The Principles of Insect Physiology*. 5th ed. London, 1953.

The following books and articles, mostly of a general nature, are of interest for the sections mentioned; nearly all of them contain bibliographies.

They have been chosen not only for the facts which they contain but for the clarity of their exposition and the help that they give to the general reader.

Section
1.   BOURNE, G. H., and KIDDER, G. W. (Eds.) (1953). *Biochemistry and Physiology of Nutrition*. New York and London.
1.16.   ORR, J. B. (1937). *Food, Health, and Income*. 2nd ed. London.
1.2.   YONGE, C. M. (1928). 'Feeding Mechanisms in the Invertebrates'. *Biological Reviews*, **3**, 21.
1.21.   JØRGENSEN, C. BARKER (1955). 'Quantitative aspects of filter feeding in invertebrates'. *Biological Reviews*, **30**, 391.
1.32.   BARRINGTON, E. J. W. (1942). 'Gastric digestion in lower vertebrates.' *Biological Reviews*, **17**, 1.

1.42. GREEN, D. E. (1954). 'Fatty acid oxidation in soluble systems of animal tissues.' *Biological Reviews*, **29,** 330.

1.5. HARRIS, L. (1955). *Vitamins in Theory and Practice*. 4th ed. Cambridge.

3.11. DIXON, M. (1937). 'Respiratory Carriers,' in *Perspectives in Biochemistry*. Ed. J. Needham and D. E. Green. Cambridge.

3.21. WIGGLESWORTH, V. B. (1930). 'The Theory of Tracheal Respiration in Insects.' *Proceedings of the Royal Society* B, **106,** 229.

3.22. BARCROFT, J. (1928). *The Respiratory Function of the Blood*. Part II, 'Haemoglobin'. Cambridge.

HALDANE, J. S., and PRIESTLEY, J. G. (1935). *Respiration*. 2nd ed. Oxford.

HILL, R. (1937). 'Haemoglobin,' in *Perspectives in Biochemistry*.

3.433. THORPE, W. H. (1950). 'Plastron respiration in aquatic insects.' *Biological Reviews*, **25,** 344.

4.1. BARKER, D. (1943). 'Recent work on flagellar movement.' *New Phytologist*, **42,** 49.

4.1. GRAY, J. (1928). *Ciliary Movement*. Cambridge.

—— (1931). *Experimental Cytology*. Cambridge.

4.2. —— Ibid.

4.3. RITCHIE, A. D. (1928). *Muscular Contraction*. Cambridge.

4.31. 'The physiology of voluntary muscle.' *British Medical Bulletin* (1956), **12** (3), especially articles by A. V. Hill, D. R. Wilkie, A. F. Huxley, H. E. Huxley, K. Bailey, D. M. Needham, and S. V. Perry.

4.34. PANTIN, C. F. A. (1956). 'Comparative physiology of muscle.' *British Medical Bulletin*, **12,** 199.

4.5. SCHAEFFER, E. A. (Ed.). *Text-book of Physiology* (1900). Vol. 2, pp. 561–91. Edinburgh.

4.6. HARVEY, E. N. (1940). *Living Light*. Princeton.

4.7. EWER, R. F. (1947). 'On the functions and mode of action of the nematocysts of *Hydra*.' *Proceedings of the Zoological Society of London*, **117,** 365.

4.8. PARKER, G. H. (1948). *Animal Colour Changes and their Neuro-humours*. Cambridge.

5.11. KNOWLES, F. G. W., and CARLISLE, D. B. (1956). 'Endocrine control in the Crustacea.' *Biological Reviews*, **31,** 396.

5.11. WIGGLESWORTH, V. B. (1954). *The Physiology of Insect Metamorphosis*. Cambridge.

5.31. HODGKIN, A. L. (1951). 'The ionic basis of activity in nerve and muscle.' *Biological Reviews*, **26,** 339.

5.33. ECCLES, J. C. (1953). *The Neurophysiological Basis of Mind.* Oxford.

5.34. PANTIN, C. F. A. (1952). 'The elementary nervous system.' *Proceedings of the Royal Society* B, **140,** 147.
ROMANES, G. J. (1885). *Jellyfish, Starfish, and Sea-Urchins.* London.

5.54. MONCRIEFF, R. W. (1944). *The Chemical Senses.* London.

5.55. LÖWENSTEIN, O. (1936). 'The Equilibrium Function of the Vertebrate Labyrinth.' *Biological Reviews,* **11,** 113.

5.56. BEATTY, R. T. (1932). *Hearing in Man and Animals.* London.

5.57. TANSLEY, K. (1950). 'Vision.' *Symposia of the Society for Experimental Biology,* **4,** 19–33.

6.1 and 6.2. JENNINGS, H. S. (1906). *Behaviour in the Lower Organisms.* New York.
LOEB, J. (1918). *Forced Movements, Tropisms, and Animal Conduct.* Philadelphia.
FRAENKEL, G. S., and GUNN, D. L. (1940). *The Orientation of Animals.* Oxford.

6.3. FABRE, J. H. (1918). *The Wonders of Instinct.* London.
HINGSTON, R. W. G. (1928). *Problems of Instinct and Intelligence.* London.
LEHRMAN, D. S. (1953). 'A critique of Konrad Lorenz's theory of instinctive behaviour.' *Quarterly Review of Biology,* **28,** 337.
PANTIN, C. F. A. (1950). 'Behaviour patterns in lower invertebrates.' *Symposia of the Society for Experimental Biology,* **4,** 175.

6.4. PAVLOV, I. P. (1927). *Conditioned Reflexes.* Oxford.
FROLOV, Y. P. (1937). *Pavlov and his School.* London.
YOUNG, J. Z. (1938). 'The Evolution of the Nervous System,' in *Evolution: Essays Presented to E. S. Goodrich.* Ed. G. R. de Beer. Oxford.

7.22. DONOVAN, B. T., and HARRIS, G. W. (1955). 'Neurohumoral mechanisms in reproduction.' *British Medical Bulletin,* **11,** 93.

7.22 and 7.23. CORNER, G. W. (1933). 'The Nature of the Menstrual Cycle.' *The Harvey Lectures 1932–3,* p. 67, or *Medicine,* **12,** 61.
HAMMOND, J. (1947). 'Animal breeding in relation to nutrition and environmental conditions.' *Biological Reviews,* **22,** 195.

8.2. NEEDHAM, J. (1931). *Chemical Embryology,* pp. 890 ff. Cambridge.
SMITH, H. W. (1936). 'The Retention and Physiological Role of Urea in the Elasmobranchii.' *Biological Reviews,* **11,** 49.

8.3.   BEADLE, L. C. (1943). 'Osmotic regulation and the faunas of inland waters.' *Biological Reviews*, **18,** 172.

——— (1957). 'Comparative physiology: osmotic and ionic regulation in aquatic animals.' *Annual Review of Physiology*, **19,** 329.

KITCHING, J. A. (1938). 'Contractile vacuoles.' *Biological Reviews*, **13,** 403.

8.4.   NEEDHAM, J. (1931). *Chemical Embryology*. Cambridge.

8.41. KAYSER, C. (1950). 'Le Sommeil hibernal.' *Biological Reviews*, **25,** 255.

8.43. FONTAINE, M. (1954). 'Du determinisme physiologique dues migrations.' *Biological Reviews*, **29,** 390.

INDEX

Where more than one reference is given that in heavy type is the more important

PRINTED IN GREAT BRITAIN
AT THE UNIVERSITY PRESS, OXFORD
BY VIVIAN RIDLER
PRINTER TO THE UNIVERSITY